ELECTROPHYSIOLOGICAL ANALYSIS OF SYNAPTIC TRANSMISSION

by

J. I. HUBBARD

B.Med.Sci., M.A., D.M., Ph.D.

*Professor of Biological Sciences, Northwestern University,
Evanston, Illinois*

R. LLINÁS

M.D., Ph.D.

*Head, Department of Neurobiology, Institute for Biomedical Research,
American Medical Association Education and Research Foundation,
Chicago, Illinois*

D. M. J. QUASTEL

M.D., Ph.D.

*Associate Professor, Department of Physiology and Biophysics,
Dalhousie University, Halifax, Nova Scotia*
*(Present address: Department of Pharmacology,
University of British Columbia, Vancouver, B.C.)*

LONDON
EDWARD ARNOLD (PUBLISHERS) LTD

Printed in Great Britain by
The Camelot Press Ltd., London and Southampton

PREFACE

THIS book was written with the object of providing a systematic basis for investigation of synaptic transmission. To this end we have attempted primarily to indicate the theoretical background for analytic techniques, and also to point out pitfalls which we, among others, have not always eluded. The scope of our text thus lies between the more descriptive texts, *Physiology of Synapses* (Eccles, 1964), *Structure and Function in the Nervous System of Invertebrates* (Bullock & Horridge, 1965), *Nerve, Muscle and Synapse* (Katz, 1966), and the technical texts such as *Electrophysiological Methods*, Parts A and B (Volumes 5 and 6 in *Physical Techniques in Biological Research*, ed. Nastuk, 1963 and 1964) and *Electronic Apparatus for Biological Research* (Donaldson, 1958).

Our prime reason for writing at this time was the knowledge that many methods have been developed in recent years for the analysis of relatively accessible peripheral synapses and that some of these methods have now been suitably modified so as to make them applicable to the more inaccessible synapses in the central nervous system. This corpus (hitherto unassembled) we have found invaluable and we would like to offer it to our colleagues in physiology and also to the numerous pharmacologists who are now investigating drug action on synapses with the techniques originally developed by physiologists. There has been an increasing convergence of the aims and interests of peripheral and central synaptologists of both physiological and pharmacological orientation. The full power of the methods available for investigating chemical synapse is unfortunately only available for synapses where the transmitter is known. However, there is increasing evidence that different transmitters are released by, and act through, fundamentally similar mechanisms at all chemical transmitting synapses, with the result that many of the methods which will be described have a wide range of applications.

Electrophysiological methods, like any others, depend enormously on the theory that has been developed, mainly on the basis of results of electrophysiological investigations. Within the last

v

twenty years a fairly complete description of electrical events at synapses has been developed although knowledge of the more fundamental mechanisms which underlie them, i.e., the physical chemistry of cell membranes, remains sadly lacking. It is hoped that the application of techniques such as we describe may make it possible not only to advance further the knowledge of how synapses function at various sites, but also to gain information which will shed light on the way in which synapses function at the molecular level.

1968   J.I.H.
                                                                     R.L.
                                                                 D.M.J.Q.

ACKNOWLEDGEMENTS

THIS book was conceived and the first draft prepared in the Department of Physiology at the Australian National University in Canberra where we were all working. We thank Sir John Eccles, the staff, and the technicians for their cheerful assistance. Of our colleagues we wish to thank particularly Drs Coombs, Landau and Vere-Jones who read and criticized individual chapters and Dr M. Kuno who read the entire manuscript. Now that we have moved to separate institutions, we are indebted to an ever-growing number of typists, technicians, and graduate students who have helped with typing and preparation of figures and tables. We thank Miss Molly Nadler for typing, Mr M. Miyamoto for preparation of tables, Mr P. Redden and Mr J. Obregon for preparation of illustrative material, and particularly Miss Ellen Adams for her assistance in the final typing and indexing.

Grateful thanks are due to the following publishers and editors for their generosity in giving permission for reproduction of illustrations: *Australian Journal of Science*; *British Journal of Pharmacology*; the Ciba Foundation; Elsevier Publishing Co.; *Experientia*; *Experimental Neurology*; *Japanese Journal of Physiology*; *Journal of Cellular Physiology*; *Journal of General Physiology*; *Journal of Neurophysiology*; *Journal of Pharmacology and Experimental Therapeutics*; *Journal of Physiology*; *Journal of Theoretical Biology*; *Nature*; *New York Academy of Sciences*; *Pflügers Archiv*; Rockefeller University Press; the Royal Society; and Springer-Verlag.

CONTENTS

I

THE STRUCTURE AND FUNCTION OF SYNAPSES

'SYNAPSES' as originally defined by Sherrington (1897) are the areas of functional contact between nerve cells which are specialized for transmission of nerve impulses from one cell to the other. It is convenient, because of the common mechanisms involved in their function, to include the close contacts between nerve and muscle cells and nerve and exocrine gland cells in the same category. The synapse was originally a physiological concept, put forward to explain certain experimental findings which at that time could not easily be reconciled with the current view of most histologists, who considered the central nervous system to be a reticulum, in which all the cells were physically joined one to another. (It was also universally held that motor nerve fibres terminated under the muscle cell membrane, the sarcolemma.) As Sherrington (1906) said, referring to the synapse,

> It would be a mechanism where nervous conduction, especially if predominantly physical in nature, might have grafted upon it characters just such as those differentiating reflex-arc conduction from nerve-trunk conduction. For instance, change from reversibility of direction of conduction to irreversibility might be referable to the membrane possessing irreciprocal permeability.

Sherrington in this passage was speculating with regard to the mechanism of the unidirectional transmission characteristic of synapses. This particular facet of the more general question of how cells communicate with each other is still being actively explored, together with the related question of how synaptic action is altered by drugs and other experimental procedures.

SYNAPTIC MECHANISMS

The synapse which has the longest history of investigation is the nerve–muscle junction. Three hypotheses regarding the mechanism

of neuromuscular transmission have successively predominated
and are of universal interest because of their extension from the
nerve–muscle junction to other synapses of the animal body—
and indeed extension to the more general problem of how cells
communicate. The longest lived (300 B.C. to about A.D. 1800) was
the 'animal spirit' hypothesis. Like its successors, the electrical and
chemical hypotheses, it was a coherent explanation of the facts
known at the time, though these were few. This hypothesis concerning the way in which nerves influence muscles is found in the
writings of the Alexandrian school of anatomists and physiologists
in the third century B.C. (Singer 1925). The views of these men, the
first known physiologists, are known through the writings in the
second century A.D. of Galen, who was concerned to refute some of
their errors. The Alexandrian, Erasistratus (about 290 B.C.), correctly observed that muscles were entered by three vessels, that is,
a vein, an artery, and a nerve. He noticed that these three divided
and continued to divide as far as he could follow them. He therefore made the logical assumption that the process of division went
on beyond his limit of observation, but also supposed that the
minute divisions of these vessels in fact made up the tissues. He
did not recognize that arteries contain blood but thought them to
contain air (as they do in cadavers), blood being present only in
veins. The nerves he thought to be hollow tubes containing a
peculiar substance, the so called 'animal spirit'. He observed that
muscles produced movement of joints by shortening and attributed
the shortening to distension by the postulated 'animal spirit' coming from the nerve. Galen satisfied himself that both arteries and
veins normally contain blood but repeated in his writings the
animal spirit hypothesis of Erasistratus and indeed, these views
were apparently considered quite satisfactory until well into the
seventeenth century—that is 1,500 years later. Indeed, as their
illustrations show, even such great anatomists as Vesalius and
Leonardo Da Vinci believed that the tendon of a muscle was a
continuation of its nerve (Belt, 1955).

The first experimental attack on the animal spirit hypothesis
came from Borelli (1608–79), an Italian who ventured to investi-
gate the nature of the postulated animal spirits. He cut open the
muscles of animals under water and found that gas did not emerge.
He therefore concluded that the animal spirit must be a liquid.
Similar views were held by Croone (1633–84), an English physiologist who conceived of muscle as a series of small bladders

explosively blown up by liquid during contractions. It is of some interest that his widow endowed a lecture, the Croonian lecture of the Royal Society, the oldest annual physiological lecture. It is still given annually on some topic in connection with the physiology of muscular motion.

Later in the same century, Swammerdam (1637–80), a Dutchman, and Glisson (1597–1677) an Englishman, performed experiments the results of which were not compatible with the animal spirit hypothesis. Glisson observed that when a man held his arm in a container of water the level of the water fell when he contracted his arm muscles rather than rising, as would be expected if there was actual swelling of the muscles. Swammerdam's experiment was similar but more convincing. Swammerdam had a frog nerve-muscle preparation in an enclosed vessel, the nerve being looped through a copper wire and the vessel filled with water. A capillary tube projected below this container but in communication with it. When the nerve was stimulated, by pulling on it with a fine silver wire, the muscle contracted. There is some doubt as to how the nerve was stimulated—either by mechanical pulling or by the use of bimetallic electrodes—since the wire was made of silver and the loop was made of copper. The important point is that when the muscle contracted water did not come out of the capillary tube. Swammerdam thus concluded, as did Glisson, that the volume of muscles does not increase on contraction.

In the eighteenth century the Swiss physiologist Haller (1708–77) assembled compelling evidence against the animal spirit theory. He observed that movement was a property of a wide variety of plant and animal tissues. In particular he emphasized that muscles could contract when stimulated in the absence of nerves. Other tissues such as the leaves of some plants moved on stimulation, without having any nerves. Nerves did not contract on stimulation themselves. Muscles were not small bladders swollen by nervous fluid as suggested by Croone and, moreover, they were not continuous with arteries or veins and could live a while without them. Also, since their nerves were few and distributed transversely, it appeared unlikely that the numerous fibres in a muscle could arise from the few nerves. Haller thus concluded that muscles were tissues in their own right. He still spoke of a nervous liquid which was of a stimulating nature forcing the elementary particles of the muscle fibre to approach nearer to each other. This liquid was of course recognized not to be of the ordinary sort. Haller had shown that nerves do not swell when ligated and found that no drops of fluid came out when nerves were cut. Nor, as the Scottish anatomist Monro (1697–1762) stated about the same time, do nerves have cavities when examined in a microscope.

During Haller's lifetime the possibility that electricity, or the electric fluid as it was called, was the agent of nervous and muscular activity *was* beginning to be discussed. Initially, the evidence was tenuous. It was known that animals could be electrified. Indeed a popular experiment of the seventeenth century was to suspend small boys on silken ropes from the ceiling, then apply a static charge to their feet and detect that they were electrified by applying an electrometer to their noses and eliciting a spark (Winckler, 1748). It was soon discovered that muscles contracted upon electrical stimulation, usually provided from a condenser. The nature of biological tissues, however, wet and apparently quite unlike the insulators and conductors used in electrical experiments did not suggest, to Haller for instance, that electricity could be the transmitter of nervous activity. It was the contribution of the Italian Galvani (1737–98) at the close of the eighteenth century, to popularize the idea that electricity could be generated by animal tissues.

Galvani's initial experiments such as the famous contraction of the frog's legs whenever the frogs, suspended from an iron balustrade by a brass hook through their spinal cords, came in contact with the iron railings, were attacked and almost completely discredited by his fellow Italian Volta (1745–1827). While Galvani thought the contraction was due to animal electricity conducted by the metal, Volta (1800) contended rightly that electricity was generated at the brass–iron contact and current flowed round the circuit hook–spinal cord–nerve–leg–railings–hook and stimulated the muscle whenever the circuit was completed by the touching of the frog leg on the iron balustrade.

Galvani's later experiments indicated that muscles could be made to twitch in the absence of metals or indeed any external source of electricity except animal tissues. In these experiments frog leg muscles contracted when the cut end of a frog's spine, connected to a muscle by the muscle nerve, was put in contact with the muscle, or when the cut muscles of one limb were brought up to touch the exposed sciatic nerve of the other limb. In this case the electrical source was what is now called the injury current, that is the current flow between injured and uninjured portions of the muscle.

This current of injury was first measured by the Italian Matteucci (1811–65) in the nineteenth century using a crude galvanometer. He showed, in both animals and man, that a current could be detected which flowed between the cut end of a muscle and its undamaged surface (Matteucci, 1838, 1842*a*). He also found that a frog muscle contraction generated enough electricity to stimulate the nerve of another nerve muscle preparation which was layered across contracting muscle (Matteucci, 1842*b*; Matteucci & Humboldt, 1843). This very famous experiment (the rheoscopic frog) has since been repeated in many physiology practical courses. Matteucci's experiments were repeated and improved by DuBois-Reymond (1818–96) working in Berlin. His most important finding was that the injury current of muscle was reduced during repeated (tetanic) stimulation. DuBois-Reymond called this the negative variation. The reduction was of course due to the action potentials of the muscle. He also went on to demonstrate the same negative variation in nerve and thus has the honour of discovering the action potential of nerve which Matteucci had also looked for, but failed to find, due to his less sensitive instruments (DuBois-Reymond, 1849).

The improvement in detection of electric currents provided by the galvanometer was paralleled in the nineteenth century by improvements in the design of microscope lenses. It became possible to examine the structure of muscle and nerve with some precision. Bowman (1840), for instance, examined the muscles of a wide range of vertebrate and invertebrate species, obtaining particularly clear pictures of insect muscles. Wide tracts of muscles were shown to lack nerves and it was found that nerves came into contact with muscles only at special areas–'endplates'—and there were divided into terminal branches. It was in these areas that muscle contraction began after nerve stimulation (Kuhne, 1862, 1888). DuBois-Reymond (1849) and Kuhne (1888) both considered chemical and electrical explanations of the nerve–muscle link. Their explanations were bound up with their explanation of the mechanism of generation of the action potential. With increasing confidence that action potentials could be explained in terms of ion movements (Bernstein, 1868) the electrical hypothesis came to be accepted. A difficulty of the electrical hypothesis clearly recognized by Kuhne (1888), at that time Professor of Physiology in Heidelberg, is that nerves evidently could not excite muscles by their action currents except when connected to the muscle at their special area of innervation—the endplate. This difficulty Kuhne (1888) explained by postulating a furthering of the excitor effects of the action potential by the endplate. This same difficulty was later to prove fatal to the electrical hypothesis at the nerve–muscle junction (Fatt & Katz, 1951).

The electrical hypothesis received some elaboration as a result of studies of the excitation of nerve and muscle by electrical stimuli. It was realized that strength and duration of the stimuli were the important variables and the French worker Lapicque (1936) concluded that nerve and muscle were uniquely matched so that the action potential in nerve was adequate to stimulate the muscle at the endplate. Agents such as curare, he thought, altered muscles so that their stimulus parameters were such that they could not respond to the action potential. This hypothesis, although it stimulated much work in connection with the excitability of nerve and muscle, was not fruitful in the area of synaptic transmission— in 1946 the last formal defence of the electrical hypothesis (Eccles, 1946a) could be illustrated by a diagram differing very little from the diagram put forward by DuBois-Reymond (1877)!

Even at the time the electrical hypothesis was formally stated experiments were being made which would result in the chemical theory for nerve–muscle transmission that is held today. In Paris, Claude Bernard (1856) was experimenting with the South American arrow poison, curare. Curarized muscle, he found, contracted in the normal way when stimulated directly, but did not contract when its nerve was stimulated. The nerve, however, appeared to conduct impulses towards the region of the nerve–muscle junction. Bernard deduced a block of transmission at the motor nerve in its most distal part where contact was made with the muscle. Later experimenters found, however, that another drug, nicotine, excited the contraction of skeletal muscle and this contraction was prevented, even in denervated preparations, by treatment with curare (Heidenhain, 1883; Langley, 1905, 1908; Edmunds & Roth, 1908). The site of drug action could only be the muscle and the nerve–muscle junction was thus established as a specific pharmacological entity.

Elliot (1905), suggested with regard to the contraction of smooth muscle caused by adrenaline, that this drug reacted with a special receptor substance in the muscle. Langley applied these ideas to skeletal muscle, and in a series of skilful quantitative experiments showed that the receptor substance for curare and nicotine was localized beneath the terminations of motor nerves on skeletal muscle (Langley, 1905, 1907, 1909, 1914). It followed from these experiments that since curare blocked the action of nerve impulses, the nerve impulse too caused muscle contraction by affecting the receptor substance. Langley (1905, 1909), following Elliot's (1904) suggestion of sympathetic nerve action by liberation of adrenaline, felt that motor nerves affected the receptor substance by releasing a chemical. A few years later Loewi (1921) demonstrated for the first time that a nerve ending could release a chemical mediator. He found that upon stimulation of the vagal nerve supply to the frog heart a chemical, later shown to be acetylcholine (ACh) was released which inhibited another isolated frog heart when added to the perfusate. A second example of what came to be called chemical transmission followed when stimulation of sympathetic nerves was shown to release an adrenaline-like substance which accelerated the heart (Cannon & Bacq, 1931; Cannon & Rosenblueth, 1933).

In a long series of investigations Dale and his colleagues extended the scope of chemical transmission from the peripheral synapses of the autonomic nervous system to the nerve–muscle junction and in so doing systematized the method of demonstrating transmitter action. The transmitter substance which had been postulated by Langley (1909) again turned out to be ACh. The principal points of their experiments, which later workers have used and refined as requirements for demonstration of transmitters (Paton, 1958), were:

(1) The demonstration of the presence of, and synthesis of, the transmitter in the animal body (Dale & Dudley, 1929) at the appropriate site (Feldberg, 1943);

(2) the demonstration that the transmitter was released from the appropriate nerve terminals in response to nerve stimulation (Dale, Feldberg, & Vogt, 1936);

(3) the mimicking of nerve stimulation by appropriate application of the transmitter and the identity of the pharmacology of the presumed transmitter and synaptic transmission (Brown, Dale, & Feldberg, 1936; Bacq & Brown, 1937; Brown, 1937). At this time the mechanism by which combination of the transmitter with muscle triggered muscle action potentials and muscle contraction was obscure.

This obscurity was clarified and electrophysiological analysis of synaptic transmission became possible when Göpfert & Schafer (1938), working in Heidelberg, found that nerve stimulation of curarized muscle set up a local electrical potential which could be recorded with leads placed over the nerve–muscle junction. This potential, which consisted of a quick negative deflection and a slower return to the initial potential level became known as the endplate potential (e.p.p.). Pharmacological evidence, such as the progressive reduction of e.p.p. amplitudes with increasing curare concentrations and the prolongation of e.p.p. time course by substances preventing ACh destruction, indicated that e.p.p.s. were set up by a reaction of the ACh released from nerve terminals with muscle receptors. An e.p.p. in turn, if its amplitude exceed a certain critical level, triggered the generation of muscle action potentials which in turn set off muscle contraction (Eccles, Katz & Kuffler, 1941, 1942; Eccles & MacFarlane, 1949).

Final proof of the chemical hypothesis was afforded by the use of intracellular recording. An accurate quantitative measure of the e.p.p. made possible the measurement of total charge displacement during neuromuscular transmission (Fatt & Katz, 1951). This charge (echoing Kuhne, 1888) could not possibly be provided by the action potential in nerve terminals, but could easily be accounted for by the ACh hypothesis. Intracellular recording also allowed new precision in analysis of synaptic events when a novel electrical phenomenon was detected. This was the apparently random appearance of small synaptic potentials (miniature potentials), too small to be detected by extracellular recording (except with microelectrodes) or to generate impulses and occurring in the absence of nerve action potentials (Fatt & Katz, 1952). Present-day analysis of synaptic transmission is concerned with both spontaneous and evoked synaptic potentials, particularly as the evoked synaptic potentials have been shown to be produced by almost synchronous release of packets of ACh which would otherwise be released singly and at random intervals to be detected as miniature potentials (del Castillo & Katz, 1954*b*) (see Chapter 4).

More recent research has been marked by an increasing knowledge of the physico-chemical basis of the transmitter process. In physical terms neuromuscular junctions in vertebrates are transducing elements in which electrical activity, in the form of action potentials in nerve terminals, is translated into the release of ACh (Fig. 1.1). ACh diffuses across the narrow synaptic cleft to react with receptors in the outer surface of the muscle membrane, causing this area to become permeable to ions (Fig. 1.1B). The resultant flow of ionic current across this localized area of membrane

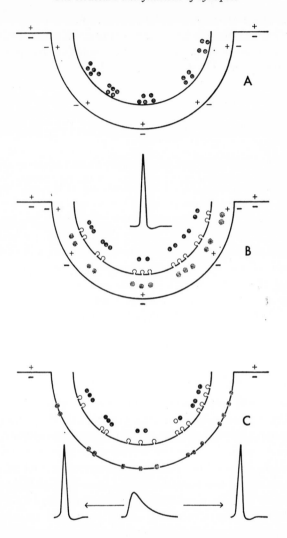

FIG. 1.1. Schematic diagram of chemically mediated synaptic transmission. A. The resting synapse. B. Invasion of presynaptic terminal by a nerve impulse and release of packets of transmitter, possibly from synaptic vesicles, into the synaptic cleft. C. Combination of transmitter with subsynaptic receptors and generation of an excitatory postsynaptic potential which triggers the generation of action potentials (shown by arrows).

generates an electrical potential which is conducted only passively. If this potential, the e.p.p., is large enough, an action potential is initiated and this is propagated along the length of the muscle cell, in either direction. The transducing cycle is complete (Fig. 1.1C) when muscular contraction is triggered in turn by the depolarization of the muscle membrane associated with the propagated action potential.

INADEQUACIES OF PRESENT KNOWLEDGE

The modern theory (Fig. 1.1) is silent about the exact mechanism of ACh release, the nature of ACh receptors and the membrane mechanism triggered by receptor action. This gross ignorance is of course true of all synapses. At many other synapses, particularly in the central nervous system, our ignorance extends still further, to the nature of the suspected transmitter. Furthermore it is now clear that the nerve–muscle junction is a model for chemically transmitting synapses only, for electrical transmission from cell to cell as postulated by DuBois-Reymond and Kuhne indeed exists.

ELECTRICALLY TRANSMITTING SYNAPSES

At electrically transmitting synapses there may be anatomical continuity between pre- and postsynaptic cell (Fig. 1.2A) or at least, a region of very close apposition of their membrane, which has a lower resistivity than the surrounding membrane (reviewed by Bennett, 1966). Fig. 1.2B is an electrical model of such a synapse in which the resistance and capacitance of the pre- and postsynaptic cell (R_I, C_I and R_{II}, C_{II}) are connected by the resistance (R_j) and capacitance (C_j) of the junctional membrane. A potential applied to cell I will spread electrotonically to cell II (Fig. 1.2C) and similarly a potential applied to II will propagate to I (Fig. 1.2D). If the degree of coupling is sufficient, an action potential in either cell will generate an action potential in the other. At the motor giant synapses of the crayfish, however, the junctional region is specialized so that it will transmit electronically only in one direction (Furshpan & Potter, 1959). Potentials applied to cell I may be transmitted to cell II (Fig. 1.2E) but the reverse does not occur (Fig. 1.2F).

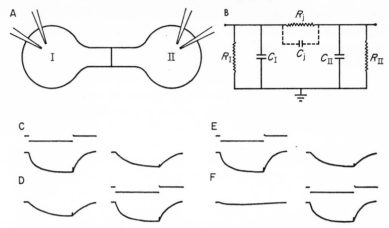

FIG. 1.2. Electrical transmission after Bennett (1966). A. Recording and stimulating electrodes in a pair of cells connected electrically. B. Electrical diagram in which the membranes of cells I and II are represented by their capacity and resistivity (R and C) and are connected by the resistance and capacitance of the junctional membrane (R_j and C_j). C. Effect of a square pulse applied to cell I. Similar potentials are recorded in I (left) and II (right). D. The reverse procedure. Stimulation of II produces a potential in II electronically transmitted to I. E, F. One-way transmission at an electrically transmitting synapse. In E a stimulating pulse applied to the left-hand cell generates a potential in that cell, recorded after electronic transmission to the adjacent cell (right). In F stimulation of this cell produces a potential which is hardly recordable in the cell which was stimulated in E.

SYNAPTIC STRUCTURE

The structure and function of a synapse is conveniently considered in three portions:

(1) the presynaptic element—in many cases a terminal sac or enlargement of the axon, which is a specialization of the axon which carries impulses to the synapse;

(2) the specialized postsynaptic or subsynaptic membrane;

(3) the space between these two elements, the synaptic cleft.

In general the usage of these terms has shown that it is often useful to employ the term 'presynaptic' in reference not only to the terminal portion but also the whole fibre and even the cell of origin. A similar situation arises with the usage of the word 'postsynaptic', which refers not only to the contacted area of a cell, but to the whole cell. It is convenient to use the term 'subsynaptic' for the area of the postsynaptic membrane immediately under the pre-synaptic element which may be distinguished from the rest of the postsynaptic membrane by its receptor and/or electrical properties.

Anatomically, synapses may have a variety of forms. Two main types may be distinguished and these can also be distinguished functionally. One type appears to be associated with chemically transmitting synapses. This type is distinguished firstly by its pre-synaptic portion, which contains abundant mitochondria and, adjacent to the terminal membrane, numerous small, approxi-mately spherical bodies of about 500 Å diameter, the synaptic vesicles, and secondly, by the presence of a synaptic cleft. The discovery that ACh was released in discrete quantal packages (Fatt & Katz, 1952; del Castillo & Katz, 1954b) was made about the same time that electron microscopists were discovering that the neuromuscular junction and other presumably chemically trans-mitting synapses were characterized by the synaptic vesicles (de Robertis & Bennett, 1955; Robertson, 1956), adjacent to the synaptic cleft on the presynaptic side. The temptation to equate quantal release with vesicle packaging (de Robertis & Bennett, 1955; del Castillo & Katz, 1955b, 1956b; Palay, 1956) was presum-ably almost irresistible. At the neuromuscular junction the results of degeneration and regeneration of nerve terminals are in accord with the hypothesis, for spontaneous release of quanta ceases and vesicles disappear at about the same time (Liley, 1956a; Reger, 1957; Birks, Katz, & Miledi, 1960). Recent attempts to produce experimental alteration in vesicle numbers in conjunction with alterations in quantal release rate have also been successful (Hub-bard & Kwanbunbumpen, 1968).

From brain tissue it has been possible to isolate vesicles, some of which have been found to contain and to take up ACh (de Robertis, 1964; Whittaker, 1965, 1966). Alterations in vesicle numbers accompanying various experimental procedures of physiological interest have also been claimed. Thus de Robertis and his col-leagues found changes in vesicle numbers after dark adaptation in rabbit retina (de Robertis & Franchi, 1956) and further striking alterations in vesicle numbers at adrenal medullary synapses after splanchnic nerve stimulation (de Robertis & Ferreira, 1957). Repetition of the adaptation experiments with well-controlled experiments has, however, failed to confirm them (Mountford, 1963) while repetition of the stimulation experiments has not apparently been attempted.

A cleft of 150–250 Å separates the terminal membrane of the presynaptic axon from the subsynaptic region of the postsynaptic cell (Palay, 1958; de Robertis, 1958; Birks, Huxley, & Katz, 1960). In the central nervous system this subsynaptic region may be sited upon the dendrites, body (soma), or axon of the postsynaptic cell, hence the synapse may be described as axo-dendritic, axo-somatic, or axo-axonic. Dendro-dendritic synapses have also been described. At many synapses some specialization is evident in both pre- and subsynaptic membrane. In osmium-fixed neuromuscular and ganglionic material, thickening and darkening of portions of the presynaptic membrane is associated with aggregations of vesicles (Birks, Huxley, & Katz, 1960; de Lorenzo, 1960; Hess, 1965). In neuromuscular material the subsynaptic specialization takes the form of complex folds (reviewed by Couteaux, 1963) while in frog ganglionic synapses bar-like structures are seen subsynaptically (Taxi, 1961). Recent investigations confirm the association of vesicles with presynaptic thickenings at the neuromuscular junction (usually opposite the subsynaptic folds) suggesting that the densities and folds are the sites of release of, and combination with, ACh respectively (Hubbard & Kwanbunbumpen, 1968). In the central nervous system of mammals, fishes, and reptiles, presynaptic thickenings and vesicle aggregation are also associated with postsynaptic thickening and increase in density (Palade, 1954; Fernandez-Morán, 1955; de Robertis, 1956; Palay, 1956, 1958; Wycoff & Young, 1956; Gray, 1959, 1961; Horstmann & Meves, 1959).

The other main type of synaptic structure is associated with electrical transmission. In the central nervous system of fish where combined functional and morphological studies have been made it is found that some synapses are formed by fusion of the opposed pre- and postsynaptic membranes. Both axo-somatic and dendro-dendritic types are found. It should be noted that presynaptic thickenings and vesicles may be seen at such synapses. The vesicles are not as numerous as in chemically transmitting synapses and are not clustered around the presynaptic thickenings in the fashion seen at chemically transmitting synapses (Pappas & Bennett, 1966).

Synapses which show a functional behaviour and structural appearance intermediate between the two main types have been described. For instance the axo-somatic synapses upon chick ciliary ganglion cells show vesicles and mitochondria in the presynaptic portion and a synaptic cleft (de Lorenzo, 1960). Transmission is both chemical and electrical at the majority of these synapses (Martin & Pilar, 1963*a*, *b*). These synapses show a further specialization, however—a myelin sheath surrounding the synapse and postsynaptic cell which presumably increases the electrical coupling between pre- and postsynaptic elements.

2

ELECTRICAL PROPERTIES OF NERVE AND MUSCLE

IT is sometimes forgotten that electrical recording techniques are popular with investigators of neural function not only because of the excellent time resolution of events which they provide but also because of the relative simplicity of the methods and the ease with which results may be interpreted. This simplicity results from the classification that has already been made of the various kinds of bioelectric phenomena and the investigation of how these phenomena stem from the electrical properties of cells. The purpose of this chapter is to review briefly what could be termed the electrical aspects of electrophysiology, and also to show how the electric potentials recorded from nerve and muscle cells have been analyzed on the basis of electrical theory. A recent monograph by Katz (1966) is recommended to those desiring a more leisurely covering of much of this ground.

BIOELECTRICITY

It is convenient to start with a consideration of electricity in the biological organism. To someone who has the usual university training in physics and electricity there may be immediate difficulties. Instead of a flow of electrons, electric current is the flow of ions, either positive or negative. Consequently the convention of current flow being from positive to negative is *not* misrepresentative. Instead of being discretely localized, circuit elements are spatially distributed. Electric potentials are generated as a result of ionic distributions and fluxes; conversely, ionic distributions and fluxes can depend on potential. Perhaps most difficult to assimilate is the fact that resistors (the simplest of circuit elements in ordinary hardware) are in general non-linear, and the changes of potential and current flow which are of physiological significance result from large alterations of resistances in response to appropriate stimuli. However, biological electric theory is made simpler than it might have been by the fact that the magnetic fields associated with current flow are in general negligible in amplitude, and inductive effects are too small to merit consideration. In all of the discussion which follows, all inductive effects will be ignored.

Electric potential

The laws of electricity relevant to bioelectric phenomena may all be derived from a few basic principles. One starts with the observation that there are two kinds of electric charge, designated positive and negative. Like charges repel, unlike charges attract. Thus, around any charged particle there is an 'electric field' which acts on any other charged particle. This field is a vector field since it is characterized at any point by two values; (1) the magnitude of the force, per unit of testing charge, which is found to be in proportion to the magnitude of the charge giving rise to the field and inversely proportional to the square of the distance away, and (2) the direction of the force which is radially away from or towards the charge. The testing charge, whose presence is necessary in order that the field be detected, will itself have a field around it, which adds linearly to the first. However, one may in principle test with a charge which is small enough to have no appreciable effect. It is convenient to substitute for the vector field which surrounds any charge a scalar field, where every point in space is characterized by a certain 'potential'. The magnitude and direction of the force is then given by the gradient of the potential. The potential at any point may be defined as the work that would be done in bringing unit charge (positive) from far away (where the field is effectively zero) to the point in question. Its units are volts, representing joules per coulomb. In practice one always measures the difference of potential between points rather than any absolute value, the reference or zero level being designated ground or earth potential.

Current

In a medium in which charged particles are free to move (e.g., a metal, which contains free electrons, or a salt solution, containing mobile ions), the force associated with a gradient of potential causes the particles to move. This movement is designated electric current, and the medium in which it flows is a conductor. The current is proportional to the number of particles moving, their mean velocity, and the charge upon each. Since current flows *only* as a result of a potential difference, it follows that if there is no current flow, the electric potential or voltage in a conductor is everywhere the same. This fact permits the measurement of electric potential at any point. It is necessary only to connect the point by a conductor to a suitable device (e.g., the grid of a triode, a field-effect transistor) which responds to the potential but does not permit an appreciable current to flow into it.

Circuit Elements

Several elements are necessary to construct electric circuits which simulate those involved in biological processes. Firstly, an active (i.e., energy producing) element—a source of voltage or current. All that need be specified is a 'black box' which produces a defined voltage or current independent of what is connected to its two terminals. It should be obvious that either of these elements is an abstraction. No mechanism could produce a voltage source that maintained its voltage across a path through which charge could move infinitely rapidly—a 'short circuit'. Conversely, constant current could in no way be maintained if there were no conducting path for the current to flow through. Nevertheless, these hypothetical devices, in association with conductors, can mimic exactly the electrical behaviour of actual voltage or current generating systems. The other circuit elements are passive conductors and capacitors.

Conductance

The most common circuit element, the conductor, is the same as a resistor. This is simply anything in which charged particles are free to move, so that current flows if a potential gradient is set up. Because current can flow, no charge separation within a conductor can be maintained, and hence there can be *no net current to or from any point*; if this occurred momentarily, it would lead to a local buildup or deficit of charge and countervailing current. Another way of stating this is that at any point at any time there is a balance of positive and negative charges, or electroneutrality. The fact that current to any point must be equal to current away from it is known as Kirchhoff's Law. Its corollary is that maintained current flow requires that there be a complete circuit around which the current may flow.

It is found experimentally that many conductors obey Ohm's Law, i.e., current is directly proportional to the voltage gradient. This implies that the moving charged particles in the presence of an electric field rapidly reach a limiting velocity at which 'frictional' forces balance the electrical force, as with small objects falling through air. Energy is therefore dissipated, as heat, at a rate proportional to the voltage gradient and the current.

In general,

$$I = \gamma \ \text{grad} \ V, \tag{1}$$

where γ is the conductivity (in mho-cm) of the medium, grad V (volts/cm) is the voltage gradient (also written ∇V), and I (amperes) is the current entering and leaving the point in question. Both I and grad V are vector quantities. In the analysis of potential and current fields in a volume conductor, this equation is the starting point for often very complicated vector algebra.

For the case in which the voltage gradient is one dimensional,

$$I = \gamma \ \frac{\mathrm{d}V}{\mathrm{d}x} \tag{2}$$

where $\mathrm{d}V/\mathrm{d}x$ is the voltage gradient.

It will be evident that for a homogeneous conductor of uniform dimensions, if a voltage of V_1 is imposed at one end and V_0 at the other, the current (I) in the direction of the end at V_0 is the same everywhere along the conductor and is proportional to $(V_1 - V_0)$,

$$I = G(V_1 - V_0) \tag{3}$$

where G is the conductance of the conductor (in mhos).

Conductors in parallel: If several conductors are placed in parallel, i.e., so that the potential across all of them is the same, then the current in each is given by the same formula (eqn. (3)). The total current is given by the formula

$$I_{\text{total}} = (V_1 - V_0)(G_1 + G_2 + G_3 + \ \dots \ ),$$

i.e., conductances in parallel add linearly, and the total current is divided between the conductors in proportion to the conductances, e.g.,

$$I_2/I_{\text{total}} = G_2/(G_1 + G_2 + G_3 + \ \dots \ ).$$

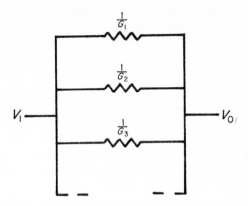

FIG. 2.1. Conductors (resistors) in parallel. The potential across each element is the same.

Conductors in series: Resistance (R) is the inverse of conductance. Since at any point the sum of currents entering and leaving is the same, the current through any of a string of conductors in series is the same.

$$I = G_1(V_0 - V_1) = G_2(V_1 - V_2) = \ldots = G_n(V_{n-1} - V_n)$$
$$V_0 - V_1 = IR_1$$
$$V_1 - V_2 = IR_2$$

etc.

Thus

$$V_0 - V_n = I(R_1 + R_2 + R_3 \ldots + R_n),$$

i.e., the resistances add linearly to give the total resistance.

Also,

$$\frac{V_1 - V_2}{V_0 - V_n} = \frac{R_2}{\sum R},$$

i.e., the total potential difference is divided between conductors in proportion to their resistances.

From these considerations it may also be deduced that the conductance of a cylindrical conductor is given by $G = \gamma \pi a^2 / l$ where a is the radius and l the length.

Capacitance

Capacitance exists whenever two conductors are separated by a nonconductor, or insulator. Since current cannot flow between the

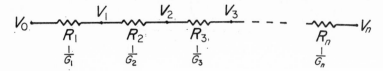

FIG. 2.2. Conductors (resistors) in series. The current through
each element is the same.

conductors, an electrical field and therefore potential difference can
be maintained between the two conductors, each of which is isopotential. The magnitude of the potential depends upon the charge
on the capacitor, that is, the relative excess of positive charge on
one side of the capacitor and deficit or negativity on the other side.
The charged capacitor, despite the charge on it, remains electrically neutral. If for any reason one were to try to charge it on either
side alone, the excess charge would not contribute to the potential
difference between the sides; because of electrostatic interaction
across the insulator the potential on both sides of the capacitor
would charge equally. The process of charging or discharging a
capacitor requires flow of charge on either side, i.e., a current to
one side of it and an equal current away from the other side. Thus,
Kirchhoff's Law applies to capacitors as well as to conductors. The
current which flows to and from a capacitor is termed capacity
current and is often spoken of as though it went through the
capacitor, though of course no charge actually crosses the insulator.

It follows from the fact that electrical fields add linearly that the
potential difference across a capacitor should be linearly related to
the charge on either side. This proportionality is written

$$V_c = Q_c/C, \quad Q_c = CV_c \tag{4}$$

where Q_c is charge in coulombs, V_c the voltage across the capacitor, and C the capacitance. For a capacitor made up of two parallel
conducting areas separated by an insulator the capacitance (or
capacity) is very nearly exactly proportional to the surface area of
each plate and inversely proportional to their separation. It also
depends upon the 'dielectric constant' of the insulator separating
the conductors. That this is greater for insulating material than for
a vacuum or air is attributed to induced charges on either surface of
the dielectric. For other geometrical arrangements, calculation of
capacitance is considerably more complicated.

Any alteration of the charge on a capacitor and therefore the potential across it is due to a flow of charge (i.e., current) to and from the capacitor. Differentiating eqn. (4), one has

$$C \frac{dV_c}{dt} = \frac{dQ_c}{dt} = I_c; \tag{5}$$

that is, capacity current is proportional to the rate of change of voltage across the capacitor.

It will be evident from the above equation that capacitors in parallel, like conductors in parallel, add linearly, and current is divided between them as by conductors in parallel.

RC circuits

From the defining properties of resistors (i.e., conductors) capacitors, and voltage or current sources, the behaviour of simple circuits containing these elements may be derived easily. For the sake of brevity the circuit shown in Fig. 2.3 will be considered. This contains many of the features which arise in circuits simulating nerve or muscle cells.

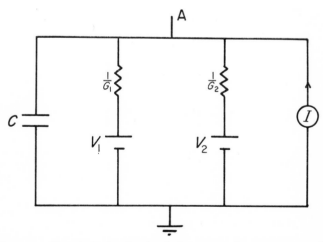

FIG. 2.3. Electrical circuit simulating area of nerve or muscle membrane.

In this circuit each conductor–battery combination is in parallel with the capacitor from the 'point of the view' of the current generator (I) or the other conductor–battery combination, but each conductor is in series with the parallel combination of capacitance and other branches of the circuit from the point of view of the corresponding battery. The circuit can therefore be turned into a pure series or parallel circuit by adjusting values of the elements.

To analyse the circuit one starts with consideration of the current at point A. At this point the potential at any time is the potential across the capacitor and will therefore be designated V_c. Applying Kirchhoff's Law, the sum of all the currents outward from this point is zero,

$$C \frac{dV_c}{dt} + G_1(V_c - V_1) + G_2(V_c - V_2) - I = 0$$

rearranging,

$$C \frac{dV_c}{dt} + (G_1 + G_2)\{V_c - (G_1V_1 + G_2V_2 + I)/(G_1 + G_2)\} = 0.$$

If G_1, G_2, V_1, V_2, and I are constant, then the term in the large brackets may be designated V_c' and $dV_c'/dt = dV_c/dt$.

Also, to simplify matters one can write

$$\tau = C/(G_1 + G_2)$$

then, the equation becomes

$$\frac{dV_c'}{dt} + \frac{1}{\tau} V_c' = 0$$

$$\frac{dV_c'}{V_c'} = -\frac{dt}{\tau}$$

integrating, $\ln V_c' = \frac{t}{\tau} + \ln k$

$$V_c' = k \; e^{-t/\tau}$$

where k is a constant of integration.

For generality let us say that at time zero V_c was equal to V_0. One could assume that at time zero one or more switches were closed to bring the circuit to the final configuration considered. Then,

$$k = V_0 - \left(\frac{G_1V_1 + G_2V_2 + I}{G_1 + G_2} \right).$$

The complete solution is

$$V_c = V_0 \, e^{-t/\tau} + \left(\frac{G_1 V_1 + G_2 V_2 + I}{G_1 + G_2}\right)(1 - e^{-t/\tau})$$

or

$$V_c - V_0 = \left(\frac{G_1 V_1 + G_2 V_2 + I}{G_1 + G_2} - V_0\right)(1 - e^{-t/\tau}). \tag{6}$$

Thus, the potential changes in such a way that the difference from its starting value rises asymptotically to a new level determined by the current and voltage sources in the circuit. By setting either V_1 or V_2 in the above equation to zero, it can be seen that each battery–conductor combination is equivalent to a current source in parallel with a conductor. In general a circuit like that above could equally well be represented as either of the simple circuits below. In the first case the value of the current source

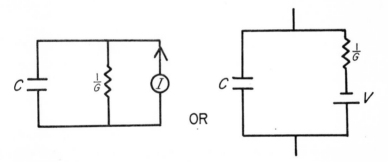

OR

FIG. 2.4. Circuits equivalent to those in Fig. 2.3. See text for further description.

is equal to $(I + G_1 V_1 + G_2 V_2)$, the value of the conductor $(G_1 + G_2)$. In the second case the value of the battery would be $(G_1 V_1 + G_2 V_2 + I)/(G_1 + G_2)$, the value of the conductor being, again, $(G_1 + G_2)$.

The 'time constant', τ, is the time at which the charging or discharging process goes to $1/e$ of completion. Its value is given by the product of the capacity and the inverse of the *total* conductance connecting the two sides of the capacitor.

It should be noted that in the circuit just considered in Fig. 2.3, it is quite irrelevant whether the resistors are drawn above or below the batteries. From the point of view of the capacitor each battery–resistor combination acts as a whole, and the resistor drawn in each may be the internal resistance of the battery or, in general, the 'source impedance'. If the active element is regarded as a voltage source, then this impedance is in series with it; if it is regarded as a current source, the impedance is in parallel with it.

A slightly different RC circuit arises in connection with recording. This is shown in Fig. 2.5A, while Fig. 2.5B shows a similar circuit without the coupling capacitor (C_c).

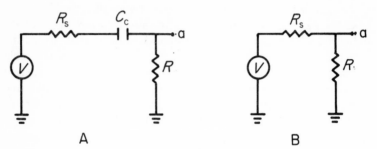

A   **B**

FIG. 2.5. Circuits encountered when potential is to be measured.

In each case the source resistance is designated R_s, and the effective resistance presented to the signal by the amplifier is R_r. For exactness, impedances (see below) should replace the resistances.

In case B the potential recorded at point 'a' is evidently

$$V_a = VR_r/(R_r + R_s).$$

Thus, if source resistance is high (as in microelectrode work), the internal resistance of the recording device must be *very* high. Hence the need for a preamplifier with very high 'input' impedance and low 'output' impedance. In case A the potential at 'a' is the same as it would be in case B at the moment when a square voltage pulse is applied and current starts to flow—the capacitor is uncharged. The capacitor charges exponentially (with time constant equal to $C_c(R_s + R_r)$), until the potential on its left is V and on its right, at point 'a', the potential is zero. Thus, this circuit cannot be used to record steady (d.c.) potentials. This is, of course, 'a.c.' recording, and its exact characteristics will become evident in the next section.

Alternating current

The behaviour of RC circuits in response to sinusoidal voltage or current is of interest for two reasons. One is that measurement of response of a 'two terminal network' to sinusoidal current of different frequencies is the most powerful method of analysing the makeup of the network. The other is that voltage or current transients of any wave form can be analysed into sinusoidal components. An understanding of response to sine waves therefore gives an immediate qualitative understanding of what the response to a complex wave form will be.

A sine wave of a given frequency and magnitude may be divided into two vectorial components at right angles to one another, as shown in Fig. 2.6. The absolute magnitude of the wave is given by

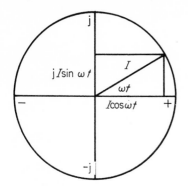

FIG. 2.6. Vector diagram showing analysis of sine wave into two components—one in phase with arbitrary reference ($I \cos \omega t$), the other 90° out of phase ($jI \sin \omega t$). The absolute value of the wave is the vector sum of the two components $(I \sqrt{\cos^2 \omega t + \sin^2 \omega t} = I)$.

the vector sum of the two components. The arithmetic using the j operator is usual, except that $j^2 = -1$. Note too that $\omega = 2\pi f$ where f is the frequency. Suppose a sinusoidal current i is passed 'through' a capacitor, then

$$C \frac{dv}{dt} = i = I(\cos \omega t + j \sin \omega t)$$

$$v = \frac{I}{C} \int (\cos \omega t + j \sin \omega t) \, dt$$

$$= \frac{I}{\omega C} (\sin \omega t - j \cos \omega t)$$

$$= -j \frac{I}{\omega C} (\cos \omega t + j \sin \omega t) \tag{7}$$

$$= -j \frac{i}{\omega C}.$$

Also,

$$i = \frac{\omega C v}{-j}$$

$$= j\omega C v.$$

The same result is obtained if one considers the application of a sinusoidal voltage and calculates the voltage resulting. In either case the result means that the current through the capacitor is ωC times the voltage and 'leads' it by 90°. The 'admittance' of a capacitor is analogous to the conductance of a conductor and is equal to $j\omega C$. The 'reactance' is the inverse of admittance.

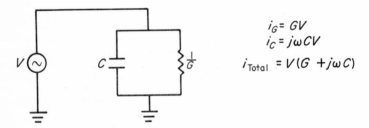

$i_G = GV$
$i_C = j\omega CV$
$i_{Total} = V(G + j\omega C)$

FIG. 2.7. A sinusoidal voltage source in series with a parallel RC circuit.

It is not difficult to work out (Fig. 2.7) the admittance (Y) and impedance (Z) of a conductor and capacitor in parallel:

$$Y = G + j\omega C$$

$$Z = \frac{1}{G + j\omega C} = \frac{G - j\omega C}{G^2 + \omega^2 C^2}. \tag{8}$$

By definition, impedance (Z) consists of the sum of a 'real' and an 'imaginary' component—the 'real' component (R) is that which gives sinusoidal voltage *in phase* with applied current, the 'imaginary' component (jX) that which is *out of phase*. By definition

$$Z = R + jX,$$
$$\theta = \tan^{-1}(X/R) \text{ where } \theta \text{ is phase shift.}$$

From eqn. (8)

$$R = G/(G^2 + \omega^2 C^2)$$
$$X = -\omega C/(G^2 + \omega^2 C^2)$$

the absolute magnitude of the impedance ($|Z|$) is what determines the actual magnitude of the voltage response:

$$|Z| = \sqrt{(R^2 + X^2)}. \tag{9}$$

It is useful to note that X and R are rather simply related

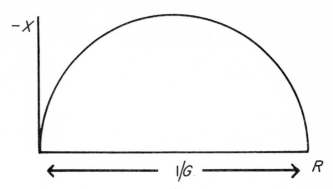

FIG. 2.8. Graph of $-X$ vs R for circuit shown in Fig. 2.7.

graphically, the plot of X versus R giving a semicircle centred at $1/2G$ since, eliminating C from the last equations,

$$X^2 = R^2 - R/G$$

$$X^2 - \left(R - \frac{1}{2G}\right)^2 = \left(\frac{1}{2G}\right)^2.$$

If the parallel RC circuit is put in series with a conductor (G_2) R is increased by $1/G_2$, independent of ω, the angular frequency of the wave. Thus, the semicircle is shifted by this amount to the right.

Perhaps the easiest method for determining θ, R, and X at different frequencies is by plotting current passing through the network versus the voltage across it, on the oscilloscope, as shown in Fig. 2.9. The absolute value of the impedance is given by the ratio of maximum voltage to maximum current.

$$|Z| = \sqrt{(R^2 + X^2)} = V_{max}/I_{max}.$$

The 'imaginary' part of the impedance, X, is given by the ratio of the voltage where current is zero (V_0) to the maximum current.

$$X = V_0/I_{max}.$$

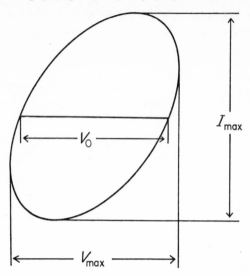

FIG. 2.9. Graph of current against voltage for circuit in Fig. 2.7. as would be observed on oscilloscope if the applied voltage modulates X deviation of the cathode ray beam, while current through circuit modulates Y deviation. From the ellipse, values of X and R can be obtained, as explained in the text.

Thus R and θ may also be obtained, making use of the relations

$$R = \sqrt{(Z^2 - X^2)}$$
$$\tan \theta = X/R.$$

Perhaps the most important result which emerges from the above discussion, for the understanding of the electrical properties of cells, is that the impedance of the RC parallel circuit is frequency dependent, becoming smaller as the frequency increases. Thus, the exponential time course of the response to a square current pulse, e.g., from switching on a constant current generator, can be looked upon as resulting from a filtering of the high-frequency components of the pulse, only the d.c. component being entirely unfiltered. The higher the frequency component of the square current pulse the less corresponding voltage appears across the circuit.

ELECTRIC POTENTIALS GENERATED BY CELLS

The membrane as a barrier for ionic movement

One of the basic concepts on which the present theory of electrobiology is based is that cells have a thin surface barrier which limits the diffusion of large molecules and charged particles into and out of the cell. Evidence for this view is very considerable and need not be considered here in any detail. It includes, for example, experiments on the movement of radioactive potassium ions into, within, and out of *sepia* (cuttle-fish) axons (Hodgkin & Keynes, 1953) or the movement of radioactive sodium and potassium ions into and out of muscle fibres (Hodgkin & Horowicz, 1959*a*) and also measurements which effectively compared the conductance within the cell cytoplasm and the conductance of the cell membrane (e.g., Hodgkin & Rushton, 1946; Katz, 1948; Falk & Fatt, 1964). Whether it is in fact the membrane itself, as visualized by the electron microscope, that forms the effective barrier remains uncertain, although it would seem to be reasonable in view of the lipoprotein or mixed lipid and protein structure that has been proposed for the membrane (e.g., Danielli & Davson, 1935). Pure bimolecular lipid artificial membranes are practically impermeable to ions (Huang, Wheeldon, & Thompson, 1964; Mueller, Rudin, Ti Tien, & Westcott, 1964). The problem then becomes to explain the conductivity that is observed. It has been shown that adsorption of certain proteins on to these lipid films greatly lowers their electrical resistance (Mueller & Rudin, 1963), i.e., greatly increases their ionic permeability. An example of the kind of theory that could explain the ionic permeability of such membranes is that of Watkins (1965). He has suggested that the protein, which contains charged groups, partially disrupts the liquid or liquid crystalline matrix of the lipid layer by penetrating the membrane at certain points. The protein chains could merely invaginate (Fig. 2.10B) or actually penetrate (Fig. 2.10C) the lipid layer. The polar discontinuities would provide channels for ion diffusion. The effects of transmitter substances and pharmacological agents which alter membrane permeability could be explained if complexes formed between one or another component of the lipid protein system at a discontinuity and the specific substance in question. Membrane permeability and conductance would vary with the size of the hydrophilic channels. Membrane capacity would be due to the intervening areas of insulating lipid separating the conducting solutions on either side of the membrane.

Although identification of the cell membrane with the physiologically defined 'surface barrier' cannot at present be altogether justified, the term 'membrane' is in fact commonly used in this context and this practice will be maintained in the discussion

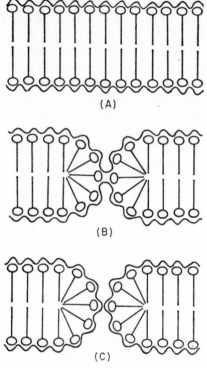

FIG. 2.10. (A) Danielli Davson concept of a cell membrane. The eliptical regions represent the 'polar head groups' of lipids, the tails of which are directed into the interior of the membrane, and the undulating lines represent adsorbed protein. (B) and (C) Schematic representation of 'polar discontinuities'. In (B) protein chains invaginate, but do not penetrate right through the membrane. In (C) protein chains are depicted making contact with both extra- and intracellular surfaces of the lipid core. The continuous lines do not necessarily represent single protein chains in either case, nor is it essential to the theory to have two such penetrating protein components (Watkins, 1965).

which follows. It should also be noted that the picture of the membrane suggested above is not at all essential to most of the arguments and discussions that follow. The analysis of cell membrane properties into membrane batteries, conductances, and capacitances may be regarded as nothing more than an operational convenience, on the basis of which cell behaviour under some conditions may be described and which is useful in predicting behaviour under closely related conditions. Other theories than the membrane theory may lead to much the same predictions. In particular, the theory of Ling (1962) can explain the membrane potential and its alterations on the basis of specific binding of ions to polyelectrolyte protein; this physical picture yields the same equations as does the more usual membrane theory. Indeed, the two theories are not exclusive and a combination of the two seems likely to develop. For the interpretation of experiments on perfused squid axons the existence of a fixed charge layer on the inside of the axon has been postulated (Baker, Hodgkin, & Shaw, 1962; M. R. Bennett, 1967). The behaviour of membranes containing fixed charges which interact specifically with ions (ion exchange membrane) can be shown to be equivalent to membranes which discriminate solely on the basis of 'pore' size, that is, simply as sieves, with the important difference that one no longer has to assume that the membrane permeability to ions depends solely on ionic dimensions. This may help to resolve the paradox that membranes are indeed sometimes more permeable to larger ions than to small ones (cf. Lettvin, Pickard, McCulloch, & Pitts, 1964).

The equilibrium potential for an ionic species—Nernst equation

It was first proposed by Bernstein (1902) that the electrochemical theory worked out by Planck, Nernst, and Ostwald could be applied to explanation of the potential difference that exists between the interior of a cell and the outside medium.

The logic goes somewhat as follows. It is an observed fact that the concentrations of some ions are very different inside cells from those outside. In particular, the concentration of potassium ions within is usually much greater, by about thirty-fold in vertebrates. How could such a difference be maintained? The answer was that if there were a net negative charge within the cell, then, even if the membrane were permeable to potassium, the outward movement of potassium would be impeded. At a certain 'membrane' potential electrical forces would balance the tendency for the ion to diffuse out, and inward and outward fluxes would be equal. The electric potential at which this balance should occur is that at which the potential energy of the ionic species is the same on either side of the membrane. It can therefore be calculated as follows.

The work done, per mole, in bringing ions to a potential V_i from a potential V_0 is simply

$$W = zF(V_i - V_0)$$

where W is work done and therefore difference of potential energy, z is valence (negative or positive), and F is the Faraday (coulombs per mole).

The difference of potential energy per mole, between two solutions of different concentrations (or, more correctly, activity) is equivalent to the work done in changing the volume in which one mole of solute molecules are distributed. According to kinetic theory this is strictly analogous to compressing a gas, since the solvent molecules serve merely to separate and distribute. Hence

$$W = - \int_{V_0}^{V_i} P \, dV$$

where P is pressure, and V is volume. The negative sign is needed, since work is done in reducing the volume. From the gas law

$$PV = RT$$

where R is the gas constant and T is absolute temperature. Hence,

$$W = - \int_{V_0}^{V_i} RT \, \frac{dV}{V} = RT \ln \frac{V_0}{V_i}$$

$$= - RT \ln \frac{A_0}{A_i}$$

where A_0 and A_i refer to concentrations or, more accurately, activities, out and in respectively (since these are reciprocally related to volume for constant amount of material). The 'chemical potential' on either side is $RT \ln A$, plus an arbitrary constant, the standard chemical potential. For equilibrium, the total potential energy per mole, or electrochemical potential, must be the same on both sides. Hence,

$$zF(V_i - V_0) - RT \ln \frac{A_0}{A_i} = 0$$

$$V_i - V_0 = \frac{RT}{zF} \ln \frac{A_0}{A_i}.$$

This equation, known as the Nernst equation, gives for any ionic species the membrane potential (voltage difference across the membrane) at which there is no net flux of the ion. It will be noted that no assumptions regarding the nature or thickness of the membrane, nor the potential gradient within it (i.e., field distribution), nor indeed the permeability of the membrane, are necessary.

There is no reason to doubt its application under any circumstances, with the proviso that it is only net passive flux that is considered; active transport could give a net flux although the membrane potential was at the equilibrium potential for the ion.

Another way of deriving the Nernst equation, which is instructive (cf. Johnson, Eyring, & Polissar, 1955), is to note that ionic flux anywhere can be obtained by adding the fluxes due to diffusion down the activity gradient (M_D) and that due to movement in an electrical field (M_E) in one dimension, corresponding to a membrane with no voltage gradient except between inside and out.

From the equation defining D, the diffusion constant,

$$M_D = - D \frac{\mathrm{d}A}{\mathrm{d}x} \tag{10}$$

where $\mathrm{d}A/\mathrm{d}x$ is the activity gradient.

$$M_E = - uA \frac{\mathrm{d}V}{\mathrm{d}x} \text{ (for a positively charged ion)}$$

where u is the mobility of the ion in aqueous solution.

According to the theory of diffusion and electrical drift,

$$D = \frac{RT}{zF} u$$

rearranging, $u = DzF/RT$.

It may also be noted at this point that permeability (P) is closely related to the diffusion constant

$$P = D\beta/a = u\beta(RT/azF) \tag{11}$$

where β is the partition coefficient between the medium and aqueous solution and a is the membrane thickness. Thus, at any point in the membrane

$$M = M_D + M_E = - D\left(\frac{\mathrm{d}A}{\mathrm{d}x} + \frac{zF}{RT} A \frac{\mathrm{d}V}{\mathrm{d}x}\right)$$

$$= - D \exp\left(-\frac{zF}{RT} V\right) \frac{\mathrm{d}}{\mathrm{d}x}\left\{A \exp\left(\frac{zF}{RT} V\right)\right\}. \tag{12}$$

This differential equation is analogous in form to the one-dimensional flux equation for an uncharged particle:

$$M_D = - D \frac{\mathrm{d}A}{\mathrm{d}x}$$

with 'electrochemical activity', the term whose derivative is in brackets in eqn. (12), replacing chemical activity (A), and with the multiplying constant now a function of V, the potential at the point. The electrochemical potential ($\bar{\mu}$), derived previously, is seen to be related to the electrochemical activity in the same way as chemical potential (μ) is related to activity.

$$\mu = RT \ln A + \mu_0$$
$$\bar{\mu} = RT \ln [A \exp (zfV/RT)] + \mu_0$$
$$= RT \ln A + zFV + \mu_0$$

where μ_0 is the standard chemical potential, which is a function only of temperature and pressure.

The differential equation (eqn. (12)) is the starting point for calculation of ionic flux, and hence ionic current (multiplying flux by zF), when net flux is not zero. Unfortunately, its integration is possible only if assumptions are made regarding the electric field within the membrane.

For the simple condition that there be *no* flux, eqn. (12) yields the Nernst equation, since then the gradient of the electrochemical activity is everywhere zero.

$$A_0 \exp \left(\frac{zFV_0}{RT} \right) = A_i \exp \left(\frac{zFV_i}{RT} \right).$$

$$V_i - V_0 = \frac{RT}{zF} \ln \frac{A_0}{A_i}.$$

Several useful consequences follow from the above considerations. If a membrane be permeable to only one ionic species, it follows that there develops across the membrane a potential with a value equal to the equilibrium potential for the ion as given by the Nernst equation. It is evident that there can be no maintained flux of the ion down its concentration gradient, since no co-ion can go with it, and the only way in which the equilibrium (no flux) condition can be brought about is by the development of a potential gradient across the membrane. The process can be visualized as follows. As permeable ions diffuse across the membrane they leave behind an excess of the opposite charge. As the charge separation increases, so does the electric potential across the membrane, until electrical forces balance the tendency to diffuse. Of course, this occurs when the membrane potential is exactly the same as the equilibrium potential for the ion.

It is interesting to note that this hypothetical membrane, although it is permeable to an ionic species and therefore permits the passage of electric current through it (one could put a wire on either side and pass current between them), also maintains indefinitely a difference of potential across it, which has developed because of charge separation. It is therefore a capacitor as well. In effect, in proposing a semipermeable membrane it has been necessary to assume a structure which behaves like a mosaic of conductances (the ionic channels) and capacitors (the areas which have no channels) which are effectively arranged in parallel. It may easily be calculated that for a membrane like that of a cell, with a capacitance of a few microfarads per square centimetre, the charge separation associated with a transmembrane potential of about 90 mV is equivalent to an excess charge on either side of the membrane corresponding to only a small proportion of the ions present in a region a few ångströms thick. Although any alteration of membrane potential will involve movement of ions, the corresponding change in ionic concentrations will be negligible.

Donnan equilibrium

A simple result emerges also if it is supposed that the hypothetical membrane is permeable to one species of co-ion as well. For example, a membrane might be permeable to both K^+ and Cl^-. Now, there can be equilibrium only if the net flux of each ion is zero—electroneutrality could otherwise be maintained only if both ions moved together, and then there would be no osmotic balance. Therefore,

$$V_i - V_o = \frac{RT}{F} \ln \frac{[K]_o}{[K]_i} = \frac{RT}{-F} \ln \frac{[Cl]_o}{[Cl]_i}$$

$$\ln \frac{[K]_o}{[K]_i} = \ln \frac{[Cl]_i}{[Cl]_o}$$

$$[K]_o[Cl]_o = [K]_i[Cl]_i. \tag{13}$$

This represents the so-called Donnan equilibrium. It is evident that for osmotic balance there must be an appropriate concentration of impermeant ions on either side of the membrane. With no impermeant ionic species, both K^+ and Cl^- will distribute equally on either side of the membrane. If there is impermeant anion on one side, to have osmotic as well as electrical balance requires that there be corresponding impermeant cation on the other side.

The three conditions for equilibrium are of course, (1) electro-neutrality on both sides of the membrane, (2) equal osmotic pressures on either side, and (3) the above equation (13). From these may be calculated the changes that will occur if the con-centration of K^+ and Cl^- outside a hypothetical cell are changed. If, for example, 10 mM KCl is added outside, then both K^+ and Cl^- inside the cell will go up by 10 mM. There will be no change in volume. If K^+ is raised but Cl^- lowered (with impermeant anion making up the difference, and impermeant cation lowered by an amount equivalent to added K^+), so that their product is kept con-stant, then neither cell volume nor intracellular concentrations will change. If either K^+ or Cl^- outside is changed independently, then although the concentration of impermeant ions is changed to main-tain isosmolarity, there will be a redistribution of the ion whose concentration outside was changed, and swelling or shrinking of the cell!

Bernstein's hypothesis

It should be emphasized that the equilibria discussed above are true equilibria. The potential established across the membrane is maintained as long as the ionic distributions are maintained, and no expenditure of energy is involved.

On this basis, Bernstein suggested in 1902 that the membrane potentials of nerve and muscle cells were generated as a result of their membranes being specifically permeable to K^+. The presence of an excess of indiffusible anion inside the cell and indiffusible cation (Na^+) outside would then lead to the observed inequality of potassium between intracellular and extracellular compartments, and the resulting membrane potential.

The main support for Bernstein's hypothesis comes from the many observations that resting potential alters in the manner predicted when the potassium concentration ratio is altered. This has been done by altering the external $[K^+]$, on a variety of tissues (e.g., Cowan, 1934; Adrian, 1956) and, in the squid giant axon, altering the intracellular $[K^+]$ as well (Baker, Hodgkin, & Shaw, 1962). However, major modifications of the hypothesis have become necessary. One of these has already been considered in principle. In a number of tissues, vertebrate muscle in particular, the membrane is permeable to Cl⁻ as well as to K⁺. In muscle, Cl⁻ is not actively transported and becomes distributed in accord with the Donnan equilibrium. Changing Cl⁻ concentration while keeping the external K⁺ constant therefore results in only a temporary change in membrane potential, while the new equilibrium is being established (Hodgkin & Horowicz, 1959*b*).

The most important modification of the theory arises from the fact that there is abundant evidence that cell membranes are not permeable only to K⁺ or Cl⁻, but also to other ions, especially Na⁺, under resting as well as active conditions (e.g., Hodgkin & Horowicz, 1959*a*). Sodium ions (and likewise divalent cations) are obviously not distributed across the membrane in the same proportion as is K⁺.

There must be therefore a net passive flux of sodium across the membrane, and a running down of the electrochemical gradient for K⁺, and cell swelling would occur were it not for an ionic 'pump' which acts to maintain these gradients. The result can only be a quasi-equilibrium situation—a steady-state system that depends upon metabolic processes and expenditure of energy. The existence of such a metabolic dependence was indeed implicit in Bernstein's hypothesis, for he proposed that electrical excitation consisted in a breakdown of the specific membrane permeability to K⁺. The system could not remain viable for years unless the sodium ions coming in with each breakdown were subsequently extruded, against both concentration and electrical gradients.

Membrane potential in non-equilibrium conditions—the Goldman–Hodgkin–Katz equation

Since there is, in fact, no true equilibrium for a cell membrane, the Nernst equation, applied to any one ionic species in particular, cannot be used to predict the membrane potential. Instead, it is necessary to go back to the differential equation describing ionic flux, integrate it for each ion concerned, and obtain the membrane potential as the potential at which there is no net movement of charge through the membrane. Goldman (1943) pointed out that if the assumption were made that the electrical field in the membrane is constant (i.e., the potential drop through it linear) such an integration of the flux equations is not difficult. As a result the following equations were derived; the derivation may be found also in Hodgkin & Katz (1949*a*).

$$I_K = -P_K \frac{F^2 V}{RT} \left(\frac{[K]_o - [K]_i e^{VF/RT}}{1 - e^{VF/RT}} \right)$$

$$I_{Na} = -P_{Na} \frac{F^2 V}{RT} \left(\frac{[Na]_o - [Na]_i e^{VF/RT}}{1 - e^{VF/RT}} \right) \qquad (14)$$

$$I_{Cl} = -P_{Cl} \frac{F^2 V}{RT} \left(\frac{[Cl]_i - [Cl]_o e^{VF/RT}}{1 - e^{VF/RT}} \right)$$

where I_{K^+}, I_{Na^+}, and I_{Cl^-} are the contributions of potassium, sodium, and chloride to the total inward current density through the membrane, and where the permeability coefficients (P) are defined by eqn. (11). V is here the transmembrane potential $(V_i - V_o)$.

The total ionic current density through the membrane is zero unless there is an extraneous source of current, hence adding eqns. (14),

$$P_K([K]_o - [K]_i e^{VF/RT}) + P_{Na}([Na]_o - [Na]_i e^{VF/RT})$$
$$+ P_{Cl}([Cl]_i - [Cl]_o e^{VF/RT}) = 0$$

solving for V,

$$V = \frac{RT}{F} \ln \frac{P_K[K]_o + P_{Na}[Na]_o + P_{Cl}[Cl]_i}{P_K[K]_i + P_{Na}[Na]_i + P_{Cl}[Cl]_o}. \qquad (15)$$

Of course, more terms may be added for any other univalent ions to be considered. This equation, known either as the Goldman–Hodgkin–Katz or constant-field equation, has been applied commonly, but often with reservations regarding its validity. It has been shown to be correct for a membrane with a uniform fixed site distribution and 'ideal behaviour', or a homogeneous uncharged membrane—in these cases the field is constant in the membrane (Finkelstein & Mauro, 1963).

It has recently been shown by Sandblom & Eisenman (1967) that the Goldman–Hodgkin–Katz equation (in a general form without restriction as to valence) applies much more generally. Since individual ionic mobilities need not be constant, the electric field need not be constant. The reasoning is fairly involved and need not be repeated here. Suffice it to say that it was possible to derive the equation by consideration of the conditions under which total membrane current is zero and the potential across a membrane is independent of the concentration profiles within the membrane, which is a necessary condition if permeability ratios are to be constant. In agreement with eqn. (11), the permeability ratio for two (univalent) ionic species of the same sign is the product of the equivalent conductance ratio and the ratio of partition coefficients (the partition coefficient for any ion is the ratio between its concentration in the membrane and its corresponding activity in the external solution).

The conditions under which the general version of the Goldman–Hodgkin–Katz equation holds are of considerable interest. They are as follows (Sandblom & Eisenman, 1967). Without any assumptions regarding the valences the equation is generally valid only in membranes permeable to species of one sign (i.e., impermeable to co-ions). The very important exception to this is when the membrane separates solutions of equal ionic strength. In this case the equation for univalent ions is equivalent to that quoted above (eqn. (15)). It is valid in the non-steady state also, if there is only one permeable co-ion.

The authors suggest that the restriction to conditions of equal ionic strength may help to explain the non-constant permeability ratios observed in biological membranes when ionic strength is unequal on the two sides of the membrane, and when permeable species of more than one sign are present (Baker, Hodgkin, & Meves, 1964; Chandler, Hodgkin, & Meves, 1965). Constant permeability ratios would, however, be expected if there were no permeant anions in the solution on either side of the membrane, and it is doubtful if this is indeed the case (Strichholm & Wallin, 1967, quoted in Sandblom & Eisenman, 1967).

With regard to charged sites in the membrane the authors point out that the equation can apply to a variety of membranes containing ion exchange sites which are fixed. It also applies to membranes containing mobile sites, but then only in the steady state, and only provided all charged species are completely dissociated.

A further interesting point is that it is not impossible that each face of the membrane should obey the Goldman–Hodgkin–Katz equation independently, and with a different set of permeability ratios. This would occur if thermodynamic isolation were maintained between the two faces (e.g., by a suitable reservoir of constant ionic composition).

Perhaps the most important restriction on application of the equation is that it depends upon the assumption that electric current is zero *everywhere* in the membrane. In a mosaic membrane there could be local circulating currents, although the total membrane current were zero, and the membrane potential would no longer be independent of the field profile within the membrane. It is difficult to imagine how one could hope to exclude experimentally the possibility of such local currents and the possibility that they exist may help to justify the alternative formulation of ionic currents as linear functions of the difference between membrane potential and ion equilibrium potential, namely:

$$I_K = G_K(V - V_K)$$
$$I_{Na} = G_{Na}(V - V_{Na}) \tag{16}$$
$$I_{Cl} = G_{Cl}(V - V_{Cl}),$$

with the understanding that the conductance terms (G_K, G_{Na}, G_{Cl}) are very likely to be non-constant functions of V (and time). Since total membrane current must be zero, unless membrane potential is changing, or current is imposed from an outside source, one obtains the 'equivalent circuit' equation:

$$V = \frac{G_K V_K + G_{Na} V_{Na} + G_{Cl} V_{Cl}}{G_K + G_{Na} + G_{Cl}}. \tag{17}$$

The advantage of the Goldman–Hodgkin–Katz equation (15) and the voltage–current relations (14) associated with it, is that they provide an indication of how ionic conductances may be expected to vary with membrane potential. The theory predicts, for example, that the instantaneous voltage–current relationship should be non-linear. This is indeed found in myelinated nerve fibres (Dodge & Frankenhaeuser, 1958, 1959) and in squid giant axon when external or internal sodium is changed (Hodgkin & Huxley, 1952*a*). However, rectification does not occur in squid giant axon under normal conditions. This lack may be explained (Noble, 1966; Frankenhaeuser, 1960; M. R. Bennett, 1967) in the following way. The rectification depends upon asymmetric distribution of permeable ions on either side of the membrane; outward current, for example, carries potassium ions into the membrane and the potassium conductance of the membrane therefore should be more when there is outward current than when there is inward current. If it is supposed that there are fixed charges on either face of the membrane, this will introduce a potential jump at this face, and the local concentration of ions will change accordingly.

A suitable fixed charge could therefore make the concentrations equal on both sides of the membrane, and no rectification would occur. At the node of Ranvier instantaneous rectification appears with both the electroresponsive sodium and potassium carrying systems (Dodge & Frankenhaeuser, 1958, 1959; Frankenhaeuser, 1962). As predicted theoretically, the rectification for each disappears when there is no concentration gradient across the membrane.

Hodgkin & Horowicz (1959*b*) examined the behaviour of frog muscle fibres in the presence of various external solutions. Their data showed that membrane potential altered with both potassium and chloride in the manner expected from the Goldman–Hodgkin–Katz equation. For a concentration of potassium less than 10 mM, deviation of membrane potential from the equilibrium potential for potassium could be explained by a resting permeability to sodium about 1% of that to potassium. Changes of chloride concentration produced changes of potential expected if resting chloride permeability were of the same order as the potassium permeability, and these changes were temporary, indicating that chloride is passively distributed. Chloride conductance could be calculated in several ways from the time course of the transients, and was found to be about double that for potassium (cf. Hutter & Noble, 1960*b*), if the muscle were in normal Ringer's solution. In depolarized fibres chloride conductance was raised; this could be explained entirely in terms of the constant-field theory—chloride permeability remained constant.

However, the alterations which were found in depolarized fibres could not be explained in terms of the theory. The membrane potential of fibres depolarized by raised (93 mM) external KCl was not sensitive to reduction of external $[K^+]$ but varied in the same way as a 'chloride electrode' when external $[Cl^-]$ was reduced. This effect indicated that potassium permeability became enormously reduced (to about 1%) when there was a large driving force for outward potassium current. This is in accord with electrical measurements showing 'anomalous rectification'—an increase rather than decrease of membrane resistance when current is outward (Katz, 1949). It is worth pointing out the remarkable agreement of absolute magnitude of resting K^+ and Cl^- conductances, about 100 and 200 mho/cm^2 respectively, with the value of 250 mho/cm^2 for total membrane conductance found by Fatt & Katz (1951). However, Hodgkin & Horowicz (1959*b*) remark on discrepancies between their flux calculations and those found using radioactive tracers.

Another point of interest is that ions may interfere with the movement of other species through the membrane. For example, although the frog muscle membrane is much less permeable to NO_3^- than to chloride, exchanging NO_3^- for external Cl^- does not result in depolarization, even temporarily, as does $SO_4^=$ substitution. This discrepancy is explained by a reduction in P_{Cl} in the presence of NO_3^- (Hutter & Padsha, 1959; Hodgkin & Horowicz, 1959*b*) as indicated by tracer studies (Harris, 1958).

That the results obtained by Hodgkin & Horowicz (1959*b*) with alterations of Cl^- are in accord with the constant-field theory may be construed as evidence that the model is a good one, especially in view of Sandblom & Eisenman's (1967) demonstration that this could be expected only under certain conditions (see above). The Goldman–Hodgkin–Katz equation, without consideration of the Cl^- is, however, expected to be valid under many more general conditions. Indeed, where Cl^- is distributed purely passively, it is evident that it makes no difference, with regard to the steady state, whether the terms for Cl^- are included or not. A change in chloride permeability could alter the membrane potential only if there were a net electrochemical activity gradient for this ion, and at equilibrium there would be none. Unfortunately for simplicity, in many tissues chloride appears not to be distributed passively. For example, in giant axons of the squid (Keynes, 1963) and of crayfish (Strichholm & Wallin, 1965) it appears that the internal Cl^- concentration is higher than is consistent with electrochemical equilibrium. An inwardly directed active transport of Cl^- is therefore indicated, and experiments with metabolic inhibitors support this (Keynes, 1963). In central neurones, if it is considered that it is an increase of chloride permeability that is the mechanism underlying the hyperpolarization associated with inhibition (rather than an increased K^+ permeability at the same time), there must be an inward electrochemical activity gradient for Cl^-, and hence an outwardly directed Cl^- pump (cf. Eccles, Eccles, & Ito, 1964*a*). In smooth muscle chloride ions are found not to be simply distributed between the intra and extracellular space (Goodford, 1964). Whether the Goldman–Hodgkin–Katz equation may legitimately be applied under these circumstances remains unclear.

In most applications the validity of the equation is, in fact, not generally a pressing problem. Either the Goldman–Hodgkin–Katz equation or the equivalent circuit equation may be looked upon as an extension of the Nernst equation to a system with permeability to more than one ionic species. Both equations reduce to the Nernst equation when permeability (or conductance) to one species becomes predominant, and both lead to change of membrane potential in the same direction if ionic permeability or conductance is changed. The basic concept of how the membrane potential is generated—diffusion of ions from high to low concentration causing membrane charging—of course remains unaltered.

Membrane capacity

It was seen in the above discussion of the generation of the membrane potential that according to present concepts, the potential is basically a diffusion potential, caused by a separation of charge which is due to unequal permeability of the membrane to ions of different sign. The separation of charge then entails a membrane potential. Implicit in this is the assumption that the membrane acts as a dielectric separating two conducting regions and there is therefore a membrane capacity. Electrical measurements independently giving evidence for a membrane capacity therefore add significantly to the validity of the electrochemical model as applied to the problem of membrane potential.

Cole (1962) has reviewed some of the early work indicating a membrane capacity (e.g. Cole, 1932). This includes impedance measurements on suspensions of spherical cells, extended later to cells of a variety of types and geometrical configuration—muscle, nerve, yeasts, bacteria, and even mitochondria. In all cases the impedance characteristics could be interpreted in terms of a surface membrane with a capacity of about a microfarad per square centimetre and an internal resistivity (within the cell) of about 100 ohm centimetres—similar to that in isosmotic external solution. Höber (1910, 1912, referred to in Cole, 1962) had provided the first measurement of the membrane capacity and, taking a normal value of three for the dielectric constant, estimated a thickness of 33 Å for the membrane. This was the first good estimate of the molecular dimensions of a living cell membrane, but is less than that estimated from electron-microscopic and X-ray diffraction studies, which indicate a thickness of about 100 Å (e.g., Robertson, 1960). This yields a rather high value of about 10 for the dielectric constant of the membrane.

There may be some objections to the simple picture of membrane capacity as merely due to the membrane lipid or lipoprotein phase (Segal, 1967). The complex impedance plot (R versus X, see p. 27) for some cell membranes is found not to follow a semicircle, as it theoretically should, but instead to follow a semicircle depressed below the axis of the real part of the impedance (Cole, 1962), indicating a phase angle for the membrane capacity of less than 90°. The explanation for this is still unsure. The calculated dielectric constant of about 10 is considered plausible since bulk phase dielectric constants of oils are about 3 and those of proteins in aqueous solution can be ten times higher. However, the high values of proteins are based upon unhindered rotation of dipoles. In a membrane 100 Å thick, with resting potential of nearly 100 mV, the field strength would be about 10^5 volts/cm. Such a high field would strongly align molecules with high dipole moments unless there were strong steric hindrance. The reduction and reversal of intramembrane field strength during an action potential (see below) would lead to freeing of the dipoles, and their rotation, and therefore there would be at this time an increase to dielectric constant and therefore in capacitance, which is observed *not* to occur (Cole & Curtis, 1939). It can therefore be concluded either that rotation of permanent dipoles does not occur (and hence the high dielectric constant is difficult to account for) or that the intramembrane field strength is considerably less than it would appear to be. The latter alternative would indicate an effective membrane considerably thicker than that visualized by the electron microscope. It is also pointed out that ion-exchange membranes (membranes containing fixed charges) may be expected to display and do display capacity-like behaviour, with characteristics very different from those of biological membranes. If biological membranes do contain fixed charges such behaviour might be experimentally found under appropriate conditions, with impedance measurements extended to sub-audio frequencies (Segal, 1967).

It remains of course undoubted that the membrane *behaves* as a capacitor and it is therefore perfectly valid to draw it as such in the electrical analogue of the membrane, with the mental reservation that what this means structurally or chemically is still to some extent obscure. Any electrical model of the membrane is of course nothing more nor less than a statement of the equations describing its behaviour.

Membrane resistance

The question of membrane resistance was in fact treated *pari passu* with the discussion of the membrane battery. It may suffice here to state that the conductance of a membrane must be attributed entirely to its non-exclusion of certain ionic species from moving through it. All current going through a membrane is ionic current, with the exception of capacity current which can, in a sense, be regarded as going through the membrane capacity. It follows also, that ionic current may be separated into the currents carried by different ionic species and the membrane conductance may be divided into partial ion conductances (with the implicit assumption that there is no interaction of movements of different species). Any mobile charged molecular species in the membrane would, of course, contribute to membrane current, and to membrane conductance, even if the species was not present in the solutions on both sides of the membrane.

It will be useful here to define the two measures of conductance encountered in the literature, which arise because of the (usual) nonlinearity of current–voltage relations:

'slope conductance'

$$G_s = \frac{dI}{dV}$$

is the slope of the current–voltage curve, at a certain voltage.

'chord conductance'

$$G_c = \frac{\Delta I}{\Delta V}$$

where ΔV is a voltage step and ΔI the current step resulting or, more commonly, ΔV is the voltage change resulting from a current step ΔI, after an elapse of sufficient time so that capacity current is zero.

In practice only chord conductance may be obtained directly, but this approximates to slope conductance if a small enough step is used, and slope conductance may in any case be obtained graphically.

Equivalent circuit for a small area of membrane

From the preceding consideration of the electrical characteristics of a membrane it follows that an equivalent electrical circuit is the following,

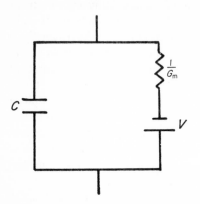

FIG. 2.11. Simplest electric circuit which simulates electrical behaviour of a cell.

where G_m is the membrane conductance, C is its capacitance, and V is the membrane potential. The value of V is given by

$$V = \frac{RT}{F} \ln \frac{P_K[K]_o + P_{Na}[Na]_o + P_{Cl}[Cl]_i}{P_K[K]_i + P_{Na}[Na]_i + P_{Cl}[Cl]_o}$$

noting,
$$\frac{RT}{F} \ln x = 58 \text{ mV} \log_{10} x \text{ at } 20°C$$

$$61 \text{ mV} \log_{10} x \text{ at } 37°C$$

or, with equal validity but with nonconstancy implied for the partial ion conductances,

$$V = \frac{G_K V_K + G_{Na} V_{Na} + G_{Cl} V_{Cl}}{G_K + G_{Na} + G_{Cl}}$$

the membrane conductance being in either case, $G_m = G_K + G_{Na} + G_{Cl}$.

It will be seen that this model gives all the information desired —the membrane potential is V, the membrane conductance is the sum of the ionic conductances and is that which will be found experimentally, and the membrane capacity is between the inside and outside of the membrane.

It is exactly the same if one writes the equivalent circuit a little differently, as in Fig. 2.12, since the complex of batteries and resistors shown now is electrically exactly the same as that shown previously (the only difference is that this implies local currents, but the energy dissipation implied would not be very large). Its

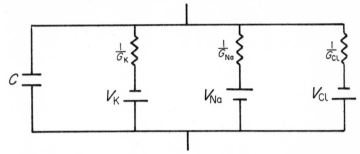

FIG. 2.12. Elaborate version of circuit in Fig. 2.11, with separation of batteries and membrane conducting channels related to potassium, sodium, and chloride.

advantage is that it expresses not only the membrane impedance to current flow (d.c. and a.c.) and the resting membrane potential but also that the flux of any ion species depends upon the difference between the potential across the membrane and the equilibrium potential for the species. It will be seen in a following section of this chapter that membrane permeability to ions may change in specific ways under certain conditions. The electrical model makes very obvious the fact that no change of membrane potential could result from an increase or decrease of membrane conductance to an ion species distributed passively, i.e., with an equilibrium potential equal to the resting potential.

For the sake of clarity it is sometimes useful to split further the membrane battery as diagrammed in Fig. 2.13.

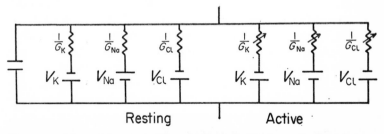

Resting   Active

FIG. 2.13. More elaborate version of circuit in Fig. 2.12, emphasizing *ad hoc* separation of 'active' and 'resting' ionic pathways.

It should be clear that no matter how many separate battery–conductance combinations are indicated, one could equally well write one battery with one conductor in series with it, both altering according to experimental results. Neither formulation should be taken to indicate the membrane structure underlying its properties. The equivalent circuit above does *not* necessarily mean that different ions go through different channels.

In recent years, the equivalent circuit of the membrane has become complicated by the likely existence of one or more non-neutral ionic pumps. The flux of charge produced by such a pump would be equivalent to a current. It could well act independently of the membrane potential and it would then constitute a constant-current generator in the membrane, as in Fig. 2.14.

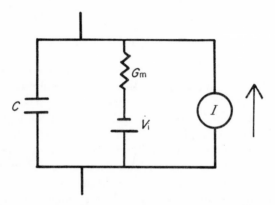

FIG. 2.14. Circuit with membrane current source. See text for description.

In this case V_i is the battery formed by combining the ionic batteries. The membrane potential would be $V_i + I/G_m$ (from the discussion earlier, see eqn. (6). The equivalent circuit could now be rewritten with the current generator combined with the membrane battery, the membrane conductance being unaltered. Essentially, the difference such a pump would make to the system is that membrane potential would change if the conductance of *any* ion changed, even if that ion were passively distributed. If the pump were directed inward (e.g., more K^+ brought in than Na^+ extruded), *any* increase in membrane conductance (e.g., G_{Cl^-}) would tend to cause hyperpolarization, and any decrease in membrane conductance would cause depolarization since the pump would be depolarizing. Conversely, if the pump were outwardly directed, it would cause hyperpolarization, and any increase in membrane conductance would tend to reduce the hyperpolarization.

Equivalent circuit for cells

The equivalent circuit for a whole cell can be the same as that for a small area of membrane only if the interior of a cell is every-where at the same potential (isopotential), under all circumstances. Then the individual 'capacitors' corresponding to each small area of membrane are effectively in parallel, as are the corresponding conducting elements, and one can add together all the membrane capacitance, and all the membrane conductance, obtaining exactly the same formal circuits as written above. This will correspond to a real cell in which the resistance between any two points within is negligible in comparison to the effective resistance between any point and the outside of the cell. Thus it will be true of a cell which is non-elongated in shape, not large, and with no areas on its membrane with conductance very much greater than average. The theoretical behaviour of such a cell has in effect been discussed previously, in the consideration of RC circuits (see eqns. (6) and (8)).

For individual cells, or groups of cells which are electrically coupled, for which the above criteria do not hold true, the equivalent electrical circuit is not the same as that for the small area of membrane. Instead, each portion which is effectively isopotential must be represented separately with resistances connecting such areas (Fig. 2.15).

In the case of a chain of small cells coupled electrotonically, i.e.,

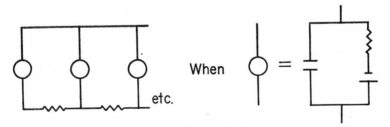

FIG. 2.15. Circuit simulating cell which is elongated, so that all of membrane is not effectively in parallel.

by fused membrane areas of low resistance, the coupling resistors each correspond to the resistance of one of these electrotonic 'bridges'. Since these are membrane areas, to be more exact one should include a coupling capacitor in parallel with each membrane resistor. Explicit solutions for the case of two such cells coupled together have been given by Bennett (1966). Electrotonic bridges connecting chains of cells have been indicated by measurements on cardiac muscle (Barr, Dewey, & Berger, 1965; Weidmann, 1966), smooth muscle, and certain neurones (Bennett, *et al.* 1967*a*, *b*, *c*, *d*). In general, it is possible to solve analytically how such chains of cells will behave if a constant current or sinusoidal current is applied, by integrating the appropriate differential equations, but this is suitable only for fairly simple problems. For cases in which a conductance is changed somewhere, with a rather arbitrary time course, which is what happens with synaptic activity or action potential generation, or when the geometry of the situation is complex, it is usually most convenient to do a stepwise numerical integration of the differential equation, e.g., one can take the case of three cells interconnected, as in Fig. 2.16.

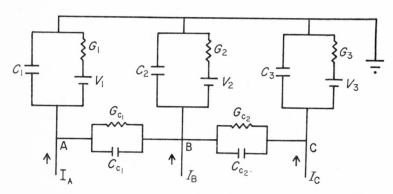

Fig. 2.16. Circuit simulating three small cells interconnected with electrotonic bridges.

Designating the potential at points A, B, and C (corresponding to the interior of each cell) as V_A, V_B, and V_C, and applying Kirchhoff's Law to the points A, B, and C by adding all the current outward at each point and equating to zero, one has

$$C_1 \frac{dV_A}{dt} + G_1(V_A - V_1) + C_{c_1} \frac{d(V_A - V_B)}{dt} + G_{c_1}(V_A - V_B) - I_A = 0$$

$$C_2 \frac{dV_B}{dt} + G_2(V_B - V_2) + C_{c_1} \frac{d(V_B - V_A)}{dt} + C_{c_2} \frac{d(V_A - V_C)}{dt}$$

$$+ G_{c_1}(V_B - V_A) + G_{c_2}(V_B - V_C) - I_B = 0$$

$$C_3 \frac{dV_C}{dt} + G_3(V_C - V_3) + C_{c_2} \frac{d(V_C - V_B)}{dt} + G_{c_2}(V_C - V_B) - I_C = 0$$

By replacing these with difference equations, they may be integrated numerically for any change of any of the parameters with any time course, the accuracy being limited only by the size of the time difference used. Digital computers are eminently suitable for such procedures and suitable methods (see e.g., Ralston and Wilf, 1960) can usually be suggested by consultants at a computer centre.

The more usual case in which the simple electrical model does not apply is that of the elongated cell, like a muscle fibre or nerve axon or dendrite, in which the membrane capacity and conductance are continuously distributed, with no appreciable areas genuinely in parallel. Such a system can be represented by a chain as in Fig. 2.15, with an infinite number of elements, the capacity and resistance of each, and the coupling resistances getting smaller as one considers more and more elements. For the case in which the 'cable' is uniform (that is, conductance, capacity, and resistance per unit length are everywhere equal), well known analytic expressions (see below, under 'geometric considerations') for the response to step current changes ('square pulses') or sinusoidal current may easily be derived. When these conditions are not met, the behaviour may be worked out by numerical integration using a finite number of elements in a model, as already explained. Here the size of the elements chosen, as well as the size of the time interval chosen, limits the accuracy obtained. In general, this method has the effect of underestimating the high-frequency components of a response more than the low-frequency components; for greatest accuracy one should use small elements (i.e., make the 'compartments' correspond to small lengths of the 'cable') where one is interested in high-frequency components. Because high-frequency components of a passively conducted signal become attenuated more rapidly than slow-frequency components as one proceeds down the line from a point where fast charges are being produced (this becomes obvious if one regards each capacitor as an admittance which increases with frequency), it is permissible to use larger and larger compartments as one gets farther away. Thus an axon or muscle fibre which is effectively infinite in length can be effectively mimicked by a finite number of compartments.

For the discussion that follows, concerning electrogenic membrane responses, the quantitative consideration of elongated cells and of cell groups is not of much importance, although it is a good idea to have a qualitative picture of how these should behave electrically. In order not to interrupt the sequence these matters will therefore be dealt with later, under 'geometric considerations'.

ELECTROGENIC MEMBRANE RESPONSES

Electrogenic membrane responses may be defined simply as alterations of membrane potential that occur under physiological conditions. There are several kinds, each with characteristics such as amplitude range, time course, etc. The most important are synaptic potentials, generator potentials, and action potentials. It is now known that these result from changes in specific membrane properties. The sensitive membrane components which are necessary for their generation may be classified as electroresponsive and chemoresponsive, and a third group, found in sensory receptors, as mechanically responsive or responsive to other physical stimuli. Grundfest (e.g., 1966) has christened the last two groups 'electrically inexcitable' to emphasize their non-electroresponsiveness, and hence their inability directly to generate action potentials.

Electroresponsive electrogenic membrane systems

It was discovered by Cole & Curtis (1939) that during an action potential there was no appreciable change in membrane capacity, but the conductance of a squid axon increased, about forty-fold, at this time. This meant that alteration of membrane conductance might be the feature responsible for the generation of the action potential. Further, the critical experiments of Hodgkin & Katz (1949a) established that at the time of the peak of an action potential the membrane potential is sensitive to alteration of external sodium concentration in the manner expected if permeability of the membrane to sodium had increased to become much larger than permeability to potassium. It was then clear that the action potential and its propagation might be explained if it was supposed that the membrane changed its properties, temporarily becoming permeable to sodium, *in response to depolarization*. The full investigation, using the giant axon of the squid, was carried out in a classic series of experiments begun by Hodgkin, Huxley, & Katz (1952) and continued by Hodgkin & Huxley (1952*a, b, c, d*).

The investigation depended upon the use of a 'voltage clamp', previously developed by Cole (1949). The theoretical basis for this concept is in retrospect very simple. It has already been seen that the electrical model of an axon is as follows (Fig. 2.17A), with

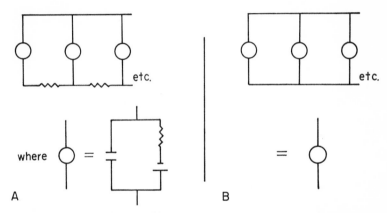

FIG. 2.17. A, Diagram showing equivalent circuit of squid axon. B, simplified circuit produced by inserting a wire along axon core.

resistor–battery combinations which can, at one's convenience, be split into any number of parallel combinations. Introducing current, or imposing a voltage at any point with the axon will produce internal current and potential drop—the voltage across the membrane will be different from one point to another.

Inserting a bare wire along the inside of the axon reduces the internal resistance, so that it is negligible (Fig. 2.17B). The equivalent circuit of the membrane is then very much simplified since one can combine the previously separated membrane capacitors and conductors which are now effectively in parallel. Membrane current (zero if there is no extraneous source) is now related fairly simply to potential:

$$i_m = G(V - V_m) + C \frac{dV}{dt}.$$

Current passes through the capacitor only if the voltage across it is changing; thus, if one had a pure voltage source and confined oneself to square voltage pulses, the equivalent circuit for the membrane would become:

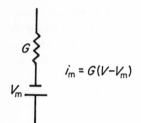

$i_m = G(V - V_m)$

FIG. 2.18. Equivalent circuit of squid axon with voltage clamp in operation, using only square voltage pulses so that capacity current is so brief it can be ignored.

Thus, the current flowing in response to an imposed voltage becomes a simple measure of the membrane conductance and membrane battery.

To produce such a voltage generator, negative feedback was used, as indicated diagrammatically in Fig. 2.19.

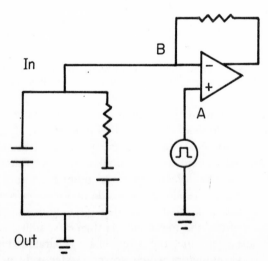

FIG. 2.19. Diagram showing basic circuit of voltage clamp. The amplifier is arranged for negative feedback, to maintain potential at B equal to the reference voltage at A.

Any deviation of the potential at B from that at A is counter-acted by current from the amplifier. Provided the gain of the amplifier is sufficient, the potential at B is held the same as the control potential at A, independent of the load, hence the name 'voltage clamp'. The clamp used by Hodgkin and Huxley was also a 'space clamp' since the potential over a wide area of membrane was controlled.

The results of this investigation are well known and need not be considered in detail here. Essentially, it was found that the current through the membrane could be expressed in the following way,

$$i_m = i_{Na} + i_K + i_l$$
$$i_{Na} = G_{Na}(V - V_{Na})$$
$$i_K = G_K(V - V_K) \qquad (17)$$
$$i_l = G_l(V - V_l)$$

equivalent to the circuit in Fig. 2.20 where G_1 and V_1 refer to

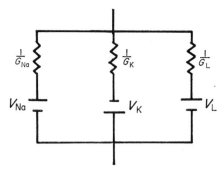

FIG. 2.20. Equivalent circuit of clamped squid axon.

leakage current. Both G_K and G_{Na} were found to be functions of transmembrane potential and of time, when membrane potential was changed, while G_1, 'leakage' conductance, was not. V_{Na} and V_K, as previously discussed, refer to the equilibrium potentials of the two ion species. The time courses with which G_K and G_{Na} altered were also functions of voltage. The famous Hodgkin–Huxley equations which were derived are essentially statements of how membrane conductances were found to vary in response to changes of membrane potential, the experimental observations being expressed in terms of differential equations with time-independent parameters. The fact that these equations, applied to an electrical

c

model of the unclamped axon, result in an action potential similar to that found experimentally (Hodgkin & Huxley, 1952*d*) confirms the view that the membrane properties measured were those involved in action potential generation and that the underlying membrane mechanisms are governed solely by transmembrane potential.

The time courses of the G_{Na} and G_K changes during an action potential in the squid axon have been calculated (Hodgkin & Huxley, 1952*d*) and are illustrated in Fig. 2.21. The dotted line is the time course of the potential change and the full lines those of the conductance changes for sodium and potassium.

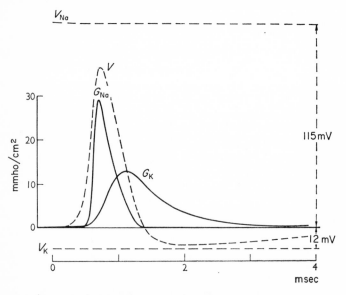

FIG. 2.21. Plot of the numerical solution for the time course of the propagated action potential (V) in squid giant axon and the related sodium (G_{Na}) and potassium (G_K) conductances at 18·5°C. Ordinate (left) conductances in millimhos/cm². Right ordinate potential in millivolts. V_{Na} sodium equilibrium potential, V_K potassium equilibrium potential. Abscissa, time in milliseconds. Modified from Hodgkin (1958).

Threshold

The critical phenomenon necessary for generation of an action potential is evidently the increase in sodium conductance that occurs rapidly but temporarily in response to depolarization. From eqn. (17), one obtains for the outward current (i_m)

$$i_m = V(G_{Na} + G_K + G_1) - G_{Na}V_{Na} - G_K V_K - G_1 V_1.$$

For a certain ΔV, there will be at any subsequent time a certain ΔG_{Na} and a ΔG_K, hence

$$\Delta i_m = \Delta V(G_{Na} + G_K + G_1 + \Delta G_{Na} + \Delta G_K)$$
$$+ \Delta G_K(V - V_K) + \Delta G_{Na}(V - V_{Na}).$$

The membrane slope conductance is therefore,

$$G_m = \frac{\Delta i_m}{\Delta V} = G_{Na} + G_K + G_1 + \Delta G_{Na} + \Delta G_K$$
$$+ \frac{\Delta G_K}{\Delta V}(V - V_K) + \frac{\Delta G_{Na}}{\Delta V}(V - V_{Na}). \tag{18}$$

For a depolarization, that is positive ΔV, all the terms on the right are positive except the last, which is negative and may be large when external $[Na^+]$ is larger than internal, as it normally is. Hence, when a depolarization is sufficient, and therefore the increase in sodium conductance sufficient, the net current in response to a depolarization is inward rather than outward. This is the 'threshold' for action potential generation. When the conductance of the membrane is negative, there results positive feedback and an action potential. To be more precise, if the point is reached at which both chord and slope input conductance is negative, then the net inward current resulting from depolarization causes still more depolarization and further increase in sodium conductance (and thus more negativity of the total input conductance). This increase continues until the new equilibrium potential corresponding to the altered membrane permeabilities is reached, or until other mechanisms come into play. These other mechanisms are inactivation of the sodium current system and increased potassium conductances, both also brought about by depolarization. These also provide the system by which repolarization is brought about, so terminating an action potential, and by which membrane is caused to become inexcitable for a short period following an impulse, preventing permanent cycling of excitation once excitation is begun.

The factors involved in determining threshold stem directly from the requirement that somewhere the net input conductance (the total conductance between the inside and outside of the cell) be negative. Thus any increase in potassium or chloride conductance will raise threshold and make a cell less excitable. So will any factor which makes less steep the relationship between sodium conductance and depolarization (i.e., reduces $\Delta G_{Na}/\Delta V$), including inactivation of the sodium conductance system by antecedent depolarization. The geometry of the cell will also be important —the threshold for excitation of a thin branch of a large cell should be higher than the threshold of an equivalent branch of a small cell. This last consideration arises from the incompleteness of eqn. (18) when one considers a cell whose interior is not always everywhere at the same potential. It is necessary to add terms (which are positive) to the right-hand side, which correspond to current flow from the area which is most depolarized to neighbouring areas.

Hodgkin–Huxley equations and observed action potentials

The membrane systems described by Hodgkin and Huxley can be seen to explain most of the characteristics of action potentials:

(1) a *threshold* level of depolarization at which a cell 'fires'.
(2) *propagation*—internal current causes depolarization of other membrane areas when one area of an elongated cell undergoes an action potential.
(3) *all-or-nothing* character—except under unusual circumstances, in which case action potential generation is limited to a small area of a cell and a 'local response' is observed.
(4) *refractory period*.

The equations also predict, as is observed, that in response to a maintained depolarizing current at one point, there results a train of action potentials with a frequency that in squid axon varies little with the intensity of the depolarization (Stein, 1967). The equations for squid axon do not account for the graded frequencies observed in vertebrate nerve cells and lobster axons in response to a maintained depolarization. It would seem likely that what appear to be minor differences in membrane response could account for this difference in behaviour. Qualitatively, repetitive firing can be explained as follows. Inward current causes depolarization which initiates an action potential. Increased G_K caused by the action potential causes subsequent hyperpolarization (towards the K equilibrium potential) which in turn tends to shut off inactivation of the sodium conductance system. With hyperpolarization G_K tends to return to its resting level; the cell subsequently depolarizes if the inward current is maintained and fires again when threshold potential is reached. The process can repeat indefinitely.

Voltage clamp analysis of electroresponsive systems in lobster axon (Julian, Moore, & Goldman, 1962*b*) and of nodes of Ranvier of myelinated nerve fibres of the toad (Dodge & Frankenhaeuser, 1958; Frankenhaeuser & Huxley, 1964) and in medullary neurones of Puffer fish (Hagiwara & Saito, 1957, 1959*b*) have indicated an action potential mechanism essentially similar to that in the giant axon of the squid. In arthropod muscle, on the other hand, it is Ca^{++} rather than Na^+ that carries inward charge (Fatt & Ginsborg, 1958; Werman & Grundfest, 1961; Hagiwara & Naka, 1964). It is possible that the same may be true for the prolonged action potentials found in mammalian smooth muscle and the plateau phase of the action potential of cardiac muscle (Hagiwara & Nakajima, 1966*a*; Reuter, 1967).

For a more detailed consideration of the problem of action potential generation the recent book by Hodgkin (1964) and the review by Noble (1966) may be recommended. Essentially it can be concluded that action potentials in general result from electro-responsive membrane systems. The potential change is due to a large increase of permeability to an ion which is distributed far from electrochemical equilibrium. The energy dissipated during an action potential therefore stems ultimately from metabolism via the ionic pump which set up the non-equilibrium ion distribution. Although transmembrane ionic flux (Na^+ or Ca^{++} inward) is involved in the action potential, altering the charge on the membrane capacity (ionic current plus capacity current always adds up to zero), the action potential does not depend on any appreciable change in *concentration* of ions on either side of the membrane. Some change of concentrations does undoubtedly occur (Hodgkin & Keynes, 1955*a*), as does movement of water as well (since when the membrane becomes permeable to Na^+ there is no longer an impermeant cation outside to balance osmotically the impermeant anion inside), and compensatory activity of the ionic pump will subsequently be needed to restore the *status quo ante* firing.

'Rectifying' electroresponsive membrane systems

An electroresponsive membrane system may be termed rectifying when membrane conductance alters as a result of altered transmembrane potential, but this is of such a nature as not to cause regenerative activity, as does the sodium conductance system. Examples are, of course, the increase in potassium conductance (G_K) which develops more slowly than the increase of G_{Na} in response to depolarization, and which is termed 'delayed rectification'. It causes membrane potential to become displaced temporarily in the direction of the equilibrium potential for potassium after an action potential. Related may be the fall in potassium permeability that is generally observed when membrane potential increases (Stämpfli, 1959; Baker, Hodgkin, & Shaw, 1962), limiting the hyperpolarization that one may obtain by reducing the potassium concentration outside a cell. Another example is the increase in the chloride conductance that occurs with depolarization in Rajid electroplaques (Bennett, 1961, discussed by Grundfest, 1966). The 'anomalous rectification' of frog muscle fibres (Katz, 1949; Adrian, 1964; Nakajima, Iwasaki & Obata, 1962) (i.e., reduced potassium conductance with depolarization and increased K^+ conductance with hyperpolarization) is an example of a rectification that is in the opposite direction.

Pharmacology of electroresponsive membrane systems

It is appropriate here to mention some of the very useful information that has recently been obtained regarding the pharmacology of the sodium and potassium current (conductance) systems. The sodium current system in a variety of species is blocked by a variety of agents: urethane (Hagiwara & Saito, 1959a), xylocaine (Hille, 1967), chlorpromazine and general anaesthetics (Hille, 1966), calcium (Blaustein & Goldman, 1966), lanthanum (Takata, Pickard, Lettvin, & Moore, 1966), all agents which also affect the potassium current system to some extent. A specific blockage of the sodium current system (blocking also the small potassium flux associated with this system) is produced by tetrodotoxin (Narahashi, Moore, & Scott, 1964; Nakamura, Nakajima, & Grundfest, 1965; Takata, Moore, Kao & Fuhrman, 1966; Hille, 1966). A similar action is produced by the dinoflagellate poison found in mussels, saxitoxin (reviewed by Grundfest, 1966). These toxins do not affect the calcium spikes in arthropod muscle (Hagiwara, 1966; Ozeki & Grundfest, 1965; Ozeki, Freeman, & Grundfest, 1966, Part I) and in heart or smooth muscle (Hagiwara & Nakajima, 1966a) (if indeed the action potentials in the latter are based upon an electrosensitive calcium conductance). Manganese ions suppress these action potentials (Fatt & Ginsborg, 1958; Hagiwara & Nakajima, 1966a).

A specific blockade of the potassium current system (delayed rectification) appears with tetraethylammonium (TEA) ion (Hagiwara & Saito, 1959a; Schmidt & Stämpfli, 1966; Koppenhöfer, 1965; Hille, 1967), which has the same effect if applied internally to a squid axon (Armstrong & Binstock, 1965).

The effect of veratrine is said to be suppression of inactivation of the sodium current system (Hille, 1967), leading to maintained inward sodium currents during depolarizing voltage clamp pulses applied to a frog node of Ranvier.

Transmitter release at nerve terminals

There is considerable evidence that transmitter release by presynaptic structures is induced by depolarization of the membrane (for review see the book by Eccles, 1964). The recent evidence that release is graded with presynaptic depolarization applied in the presence of tetrodotoxin and/or TEA in the squid giant synapse (Bloedel, Gage, Llinás, & Quastel, 1966; Kusano, Livengood, & Werman, 1967; Katz & Miledi, 1967e) and at the frog neuromuscular junction (Katz & Miledi, 1966), support the idea that the terminal membrane contains a specific electro-responsive membrane system mediating release of transmitter. It has been suggested by Katz & Miledi (1967d) that an increase in calcium permeability with depolarization is involved, but evidence for this remains indirect.

CHEMORESPONSIVE ELECTROGENIC SYSTEMS

Although electroresponsive membrane systems must have a chemical basis and are therefore sensitive to a variety of chemical agents (as already briefly described), there is no ambiguity in restricting the term chemoresponsive to another kind of electro-genic membrane system. This includes all electrogenic mechanisms which are *not* electroresponsive (i.e., 'electrically inexcitable') and which can be demonstrated to respond normally to a specific chemical stimulus. Two varieties may be distinguished. First, the systems involved in the postsynaptic response to transmitter substance that is released presynaptically. Second, the ionic pump or pumps which apparently respond to changes in the concentration of certain ions, on either side of the membrane, and which may be electrogenic.

Electrogenesis at synapses

At synapses transient potential changes can be observed which appear to be generated locally and are propagated only by electrotonic (passive) spread. If of sufficient amplitude they give rise to action potentials and this appears to be the only way in which cells (except sensory receptors) are normally stimulated to give action potentials. Synaptic potentials may be distinguished from action potentials by their smaller amplitude, slower time course, and lack of refractory period; that is, successive synaptic potentials may add. Synaptic potentials may be either positive (depolarizing) or negative (hyperpolarizing) in sign. Excitatory synaptic potentials are always depolarizing, and the excitatory function seems to be mediated entirely by the potential change. Inhibitory synaptic potentials are usually, but not always, hyperpolarizing. The inhibitory action is evidently mediated not only by the potential change but also directly by the underlying mechanism, which is an increased conductance to certain ions. From the previous discussion of 'threshold' it will be evident that an increased conductance alone can increase threshold appreciably.

The evidence for the mechanism of the excitatory synapse is most complete in the case of the neuromuscular synapse.

In the first investigation of the endplate potential (EPP, the synaptic potential at the motor endplate) using intracellular microelectrodes, Fatt & Katz (1951) established that the time course and spatial spread of the endplate potential could be accounted for on the basis of the passive electrical properties of muscle fibres, if the effect of transmitter substance (acetylcholine, ACh) was to cause within a total of 2 msec or less a deposition of positive charge on the inside of the endplate region. Their results indicated that the movement of charge was associated with a local increase in membrane conductance to both sodium and potassium and perhaps other ions.

The correctness of this interpretation was established firmly by the experiments of Takeuchi & Takeuchi (1960b) which made use of the voltage clamp technique, previously applied to the squid giant synapse by Hagiwara and Tasaki. It was possible to apply the voltage clamp without a space clamp since the endplate potential is generated at a very small area of the muscle membrane. The clamp prevents any change of potential in the region of interest, and therefore prevents any spread of current along the fibre as a result of endplate activity. The feedback current which flows through the muscle membrane to hold the membrane potential at its present value is equal and opposite to the current that flows through the membrane as a result of transmitter activity, since without change in membrane potential the sum total of membrane current (all ionic) must be zero. The feedback current was delivered through a microelectrode whose tip was placed very close (within 50 μ) to the voltage recording electrode.

This investigation showed the following results. The amplitude of endplate current was *linearly related* to the clamped membrane potential, indicating that the increases of ionic conductance generating the endplate current were independent of membrane potential. Extrapolation of the line of the voltage axis gave an endplate current equilibrium potential of 10–20 mV (inside negative). This equilibrium potential was the same for all times during the endplate current and was not affected by curare (which makes the endplate less sensitive to transmitter). It was greatly affected, however, by external sodium and potassium concentrations.

The simplest equation representing endplate current was the following:

$$I_{\text{e.p.c.}} = (\Delta G_{\text{Na}} + \Delta G_{\text{K}})\left(V - \frac{\Delta G_{\text{Na}}V_{\text{Na}} + \Delta G_{\text{K}}V_{\text{K}}}{\Delta G_{\text{Na}} + \Delta G_{\text{K}}}\right)$$

corresponding to the model (Fig. 2.22A).

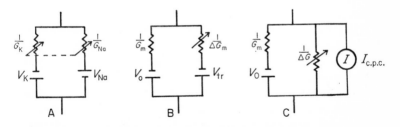

FIG. 2.22. Three models which are equivalent, each showing the modification of the electrical circuit representing the subsynaptic membrane which is required to describe the effect of transmitter at the neuromuscular junction.

The equation may, of course, be written

$$I_{e.p.c.} = \Delta G_m(V - V_{tr})$$

where ΔG_m is the change of membrane conductance and V_{tr} is the equilibrium potential for the transmitter sensitive membrane system. The experimental results indicated a ratio of $\Delta G_{Na}/\Delta G_K$ of 1·29. Chloride concentration changes were found to have no effect on the equilibrium potential for the system. Chloride therefore does not carry endplate current. Calcium ions (N. Takeuchi, 1963b) probably do contribute to a small extent.

The equivalent circuit (Fig. 2.22A) may be written equally well as a series battery–resistor combination in Fig. 2.22B or as a current source in parallel with a conductance (Fig. 2.22C) depending on which point of view is most convenient. The configuration shown in Fig. 2.22B emphasizes what may be one of the most important features of the synaptic potential from the point of view of investigation, that the synaptic potential is graded with potential across the postsynaptic membrane, and there is a certain trans-membrane potential at which synaptic current will be zero (the equilibrium potential of the transmitter) and therefore no voltage change will occur. Although geometric complexities make it sometimes difficult, such a 'transmitter equilibrium potential' may in principle be determined for any synapse by passing increasing currents into the postsynaptic cell until the synaptic potential becomes zero and then reverses. No voltage clamp is needed. Reversal of a synaptic potential by changing the membrane potential constitutes powerful evidence that the potential results from a postsynaptic change of permeability to certain ions. The ions involved in synaptic current can be determined if it is possible to alter the ionic environment on either side of the synaptic membrane.

The other configuration, that of the current source with the parallel conductor (Fig. 2.22C), is particularly convenient when it comes to calculating the voltage change that will occur post-synaptically as the result of transmitter action. Provided the synaptic potential is going to be small, compared with resting potential of the cell, it may be permissible to ignore its effect on synaptic current and state the current to be $I_{syn} = \Delta G_m(V_m - V_{tr})$ where V_m is resting potential at all times. If ΔG is small compared to the input conductance of the cell at the synapse then the voltage change resulting from the current is easy to calculate. If the conductance change is not small, then it will contribute significantly to the total input conductance, across which the synaptic potential is generated by the synaptic current, and will also alter the time constant. It is therefore implicit in the mechanism of the synaptic potential that if there is more than one synapse active at the same time on a cell, then each tends to occlude the potential change produced by the other. This aspect of synaptic activity has recently been emphasized by Rall (1967).

The relation between the amplitude of a synaptic potential and the conductance change giving rise to it can be deduced from the equivalent circuit (Fig. 2.23). For the case of the cell without appreciable intracellular voltage gradient (A), one has, from Kirchhoff's Law,

$$C \frac{dV}{dt} + G_m(V - V_m) + G_{tr}(V - V_{tr}) = 0.$$

For a step increase in G_{tr} from zero to a constant value, the solution may be written down (cf. eqn. (6)),

$$v = V - V_m$$

$$= \frac{G_{tr}}{G_m + G_{tr}} (V_{tr} - V_m)\{1 - e^{-t}(G_m + G_{tr}/C)\}.$$

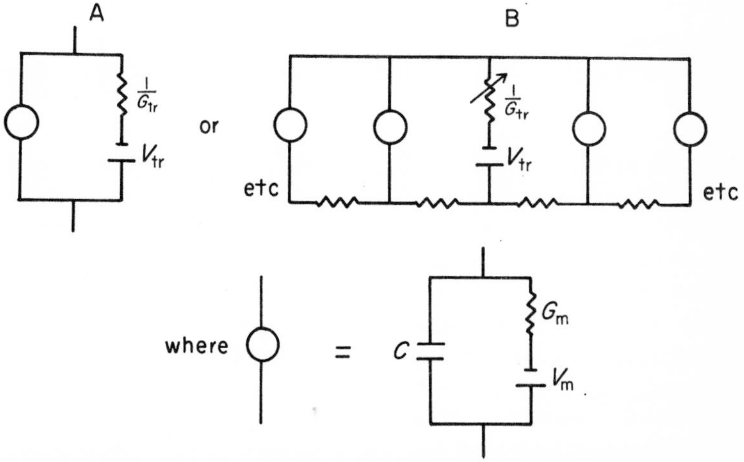

FIG. 2.23. A, electrical model of cell with active synapse. B, model of cable-like cell (dendrite or muscle fibre) with active synapse.

For a time t, which is short compared to the time constant $\{C/(G_m + G_{tr})\}$, the exponential may be approximated by the first two terms of its expansion,

$$v_{(t \sim 0)} \equiv \frac{G_{tr}}{G_{tr} + G_m} (V_{tr} - V_m) \cdot \frac{t}{C} (G_m + G_{tr}) \qquad (19)$$

$$= \frac{t}{C} (V_{tr} - V_m) \cdot G_{tr}.$$

Thus, for small t the synaptic potential (voltage response) should be independent of input conductance of the cell membrane and linearly related to t.

For a time t, which is long compared to the time constant, the second term in brackets disappears,

$$v_{(t \to \infty)} = \frac{G_{tr}}{G_m + G_{tr}} (V_{tr} - V_m)$$

rearranging,

$$\frac{G_{tr}}{G_m} = \frac{v}{V_{tr} - V_m - v}. \qquad (20)$$

This expression was derived by Martin (1955) and used to 'correct' endplate potential amplitude to be linear with conductance charge.

However, one must take into account that the time constant changes because of the conductance introduced by the transmitter. Thus a 'short' time of application of G_{tr} may become 'large' when G_{tr} is large. As a result, for the simple model, the conductance change is somewhere between being linearly related to voltage change and being linearly related to voltage change corrected by Martin's equation (20). For a G_{tr} duration of one-tenth the original time constant, deviation from a constant fraction of the correct value turns out to be about the same for the two functions. For a greater duration, the conductance change is more close to being linearly related to the 'corrected' voltage change.

For conductance changes which are not constant, but rise quickly and then fall off, as found experimentally (Takeuchi & Takeuchi, 1959, 1960b), one need only note that the synaptic potential will continue to rise until

$$v = \frac{G_{tr}}{G_m + G_{tr}} (V_{tr} - V_m)$$

and then fall. When this will occur is difficult to predict, but it is evident that it will be sooner for a large transmitter action than a small one, since the time constant in the former case is reduced to a greater extent. It would therefore appear that Martin's correction will tend to overcorrect only a little, to an extent depending on the effective duration of transmitter action.

Under real conditions there is another factor to be considered; this is the extracellular potential change caused by current flow at the synapse. Extracellular synaptic potentials may be recorded quite easily at the neuromuscular junction, for example, and are often as large or larger in amplitude than those recorded intracellularly. These result from the funnelling of current through the extracellular medium in through the small area of membrane involved in generating the synaptic potential. This extracellular potential will reduce the driving force for ions to move through the channels opened up by the transmitter substance. The equivalent circuit should be modified by inserting in series with $1/G_{tr}$ a resistor R_e ($1/G_e$). One must then substitute in eqn. (19), $G_{tr}G_e/(G_{tr} + G_e)$ where G_{tr} was alone, obtaining,

$$G_{tr} = \frac{C}{t} \ \frac{v}{V_{tr} - V_m - v(CR_e/t)}.$$

Thus, a correction rather like Martin's correction has to be introduced, even for an extremely brief synaptic potential, with the magnitude of the correction depending on R_e and, therefore, upon the actual area of membrane involved in the synaptic conductance change. This result suggests that Martin's correction may not overcorrect as much as otherwise would be the case, and might well undercorrect.

Similar considerations apply to the voltage change—the synaptic potential—in a cable-like structure, like a muscle fibre or neurone dendrite. The calculations—numerical integration of a number of simultaneous differential equations (see above)—have been done. The results (Quastel, unpublished) indicate that Martin's correction may overcorrect a little at the focus (the point where the conductance change takes place) if the synaptic conductance falls very rapidly from its initial peak (with a time constant less than one-tenth of the resting time constant). However, for distances of the recording electrode between about 0·05 and 0·2 of a length constant (see below) from the focus it should give a very accurate linearity with conductance changes up to five times the input conductance. With synaptic activity of longer duration it tends to undercorrect at distances of more than about one-tenth of a length constant. When one takes into account extracellular potential changes at the focus as well, it seems unlikely that Martin's correction ever overcorrects and probably, in general, undercorrects.

Electrogenesis due to active transport

In the first section of this chapter the effects of a pure current source in the membrane, without any associated conductance, were discussed. This would be the equivalent circuit of an electrogenic ionic pump. The sodium–potassium pump, as is well known, responds to changes in concentration of Na^+ (inside) or K^+ (outside) and it is likely that any electrogenic ionic pump would be ion sensitive in this way. Thus, electrogenesis resulting directly from active transport of an ion or ions would have to be classified under chemoresponsive systems.

Electrogenesis by the sodium–potassium pump would have to be due to an imbalance between Na^+ being moved out and K^+ moved in. It has recently been reported (Alving & Carpenter, 1967) that in *Aplysia* membrane potential of neurones may exceed the K^+ equilibrium potential. This resting hyperpolarization is blocked by ouabain or the absence of external K^+, both known to block the sodium–potassium pump in a variety of tissues. Also, a neurone in a nudibranch mollusc responds with a hyperpolarization following antidromic stimulation, and invasion (Gorman, Mirolli, & Salmoiraghi, 1967). The hyperpolarization had no evident equilibrium potential, suggesting that it was due not to an ionic conductange change, but to an electrogenic pump. In amphibian sympathetic ganglia the slow IPSP and post-tetanic hyperpolarization are evidently associated with metabolically driven extrusion of Na^+ ions (Nishi & Koketsu, 1968).

'SPECIFIC' ELECTROGENIC
MEMBRANE SYSTEMS—GENERATOR POTENTIALS

For the sake of completeness, mention should be made of the potentials generated at sensory nerve terminals. These share many of the characteristics of synaptic potentials—they are graded in amplitude with the intensity of the stimulus, and act to trigger action potentials in the adjoining axon. Receptor activity seems to depend upon specific sensitivity of the sensory structure to specific types of stimuli—light, vibration, mechanical pressure, etc. Of course, many types may be specifically sensitive to chemical substances, e.g., the chemoreceptors of the carotid body, or medulla, or even pain receptors which may respond to substances released as the result of tissue damage.

What specific investigation has been made suggests that generator potentials are brought about by an increase in sodium and perhaps potassium conductance—like the muscle membrane response to acetylcholine. For example, the amplitude of the generator potential of the Paccinian corpuscle depends upon the presence of external Na^+ (Diamond, Gray, & Inman, 1958) and generation of the potential appears to be associated with an increase in sodium permeability (Ozeki & Sato, 1964). Investigation of the crustacean stretch receptor (Terzuolo & Washizu, 1962), and muscle spindle (Ottoson & Shepherd, 1965) has led to the same conclusion.

GEOMETRIC CONSIDERATIONS

It has been seen above that to a very large degree the events which take place in a nerve or muscle cell during an action potential or synaptic potential are electrical in nature, and the behaviour of the cell may be simulated, more or less accurately, by an electrical model which is the equivalent of a mathematical model. In order to apply the information which is available regarding the electrical properties of the cell membrane and the way in which these electrical properties alter during activity, it is necessary to construct electrical models of cells which correspond as closely as possible to reality. The major complicating factor arises always from the geometry of the cells in which one is interested, which is such that it is *not* in general true that the whole of a cell interior is always at the same potential. Indeed, this fact is of enormous importance both to the functioning of cells and to their experimental analysis, since upon it depends the mechanism of propagation of action potentials and the generation of extracellular field potentials, which are of such importance in the investigation of the central nervous system.

The core conductor model

The simplest case to be considered here is that of the uniform, semi-infinite core conductor, that is, a long cylindrical cell with a conducting interior which offers an appreciable resistance to current flow, and a thin surface membrane with a low leakage conductance and fairly high capacity per unit area. This corresponds to such cells as the giant axons of squid and lobster (e.g., Cole & Curtis, 1939; Cole & Hodgkin, 1939). Such a 'cable' can be represented as an infinite series of elements, each element consisting of a capacitor and conductor in series, and a conductor on either side (thus taking into account the resistance of the external fluid) linking it to the next element in the series (Fig. 2.24).

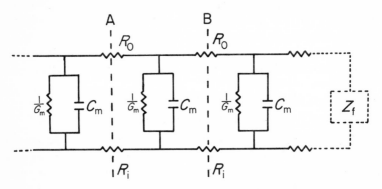

FIG. 2.24. Electrical model of cable-like cell.

The membrane battery may be ignored if one is interested only in changes of potential. The values of G_m, C_m, and R_i are each related to the length (Δx) of the membrane element being considered:

$$G_m = g_m \, \Delta x \qquad (R_m = r_m / \Delta x)$$
$$C_m = C \, \Delta x$$
$$R_i = r_i \, \Delta x$$
$$R_o = r_o \, \Delta x$$

where g_m, (r_m), C, r_i and r_o are each conductance, capacitance, and resistance in and out, for unit length of cable.

Input resistance

To see how such a system will behave under a variety of conditions, it is useful first to consider the steady-state behaviour (when dV/dt is everywhere zero and therefore the capacitors can be ignored), in response to a steady current applied between inside and out at any point. If the cable is infinitely long, then it is evident, for reasons of symmetry, that the response will be independent of where the current is applied. The effective resistance between inside and out ('input resistance') will be the same everywhere. Imagine this resistance to be split into two parts, one on either side of where the current is applied, and call the effective resistance on either side R_f, then the input resistance (R_i) is equal to $\frac{1}{2} R_f$. The circuit shown in Fig. 2.25 may be split

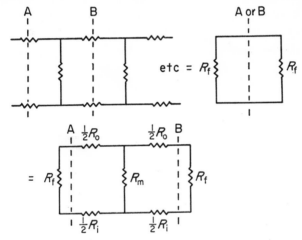

FIG. 2.25. Equivalent circuit of Fig. 2.24, with membrane capacity omitted, to show how input resistance of cable may be derived. For description see text.

at plane A or B, and in each case the resistance to the right of the split is equal to R_f, despite the larger network seen when the division is at A. Hence,

$$R_f = \tfrac{1}{2}R_0 + \tfrac{1}{2}R_i + \frac{1}{1/R_m + 1/(R_f + \tfrac{1}{2}R_0 + \tfrac{1}{2}R_i)}$$

$$= \tfrac{1}{2}(R_0 + R_i) + \frac{R_m(R_f + \tfrac{1}{2}R_0 + \tfrac{1}{2}R_i)}{R_m + R_f + \tfrac{1}{2}(R_0 + R_i)}$$

$$R_f\{R_m + R_f + \tfrac{1}{2}(R_0 + R_i)\} = \tfrac{1}{2}R_f(R_0 + R_i + 2R_m) + R_m(R_0 + R_i) + \tfrac{1}{4}(R_0 + R_i)^2$$

$$R_f{}^2 = R_m(R_0 + R_i) + \tfrac{1}{4}(R_0 + R_i)^2.$$

Substituting the electrical constants per length of cable

$$R_\mathrm{f}{}^2 = \frac{r_\mathrm{m}}{\Delta x}(r_0 + r_\mathrm{i})\Delta x + \tfrac{1}{4}(r_0 + r_\mathrm{i})^2\Delta x^2$$

when Δx is made small, the second term on the right becomes negligible, but the first remains constant, therefore,

$$R_\mathrm{I} = \tfrac{1}{2}R_\mathrm{f} = \tfrac{1}{2}\sqrt{\{r_\mathrm{m}(r_0 + r_\mathrm{i})\}}. \tag{21}$$

The formula for spatial decrement is also easily derived from basic principles. Consider any two points, one outside, the other in, with potential V_0 and V_i respectively, at some distance x, to the right of where current I is applied inside. Each compartment is to be considered vanishingly small in length ($\mathrm{d}x$).

The voltage gradient on the outside, at x is

$$\frac{\mathrm{d}V_0}{\mathrm{d}x} = r_0 i$$

where i is the longitudinal current,

also,
$$\frac{\mathrm{d}V_\mathrm{i}}{\mathrm{d}x} = -r_\mathrm{i}i$$

the internal and external currents are the same, but opposite in direction. The current, i, at point x is simply that going through the cable to the right of point x, whose equivalent circuit is simply a resistor of magnitude R_f,

i.e.,
$$i = (V_\mathrm{i} - V_0)/R_\mathrm{f}$$

$$\frac{\mathrm{d}(V_\mathrm{i} - V_0)}{\mathrm{d}x} = \frac{\mathrm{d}V_\mathrm{i}}{\mathrm{d}x} - \frac{\mathrm{d}V_0}{\mathrm{d}x}$$

$$= -(r_\mathrm{i} + r_0)i$$

$$= -(r_\mathrm{i} + r_0)\frac{(V_\mathrm{i} - V_0)}{R_\mathrm{f}}$$

$$\frac{1}{(V_\mathrm{i} - V_0)}\frac{\mathrm{d}(V_\mathrm{i} - V_0)}{\mathrm{d}x} = -\frac{(r_\mathrm{i} + r_0)}{R_\mathrm{f}}.$$

Integrating,

$$\ln(V_\mathrm{i} - V_0) = -x\frac{(r_\mathrm{i} + r_0)}{R_\mathrm{f}} + K'$$

$$V_\mathrm{i} - V_0 = K\exp\{-x(r_\mathrm{i} + r_0)/R_\mathrm{f}\}$$

where K is a constant of integration. It is equal to $I\,R_I$, since at $x=0$, the point where current is applied, the transmembrane potential ($V_m = V_i - V_o$) is $I\,R_I$.

Thus,
$$V_{m,\,x} = I\,R_I \exp\left(-x/\lambda\right) \qquad (22)$$

where λ, the 'length constant' or 'space constant' is given by,

$$\lambda = R_f/(r_i + r_o) = \sqrt{\{r_m/(r_i + r_o)\}}.$$

The actual potential on either side of the membrane depends upon what point is designated to be at the zero reference potential.

From the above quations,

$$\frac{dV_i}{dx} = -r_i\,i = \frac{r_i}{(r_i + r_o)}\,\frac{d(V_i - V_o)}{dx}$$

therefore,

$$V_i = (V_i - V_o)\,\frac{r_i}{r_i + r_o} + K$$

where K is the integration constant, and a similar equation holds for V_o.

If the potential at $x = \infty$ is designated 0, then $K = 0$, and one has the simple relations

$$V_{i(x)} = I\,R_I\,\frac{r_i}{(r_i + r_o)}\exp\left(-x/\lambda\right)$$

$$V_{o(x)} = -I\,R_I\,\frac{r_o}{(r_i + r_o)}\exp\left(-x/\lambda\right).$$

Thus, for an ingoing current, the potential inside is everywhere positive while that outside is everywhere negative.

If, instead, the point $x = 0$ is grounded so that it will be at zero potential, then

$$K = I\,R_I\,r_o/(r_o + r_i),$$

and
$$V_{i(x)} = I\,R_I\left\{\frac{r_o}{r_o + r_i} + \frac{r_i}{r_o + r_i}\exp\left(-x/\lambda\right)\right\}$$

$$V_{o(x)} = I\,R_I\,\frac{r_o}{(r_i + r_o)}\left\{1 - \exp\left(-x/\lambda\right)\right\}.$$

Note that, in this case, at $x = \infty$

$$V_{i(x=\infty)} = V_{o(x=\infty)} = I\,R_I\,\frac{r_o}{r_o + r_i}.$$

These formulae conform with the intuitive result that with a ladder network as in Fig. 2.25, the potential across the leak conductors should fall in geometric progression from one compartment to the next; for infinitely small compartments this becomes an exponential decay.

The response of the core conductor to alternating current can now be seen intuitively without further mathematics—the actual formulae, given by Falk & Fatt (1964) unfortunately do not appreciably sharpen one's mental picture. One need only substitute for the leak conductances in Fig. 2.26 'admittances' which

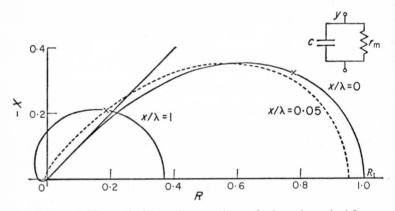

FIG. 2.26. Theoretical impedance and transfer impedance loci for the simple fibre model in which y consists of a resistance and a capacitance in parallel (shown at the right). The straight line for $R = -X$ is also shown. x indicates the positions of the loci (for $x/\lambda = 0$ and $1\cdot0$) corresponding to the characteristic frequency, at which $\omega = 1/cr_m$. The scales are given in terms of the d.c. input resistance (R_i).

behave like frequency dependent conductances and make the appropriate changes where g_m appears in the equations. Thus, the input impedance of the cable will go down as the frequency of sinusoidal current is increased, and so will the 'length constant'. The higher the frequency component of a current signal, the less the voltage response where it is applied and, moreover, the more the response will be attenuated along the cable. Phase shifting will be quite complicated, however. Theoretical impedance and transfer impedance loci for the core conductor model are shown in Fig. 2.26.

To obtain the time course of response to applied current, membrane capacity has to be taken into account formally, the simple substitution used previously $(i = V_m/R_t)$ is incorrect. Instead, one notes that membrane current at any point is equal to the change in axial current within the cable.

$$i_m = \frac{di}{dx}.$$

As before,
$$\frac{dV_m}{dx} = -(r_i + r_o)i$$

differentiating,
$$\frac{d^2V_m}{d^2x} = -(r_i + r_o)\frac{di}{dx}$$

whence,
$$\frac{d^2V_m}{d^2x} = (r_i + r_o)i_m.$$

The membrane current per unit length (i_m) is now subdivided into its two components, the capacity current (i_c) and the conductor (ionic) current, i_i

$$i_m = i_c + i_i$$

$$= C\frac{dV_m}{dt} + i_i$$

therefore,
$$\frac{1}{(r_i + r_o)}\frac{d^2V_m}{dx^2} = C\frac{dV_m}{dt} + i_i.$$

This equation, of course, describes the membrane potential, as a function of x and t under all conditions, including those when the ionic conductance behaves non-linearly, e.g., in the case of electroresponsive membrane. However, its solution is straightforward only if a linear membrane conductance, and simple geometry of the system is assumed. In this case the equation simplifies to

$$\lambda^2\frac{d^2V_m}{dx^2} = \tau_m\frac{dV_m}{dt} + V_m$$

where $\lambda = \sqrt{\dfrac{r_m}{(r_i + r_o)}}$, the length constant

and $\tau_m = r_m C$, the time constant of the surface membrane.

This equation is further simplified to

$$\frac{d^2V_m}{dX^2} = \frac{dV_m}{dT} + V_m \tag{23}$$

by the substitutions $X = x/\lambda$ and $T = t/\tau$, and is now the same as that encountered in the theory of heat conduction and the theory of diffusion. It may be solved analytically for a number of boundary conditions—in particular for the cases where a constant current I_0 is introduced abruptly at a point in the fibre ($x = 0$) (e.g., Hodgkin and Rushton, 1946), or a finite amount of charge is deposited in an infinitesimal time (Fatt & Katz, 1951).

For a constant current introduced at $x = 0$, at time zero, two useful results are:

$$V_m(x = 0, T) = I_0 R_I \operatorname{erf} \sqrt{T} \qquad (24)$$

where
$$\operatorname{erf} y = \frac{2}{\sqrt{\pi}} \int_0^y \exp(-m^2)\, dm$$

is the Error function, which is tabulated (Carslaw & Jaeger, 1947). $R_I = \frac{1}{2} \sqrt{\{(r_0 + r_i)r_m\}}$, the input resistance, the effective resistance between inside and outside.

When T is large, i.e., when a steady state is reached, one has, as before, (eqn. (22))

$$V_m(X, T \to \infty) = I_0 . R_I \exp(-X).$$

R_I, λ, and τ_m can be obtained from measurement of the voltage response to a current step function applied at a point, it being necessary to record the final height of the response at several distances, and to estimate the time course of the response at the point where current is applied.

When a current pulse is very brief compared to the membrane time constant, the expression for V_m as a function of X and T is also fairly simple:

$$V_m(X, T) = \frac{q_0}{2C\lambda} . \frac{1}{\sqrt{(\pi T)}} \exp\left(\frac{X^2}{4T} - T\right) \qquad (25)$$

where q_0 is the amount of charge injected.

For the peak of the potential wave which results, at any position x, $dV_m/dt = 0$. By differentiating and equating to zero, one finds that

$$X^2 = 4T^2 + 2T$$

for the time of the peak potential charge at distance x.

Equation (23) is especially useful because it can also be used where the geometry of a cell is complicated, such as a neuron with soma and dendrites (Rall, 1960). In this case the geometrical complexities are avoided by correcting the true distance from the point of interest (the soma), by taking into account changes in λ. The solutions then depend on the degree of dendritic dominance (ρ, the ratio of total dendritic conductance to somatic membrane conductance); when $\rho = \infty$, this corresponds to the uniform cable considered above. The situation when $\rho = 0$, the other limiting case, can be interpreted as a 'soma without dendrites', or a cell in which there is no axial current at any time. In the latter case the

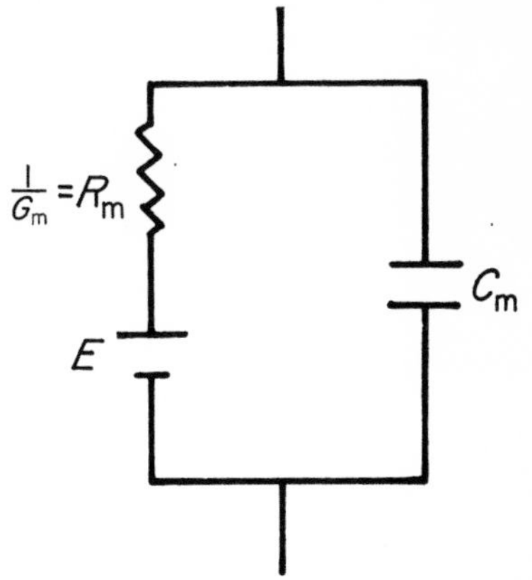

FIG. 2.27. Simple electrical model, corresponding to a neurone soma without dendrites.

$$\frac{1}{G_m} = R_m$$

$$C_m$$

$$E$$

electrical model is very simple as in Fig. 2.27, and eqn. (23) reduces to

$$\frac{dV_m}{dT} + V_m = 0$$

since dV_m/dx is always zero.

If this model is matched to the cable model, with R_m made equal to the input resistance of the cable, and $R_m C_m = \gamma_m$, then the response to a constant current step function is, of course:

$$V_m = I_0 R_m (1 - e^{-T}). \tag{26}$$

This is appreciably slower than $\operatorname{erf}\sqrt{T}$, the transient produced at $x = 0$ in the cable. (Fig. 2.28.)

Depending upon the degree of dendritic dominance (ρ) in the model cell, the solution for the voltage response to a step current function lies between these two extremes. However, as ρ increases

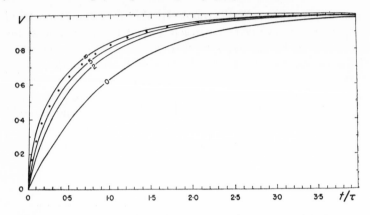

FIG. 2.28. Transients of passive soma membrane potential when a constant current step is applied across the soma membrane at zero time. The electrotonic potential, V, is expressed relative to its final steady value during constant applied current. Time is expressed relative to the membrane time constant. Curves are drawn for $\rho = 0$, 2, 5, and ∞, the dots correspond to $\rho = 10$. The uppermost curve, $\rho = \infty$, represents the limiting case in which the dendrites are completely dominant. The lowermost curve, $\rho = 0$, represents the limiting case of a soma without dendrites.

the curve rapidly approximates that for $\rho = \infty$, and it is likely that any real neuron, with dendrites, should behave much more like the ideal leaky cable than like a simple resistance and capacitance in parallel.

Experimental evidence that the cable model does in fact apply to a nerve or muscle fibre is very considerable.

These include the results of Hodgkins & Rushton (1946) who found that the response of the lobster axon to small steady currents applied at a point followed closely the error function predicted (eqn. (24)). Moreover, the equilibrium distribution of potential along the length of the fibre was exponential, as predicted (eqn. (22)). In their investigation of the endplate potential in frog sartorius muscle Fatt & Katz (1951) showed that the total charge transferred into the fibre by an endplate potential decayed exponentially with time, which would be true of either the cable or a simple RC circuit with the slope giving τ_{m}. The plot of $\{4t_{\rho}^{2}/r_{\mathrm{m}}^{2} + 2t_{\rho}/\tau_{\mathrm{m}}\}$ against x^2 then gave a straight line (eqn. (26)). Equation (26) would be expected to hold because the endplate current is brief (about 2 msec) compared to the time constant of the muscle membrane (about 24 msec) and therefore corresponds to a fast dumping in of charge. They also used rectangular current pulse analysis, like that of Hodgkin & Rushton (1946), with results which matched those obtained from consideration of the endplate potential as recorded by an intracellular electrode at various distances from the endplate. Thus it can be stated that the muscle fibre, apart from the region where the endplate potential is generated, may be considered to be equivalent to the simple model involving only resistive and capacitive elements.

Rall (1960) applied his theoretical analysis to the results obtained by Coombs, Curtis, & Eccles (1959), who applied current steps to motoneurons. Here an examination was made of the shape of the transient response. Solving eqn. (23), one obtains the following relationships at $x=0$, for the response to an applied constant current.

$$\frac{dV_m}{dt}=\frac{I_0 \cdot R \exp(-t/\tau_m)}{\sqrt{(\pi \gamma_m t)}} \quad \text{when } \rho = \infty \text{ (i.e., cable)}$$

$$\frac{dV_m}{dt}=\frac{I_0 R \exp(-t/\tau_m)}{\gamma_m} \quad \text{when } \rho = 0.$$

Therefore, $\log \{\sqrt{t}(dV_m/dt)\}$ was plotted against t. If ρ is large, the points should fall on a straight line. When calculated with natural logarithms the negative slope of this line gives $1/\tau_m$. The results of this procedure are shown in Fig. 2.29 and indicate the close correspondence between theory and experimental results. There is a similar correspondence between predicted and observed responses to brief current pulses.

More recently the adequacy of this resistance–capacitance model to explain the electrical properties of nerve and muscle membrane has been questioned. A careful study of the response of motoneurons to current steps introduced in the soma has been made by Ito & Oshima (1965), who found that at the onset and cessation of the current steps there were marked overshoots and undershoots of the shifts in membrane potential. These over- and undershoots varied according to the membrane potential and were attributed tentatively to changes in activity of the electrogenic, hyperpolarizing sodium pump, which appears to exist in cat motoneurons (Eccles, Eccles, & Ito, 1964*a*, *b*; Ito & Oshima, 1964*a*), the changes perhaps being caused by potassium ion movements out of or into the extracellular space.

For a consideration of the transients, to test the electrical model,

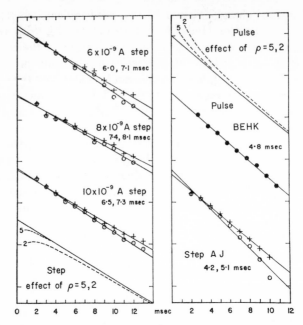

FIG. 2.29. Linear plots of experimental transient data. The left side is based upon transients obtained with applied current steps of three different amplitudes in a single neurone; the right side is based upon experiments with a different motoneuron, that was subjected to both pulses and steps of applied current. The open circles (both left and right) represent current step experiments; their ordinates represent the natural logarithm of the product $\sqrt{t}(dV/dt)$; their abscissae represent time from onset of the applied step. The crosses include a correction for the time constant of the recording system. The straight lines represent least-square fits; the value of τ corresponding to each slope is stated in the figure. The filled circles represent current pulse experiments; their ordinates represent the natural logarithm of the product, $\sqrt{t}(-dV/dt)/(1+\tau/2t)$; correction for the recording system time constant is negligible in this case; the abscissae represent time from the mid-point of the pulse. The (dashed) curves at lower left illustrate the effect of $\rho = 5$ and 2 to be expected with the step transient plotting procedure; the (dashed) curves in the upper right illustrate the corresponding effect to be expected with the pulse transient plotting procedure. The unit of the ordinate scale is one (i.e., the natural logarithm of e) (Rall, 1960).

it was necessary to make corrections for the effects of the over- and undershoots. It was found that the initial responses to step current could be accurately described as the sum of two exponentials, whereas a plot of log $\{\sqrt{t}(dV_m/dt)\}$ against t showed small but appreciable deviations from linearity, whether one used V_m directly or corrected for the effects of the over- or undershoot. The deviation took the form of a relatively high slope of decay at the very early phase. Although the authors conclude that the best representation of the whole response is in the form of the sum of three exponentials, it is not likely that their suggestion that the faster two of these exponentials represent dendritic and somatic time constants respectively can be exactly correct, since dendritic resistance and capacitance would be distributed rather than lumped. The alternative suggestion that the deviation may derive from the effect of the endoplasmic reticulum, like the deviation in skeletal muscle studied in detail by Falk & Fatt (1964, see below) is far more plausible. It may be pointed out that the use of the sum of two exponentials as an empirical description of the voltage response allows no prediction to be made regarding the time course of potential response at the soma to a current pulse anywhere but at the soma. The calculation of the time course of transmitter action during an EPSP (Ito & Oshima, 1965) is therefore valid only if the EPSP was generated on the soma, or very close by, so that the synaptic currents were in fact mimicked effectively by the currents which were applied during the current pulse analysis.

One difficulty with the simple model of the muscle fibre considered above has been the rather high values of membrane capacitance calculated from the results of investigation of frog muscle—the values of 5–8 $\mu F/cm^2$ (and of 20 $\mu F/cm^2$ for crayfish muscle) obtained using internal electrodes are very large for a dialectric membrane of 75 Å in thickness. Moreover, they conflict with values of 1–2 $\mu F/cm^2$ obtained for most biological membranes (Cole, 1962) and 2·5 $\mu F/cm^2$ obtained in measurements of frog muscle fibres with a transverse applied electric field (Fatt, 1964).

Falk and Fatt have resolved this discrepancy (Falk & Fatt, 1964) by showing that there are at least two distinct components of the capacitance between the inside and outside of the fibre, one, which has a resistance in series with it probably due to components of the sarcoplasmic reticulum which form a system of tubules leading from the surface of the fibre to the interior (Gage & Eisenberg, 1967). In the investigation measurements were made of the voltage response to sinusoidal current of frequencies between 1 Hz and 10 kHz. The relationship obtained between the real and imaginary parts of the impedance (R and X), and the phase shift over this frequency range, was compared with those of theoretical models. This method permits far more accurate assessment of the impedance and transfer impedance properties of the muscle fibre than the more commonly used method of measuring the time course of response to a current step function. As pointed out by Schwan (1965), to whom the reader is referred for a complete discussion of techniques used in determination of biological impedances, a.c. 'steady state' measurements can be carried out with an accuracy limited only by the investment in instrumentation, whereas to detect more than one or two time constants from an oscilloscope record of a transient response is rather involved. In Fig. 2.30 are shown the impedance locus plots

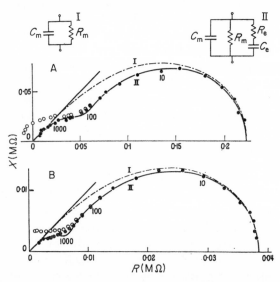

FIG. 2.30. Impedance-locus plots obtained with intracellular microelectrodes from a fibre of (A) frog sartorius and (B) crayfish carpopodite-extensor muscle. Current-applying and voltage-recording electrodes were placed close together, distant from the end of the fibre. Hollow circles give uncorrected observations, filled circles after correction for stray capacitances around the microelectrodes. Measurements were made at frequencies (6 per decade) from 1 c/s to 10 kc/s; frequencies (in c/s) are labelled on a few points. The dot-dashed line gives the theoretical impedance locus for the model of inside-outside admittance shown at upper left (I), fitted to the limiting value of R obtained at low frequencies. The solid line gives the theoretical locus for the more complicated model of inside-outside admittance shown at upper right (II), with the additional parameters R_e/R_m and C_e/C_m adjusted to give the best fit of the observations (Falk & Fatt, 1965).

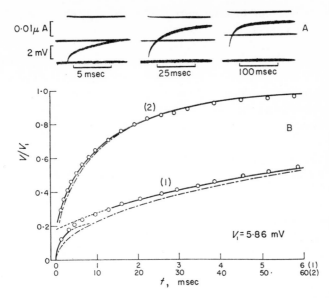

FIG. 2.31. Transient voltage response in a frog sartorius muscle fibre to a step-function current, obtained with current and voltage electrodes close together. Records shown in (A) were obtained on the same fibre as the a.c. impedance determination, the two sets of observations being made without displacing the electrodes. Records are shown with constant current and voltage amplification, but different sweep speeds; the top trace gives the current and the bottom trace the voltage. Each record is formed of 10 superimposed sweeps of the response, with an equal number of the base-line. In (B) measurements of the voltage (including information from records taken at other sweep speeds, not illustrated) are plotted on two time scales, labelled (1) and (2). The voltage is normalized to the level attained at 130 msec. The theoretical curves are computed from the results of the a.c. analysis, the dot-dashed line being for the simple fibre model and the solid line for the two-time-constant model. The dashed portions of the curves in (1) represent regions in which the equations used in computing the solid-line curve (for $t < 0.3$ msec and $t > 1.3$ msec) would no longer hold (Falk & Fatt, 1964).

obtained by Falk & Fatt (1964). The results indicate that the more complex model is required for a description of the passive electrical properties of the muscle fibre. In view of the results of Ito & Oshima (1965), it seems likely that a similar model should apply also to the motoneurons.

Unfortunately this two-time-constant model responds in a rather complicated manner to applied current. The solution for the transient response to a step current function is given in Falk & Fatt (1964). It is such that a complete integration (which has to be carried out numerically) must be made from 0 to t for each value of t for which V (the voltage response) is to be evaluated. Qualitatively, it may be stated that for short times, less than a few msec, the response is influenced considerably by a time constant considerably shorter than that obtained by ignoring R_e. For times less than about 0·3 msec the behaviour is similar to that of the simpler model, with a time constant approximately equal to $C_m r_e / \{1 + (C_m/C_e) + (r_e/r_m)\}$. For example, for a typical fibre with $C_e = C_m$ and 0·1r_m, and $r_m C_m = 10$ msec the apparent time constant at such times is about 0·5 msec, the apparent input resistance of the fibre being 22% of the d.c. input resistance. (The ratio is given, approximately, by $(r_e/r_m)^{\frac{1}{2}}\{1 + (C_m/C_e) + (r_e/r_m)\}^{-\frac{1}{2}}$.) Fig. 2.31 shows the transient response, observed and calculated, in a typical frog muscle fibre.

3

MEASUREMENT OF CELL ELECTRICAL PROPERTIES

External recording

Recording membrane potential without penetrating the cell with a microelectrode depends upon manufacturing an artificial situation in which the transmembrane potential of some part of the tissue (Fig. 3.1, (1)B) is reduced to a value (preferably zero) which is less than that close to the other recording point (Fig. 3.1, (1)A), e.g., by damaging it or applying isotonic KCl to it. A current—the injury current—then flows between A and B both inside and outside the cell. The extracellular component can be detected by recording the potential difference (the demarcation potential) created between A and B by the current which flows through the longitudinal extracellular resistance (r_1) between these two points. The (equal) current which flows inside the cell through the longitudinal internal resistance (Fig. 3.1 (2) r_2) necessarily tends to short-circuit the recording device. The measured potential, V, must be less than the transmembrane potential, V_m, in the proportion $V/V_m = r_1/(r_1 + r_2)$. The ratio $r_1/(r_1 + r_2)$ is termed the short-circuit factor. Evidently, the higher the external resistance (r_1) the closer V_m approaches to V. The value of r_1 can be assessed by measuring the electrotonic spread of an applied current in the extracellular medium while r_2 can be determined from a knowledge of the specific resistance of the cell protoplasm (R_i) and the dimensions of the cell.

This method in its original form is now only of historical interest, having been generally abandoned in favour of microelectrode recording which can directly give the potential difference across the membrane (between A and C in Fig. 3.1, 1–3). There are, however, cells which are very difficult or even impossible to penetrate with a microelectrode, yet are long enough for two

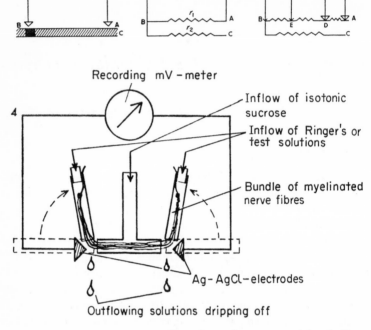

FIG. 3.1. Extracellular recording of membrane potential. 1 indicates the recording of the potential difference between an electrode on uninjured membrane at A and an electrode on a depolarized area B. 2 indicates the resistance of the extracellular (r_1) and intracellular (r_2) paths between A and B. 3 indicates the Huxley & Stämpfli (1951) method for measuring extracellular potentials. B is a depolarized area. There is a current source between B and E which is adjusted so that no current is detected between A and D. 4. The sucrose gap (after Stampfli, 1954) showing frog nerve fibres pulled through three polythene tubes. The middle tube is circulated with isotonic sucrose solution of high specific resistance, the outer tubes with Ringer's solution on one side and Ringer's solution or test solutions on the other side. After introduction of the nerve fibres both tubes are moved into the vertical position in order to have a sharp change of resistance at both ends of the middle section by spilling the sucrose solution away.

extracellular electrodes to be applied to them. Such cells include small diameter nerve fibres, both myelinated and unmyelinated, and smooth muscle fibres. Modifications of the injury-current technique have therefore been devised which are more convenient than older methods in that the injury current is greatly reduced or abolished so that the preparation survives better, while a knowledge of the short-circuit factor is not required.

The first of these methods (Huxley & Stämpfli, 1951) simply balanced out the injury current by applying a counter current to the injured region (Fig. 3.1 (3)B, E) so that B was made positive to E and no current was detected by the external recording system (Fig. 3.1 (3)A, D). Since current flow between C and B is the same as that between A and D, it too must be zero, and these points are at the same potential. The same is true for the path ED. Thus the potential difference between B and E, which can be measured, is the same as the membrane potential. Action potentials can be measured by a similar balancing technique.

A development of this technique which has enjoyed greater popularity is the 'sucrose-gap' method (Stämpfli, 1954; Straub, 1956). In this method the resistance r_1 (Fig. 3.1 (2)) is made so large that $r_1 + r_2$ is virtually equal to r_1, i.e., the short-circuit factor is almost unity and the external electrodes (Fig. 3.1 (2)A and B) record almost the true resting potential. The technique is illustrated in Fig. 3.1 (4). The high longitudinal extracellular resistance (r_1) is ensured by putting the tissue (in the experiment illustrated, frog myelinated nerve fibres) into a polyethylene tube (of slightly greater internal diameter than the tissue itself) through which isotonic sucrose flows at a constant rate. The sucrose flows inwards from the middle of the tube (Fig. 3.1 (4)) and spills out at the two ends of the tube where the nerve is bent upward into further tubing. A minute injury current is generated by flowing isotonic KCl around the nerve at one end, while normal Ringer's solution flows across the other end. Potential measurements are made from the tissue at the sucrose–KCl and sucrose–Ringer interfaces. Action potentials can be measured by this technique (Ritchie & Straub, 1956; Burnstock & Straub, 1958) and if desired the short-circuit factor can be calculated (Bennett & Burnstock, 1966). It should be noted that in practice the sucrose gap is difficult to set up satisfactorily, and those interested would be well advised to seek the help of colleagues with some experience in the method.

Internal recording

The best method of measuring membrane potential is to insert an electrode into the interior of the cell (Fig. 3.1 (1)C)

D

and measure the potential difference between it and a reference electrode. The microelectrode technique permits this for a large variety of cell types. Certain tissues, e.g., the squid giant axon, also allow the insertion of a metal wire from one end of the preparation, remote from the area of recording.

Artefacts in membrane potential measurement

When recording membrane potential, there are (besides the potential developed between the inside and outside of the cell) other potentials generated at the liquid–metal and liquid–liquid junctions in the recording circuit. With a microelectrode outside a cell, there will be junctional potentials (1) between the solution filling the electrode and the extracellular solution, (2) between the (usually) silver wires connecting the electrode to the recording circuit and the solution filling the electrode, and (3) between the extracellular solution and the indifferent electrode. These junction potentials can be balanced out by an opposing current from the familiar backing or bucking-off circuit employed in every electrophysiological laboratory—and can be reduced by judicious selection of solutions for filling electrodes and proper chloriding of the silver wires used to connect the electrode solution with the recording system (see e.g., Silver, 1958; Frank & Becker, 1964).

If the microelectrode is inserted into a cell, the potentials recorded will now be the sum of the membrane potential, and a potential between the electrode contents and the intracellular medium round the electrode tip, the nature of which cannot be accurately predicted. This potential—the tip potential—can be measured with the electrode placed in various salt solutions by simply comparing the potential between the electrode and a silver–silver chloride reference electrode system before and after the tip of the electrode is broken off. The potentials are about -2 to -5 mV for recently filled 0.5–$1.0\,\mu$ tip diameter 3 M KCl filled electrodes (Levine, 1966a), but can be up to -70 mV for high-resistance electrodes (Adrian, 1956).

Tip potentials are often much larger than potentials expected at a liquid–liquid junction. Adrian (1956) suggested that the potentials were junctional potentials produced by partial plugging of the electrode tip so that chloride mobility was reduced and potassium and sodium mobility increased, thus producing a potential difference. Later experiments suggest that the tip potential is generated at the interface between the glass of the electrode tip and the electrolyte solution. The internal interfacial potential would be negligible since these potentials are reduced in solutions of high ionic strength but the external potential could be large and would depend on the ionic strength and ionic species of the external solution. In agreement with this view, tip potentials are much reduced by traces of heavy metals in the outside solution (Agin & Holtzman, 1966). It is of interest that these authors found that 2 mM $CaCl_2$ in the outside solution also reduces tip potentials.

Del Castillo & Katz (1955*b*) and Adrian (1956) suggest that the presence of tip potentials should be suspected if:

(1) different mean values for the membrane potential of the same preparation are found with different electrodes,

(2) breaking the electrode tip increases the resting potential measured when the electrode is reinserted,

(3) high resistance microelectrodes penetrate cells easily but give low resting potentials.

The magnitude of tip potentials depends on the salt used to fill the electrode, the method of electrode filling and the age of the electrode. Isotonic KCl was the first salt used to fill microelectrodes (Graham & Gerard, 1946; Ling & Gerard, 1949*a*). The familiar 3 M KCl was introduced by Nastuk & Hodgkin (1950) primarily because its higher conductivity reduced the electrode time constant, but also because the junction potential between the estimated intracellular KCl of some 150 mM and 3 M KCl should be small. Although electrodes filled with a wide variety of other salts have subsequently been used (e.g., Coombs, Eccles, & Fatt, 1955*a*, *b*), no systematic studies of tip potentials with other than KCl-filled microelectrodes appear to have been made. Experiment has shown that KCl electrodes filled by boiling under reduced pressure, or by methods not involving heat, have lower tip potentials than electrodes filled by the earlier method of boiling in the KCl solution (Nastuk, 1953; Levine, 1966*a*). Several systematic studies indicate that 3 M KCl-filled electrodes develop increasing tip potentials as they get older (Adrian, 1956; Ito and Oshima, 1964*a*; Levine, 1966*a*) and it seems wise therefore to use them within two days of filling. For highly accurate work it is desirable to have some means of measuring electrode resistance continuously so that changes in resistance and tip potentials due, for example, to breakage of the electrode or its plugging by cell constituents, can be detected during the progress of an experiment. The possibility of tip potentials makes it unwise to assume that the highest obtainable resting potentials are the closest to the true *in vivo* potential.

A further difficulty arises when comparing the effect of solutions of different conductivity upon resting potential. For example, del Castillo & Katz (1955*b*) found that the tip potential nearly doubled when the solution into which a microelectrode was dipped was changed from Ringer to sodium-free sucrose Ringer. This trouble may be minimized by selecting electrodes with low tip potentials and by changing the solution with the microelectrode still in the cell. A correction must then be made for the change in the junctional potential at the indifferent electrode.

Experimental alterations of resting potential

Even if tip potentials have been avoided, the measured membrane potential may be less than the true potential. Three possibilities are always present. Firstly, the cell may be directly damaged by the experimental procedure; secondly, the cell may be unable to maintain its normal ionic concentrations in the experimental environment; and thirdly, the cell may be depolarized by continuous synaptic bombardment (see Chapter 6, p. 216).

The most common damage is of course damage by the microelectrode. An obvious sign of damage in all cells is a rapid fall in resting potential after penetration. In neurones other signs include repetitive firing at an initially high frequency which rapidly decreases (Frank & Fuortes, 1955), small action potentials with large afterhyperpolarization and late rising from synaptic potentials (R. M. Eccles, 1955), and in very deteriorated cells an inability to generate action potentials (Eccles, Hubbard, & Oscarsson, 1961).

An inadequate environment is the great weakness of *in vitro* preparations maintained in salt solutions. For instance, Kernan (1960) found that when frog plasma was the bathing medium for frog sartorii, the membrane potential was little different from the equilibrium potential for K^+ even with an extracellular K concentration of 2·5 mM. This is probably because in plasma the permeability of amphibian and mammalian muscle fibres *in vitro* stays closer to the normal *in vivo* value than is the case in ordinary Ringer's solution (Carey & Conway, 1954; Creese & Northover, 1961).

The oxygen supply of an *in vitro* preparation is also of great importance for maintenance of membrane potential, especially in mammalian tissues kept at body temperature. These tissues have a high oxygen consumption (Creese, Scholes, & Whalen, 1958), and the possibility arises that the oxygen supply provided when oxygen and carbon dioxide are bubbled through the bathing medium at some distance from the preparation may not be adequate. Using such indirect oxygenation, rat diaphragm muscles gain sodium and lose potassium (Creese, 1954). Later studies (Creese *et al.*, 1958; Creese, 1960) indicated that this change was due to loss of K^+ from the inner fibres. As expected these fibres also showed reduced resting potentials when compared with surface fibres. Indirect oxygenation is thus only adequate for electrical studies upon surface fibres. Another often used preparation, the frog sartorius muscle, is probably adequately oxygenated by indirect means (Keynes, 1954; Harris & Steinbach, 1956; discussed by Creese, 1960).

Experimental alterations of the composition of the bathing medium may also have long-term deleterious effects upon the ionic composition of the preparation and thus affect membrane potential. Thus Creese & Roberts (1954) found that in bathing solutions with a low Ca concentration, rat diaphragm muscles slowly gained Na^+ and lost K^+. Experimenters who vary Ca/Mg ratios in bathing solutions to block neuromuscular transmission may thus find it desirable to keep the calcium content normal and raise the magnesium concentration rather than use a lowered $CaCl_2$ and raised $MgCl_2$. Constancy of the CO_2 concentration of the bathing medium is also important. An increase in CO_2 tension causes a fall in intracellular K^+ in mammalian muscle while a fall in CO_2 tension has an 'anticurare action' (Creese, 1953).

MEASUREMENT OF MEMBRANE RESISTANCE AND CAPACITANCE

Cell membranes are characterized electrically by their transverse resistance (R_m) and transverse capacitance (C_m). The units of these constants are ohm.cm^2 and $\mu F/cm^2$ respectively as they relate to unit area of the membrane. The terms 'specific membrane resistance' and 'specific membrane capacitance' have been applied to these constants (Coombs, Eccles, & Fatt, 1955*a*, Coombs, Eccles,

& Curtis, 1959) but it seems preferable to confine the term 'specific' to the resistance of unit length of a material (ohm.cm) as in physics. Representative values are shown in Table 3.1.

The most commonly used technique for measuring these constants has been to apply sudden current pulses through the membrane, and to measure the time required for the trans-membrane potential to reach a steady level and the magnitude of this response. In the past some investigators have used current steps applied through the membrane by means of two extracellular electrodes in contact with the external surface of the nerve membrane (Hodgkin & Rushton, 1946; Lorente de Nó, 1947*b*). The form of the potential changes recorded with this technique (Fig. 3.2) is quite similar to that obtained with the nowadays more usual method of applying square current pulses across the membrane

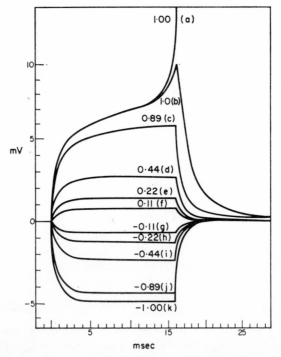

FIG. 3.2. Response of a crab axon to rectangular current pulses of different intensity; recorded at a polarizing electrode of width about 200 μ. The numbers on each record give the strength of current relative to threshold. Depolarization of the nerve is shown as positive (Hodgkin & Rushton, 1946).

TABLE 3.1

Passive properties of cell membranes

Tissue	R_o kΩ or MΩ	λ mm	τ msec	R_m Ωcm²	C_m μF/cm²	d μ	Reference
Muscle							
human intercostal	570 kΩ	18·9	22·0	4070	4·8	—	Elmqvist, Johns, & Thesleff (1960)
							Elmqvist et al (1964)
rat EDL	—	0·57	3·1	542	5·9	—	Kiyohara & Sato (1967)
SOL	—	0·46	2·0	540	3·8	—	Kiyohara & Sato (1967)
cat tenuissimus	—	1·10	4·9	1430	3·5	30–60	Boyd & Martin (1959)
frog sartorius	—	1·61	21·5	2065*	10·6	129	Del Castillo & Machne (1953)
tortoise retractor capitis	980	1·47	33·6	4860	7·2	50	Levine (1966b)
terrapin retractor	1020	2·31	33·6	5570	5·9	—	Levine (1966b)

$$*\ \frac{\text{Denervated } R_m}{\text{Normal } R_m} = 1\cdot 7$$

Tissue	R_o kΩ or MΩ	λ mm	τ msec	R_m Ωcm²	C_m μF/cm²	d μ	Reference
Neurone							
Cat motor cortex	6·7 MΩ	—	8·4	1000–6000 (soma)	1·5–5·0 (soma)	—	Hubbard, S. J. (1963)
hippocampal	13	—	9·9	600	5	20μ	Lux & Pollen (1966)
motor	1·2	—	3·1		370	70μ	Spencer & Kandel (1961a)
Toad motor	3–6	—	1·5–8			—	Coombs, Curtis, & Eccles (1959)
Toad spinal ganglion large cells	16–22	—	2·1–4·6	2200–4000	1·1	—	Araki & Otani (1955) Ito (1957J)
Aplysia ganglion	2·2	—	50	2200	23	—	Fessard & Tauc (1957)

between an intracellular electrode and the external medium, and simultaneously recording the time course of the potential generated by this current with the same or another intracellular electrode. As Fig. 3.2 shows, the membrane potential changes generated in response to both hyperpolarizing and depolarizing currents rise exponentially to a steady level and decline with a similar time course. At a certain depolarizing strength (Fig. 3.2b), however, irregularities appear on the responses—abortive action potentials. Stronger pulses will excite action potentials consistently. Investigation in the depolarizing direction must thus be confined to a limited range of current steps.

Two forms of the microelectrode technique have been developed to measure membrane constants. In one case the current pulse is applied through one electrode and the transmembrane potential is measured by a second intracellular electrode. This method is particularly useful if the two electrodes can be independently introduced into the cell (Tauc, 1955; Bennett, Crain, & Grundfest, 1959; Hagiwara, Watanabe, & Saito, 1959). In the central nervous system, the insertion of two microelectrodes into the same cell is for all practical purposes impossible. This impossibility resulted in the development of the 'double barrel' microelectrode in which two micropipettes are drawn together (Fig. 3.3). Such a microelectrode allowed successful application of the method outlined above to the spinal mononeurone (Coombs, Eccles, & Fatt, 1955*a*; Coombs, Curtis & Eccles, 1959). A 'parallel' electrode technique, in which the two micropipettes are in contact only in a very small portion near their tips has also been used (Terzuolo & Araki, 1961). These methods must be used in association with special circuits since, due to the proximity of the two micropipettes, large artefacts are recorded across the capacitance of the microelectrode walls (Fig. 3.3B). This problem, however, can be overcome in a number of ways (Coombs, Curtis, & Eccles, 1957; Araki & Terzuolo, 1962; Lux & Pollen, 1966). A more formidable problem is its limitation to the study of large cells which are able to withstand twin impalement.

Wheatstone bridge

The Wheatstone bridge technique was developed by Araki & Otani (1955) and utilizes a bridge arrangement in which one of the resistive arms is the recording micropipette. This technique allows

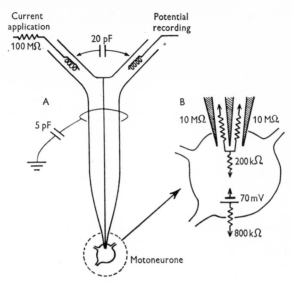

FIG. 3.3. A. Double-barrelled microelectrode and its immediate connections. Typical values are given of the several electrical characteristics which are significant in the use of the electrode. B. Enlarged view of the microelectrode tip in a motoneurone. The motoneurone properties represented are the potential and resistance (ignoring the reactance) between the inside and outside of the inactive cell. For diagrammatic purposes the microelectrode tip is shown greatly magnified relative to the motoneurone (Coombs, Eccles, & Fatt, 1955a).

direct stimulation of the impaled cell through the same electrode used for recording the intracellular potential change, and thus any cell which can be impaled correctly can, in principle, be tested.

The principle of this technique is the well-known four-arm Wheatstone bridge, the usual device employed in resistance measurements (Fig. 3.4A). This network is arranged in such a manner that the zero potential differences between two terminals, during the application of a current between the other two terminals (see Fig. 3.4), indicates that a precise relation exists between the electrical parameters of the resistances in the bridge, i.e.,

$$\frac{R_1}{R_3}=\frac{R_2}{R_4}.$$

When no potential difference is recorded between points c and d of the bridge, the device is said to be 'balanced'. Given this dynamic condition, if the resistive value of one of the arms is

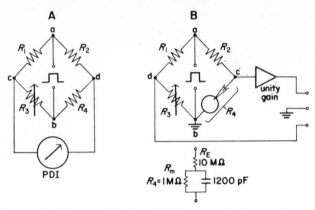

Fig. 3.4. A. Diagram of a simple Wheatstone bridge to illustrate the relation of the resistors to the current source (Π) and potential difference indicator (PDI). B. Experimental arrangement for the utilization of a bridge circuit in order to record potential and to apply current across a cell membrane with a single electrode; see text.

altered it is possible to calculate the magnitude of the change by rebalancing the bridge to a null reading in the potential difference indicator (PDI). This is known as the bridge balance method. An alternative to this method is to read directly the potential difference produced by the disbalance and, knowing the current applied and the magnitude of the potential difference, it is possible to calculate the resistance using Ohm's law. This is the bridge imbalance method. It must be remembered that the bridge sensitivity is maximum when the four arms have similar resistive values, and the volt-meter has an input impedance of the same order of magnitude as that of any one of the arms.

Figure 3.4B shows one of the many arrangements which allow the use of the circuit to measure the input resistance and capacitance of a given cell. R_1 and R_2 are fixed resistors. R_2 is the current limiting resistor and in general has a value of about $5 \times 10^8 \ \Omega$. The values for R_1 and R_3 must be selected depending on the resistance of the electrodes to be utilized and the input resistance of the cell to be studied. R_4 is shown separately on the lower part of Fig. 3.4 and must be calculated as two resistances in series, that of the microelectrode—R_E (depicted as 10 MΩ), and that of the cell—R_m (1 MΩ). The capacity in parallel with the 1 MΩ resistor represents the capacitance of the cell (Eccles, 1957). Unless a fairly accurate calculation of the resistance is obtained by measuring the bridge imbalance produced by an RC circuit (dummy cell), the bridge circuit should not be utilized. Furthermore, it must be remembered that the bridge technique is by no means accurate (see below) and only a first approximation measurement can be obtained. The bridge must be balanced before the impalement of the cell, and the input capacity compensated by negative feedback (Donaldson, 1958). Under these conditions, when the microelectrode penetrates a cell the RC circuit is added to one of the arms of the bridge. The amplitude of the imbalance is related to the value of the added resistance, while the time that the potential requires to reach the asymptote represents the value of the capacity. Given that the amplitude of the potential and the amount of current applied are known, the resistance can be calculated. The capacity can be calculated by measuring τ* which is the RC value of the added circuit. The measurement of membrane capacitance is in fact quite complex in the case of central neurones since the presence of a dendritic tree adds a very complex RC load to the soma. Some approximate value for the capacity can be obtained, however, following the calculation of ρ as specified by Rall (1962*a*), see p. 260. On the other hand, as pointed out by Thomas-Green (1964), resistance measurements by means of a Wheatstone bridge have several inherent sources of error. For example, the potential difference produced by the bridge imbalance is not a function of the input resistance of the cell exclusively. Actually it is

$$V_m = V \frac{\{R_1(R_E + R_m) - R_2 R_3\}}{(R_1 + R_3)(R_2 + R_E + R_m)} \qquad \text{(see Fig. 3.4B)}$$

The second source of error pointed out by this author is that the current flow through the electrode arm is assumed to be

$$I = \frac{E}{R_1 + R_3} \cdot \frac{R_1}{R_2}$$

but since in the unbalanced condition this is not the case, given that the current flowing through R_1 is not proportional to the electrode arm, this assumption does not hold. However, if the usual assumptions are followed, the calculated input resistance of the cell should be

* τ is calculated as the time needed for the potential to attain $1/e$ of its asymptote value.

$$R_m \, \text{Calc} = \frac{R_m R_2}{R_2 + R_E + R_m}$$

which this author found to deviate only 2% from the measured input resistance.

This simple equation should always be employed to estimate the magnitude of the error introduced by this method. Another inherent error of the Wheatstone bridge approach is the assumption that the resistance of the microelectrode does not change during impalement, and thus that the bridge imbalance is produced solely by R_m. Since there is a strong possibility that the electrode changes its resistive characteristics when it penetrates the cell, this problem is in fact very serious. A clear solution to this impasse is to balance the resistive component of the microelectrode inside the cell itself (Purple, 1964). This method utilizes the fact that the RC value of the membrane is large compared with the RC of the microelectrode. In this manner, if a short-lasting current pulse—too short to charge the capacity of the membrane to any appreciable degree—is passed across the cell, it will allow a verification of the balanced state of the bridge since the cell membrane is 'transparent' to the short-duration pulses. Care must be taken, however, that no current is lost across the stray capacity of the electrode. Finally, the value of R_2—the current limiting resistance—should be as large as possible, in order to prevent a certain amount of shunting of the cell's potential through this pathway. In order to make this resistance as large as practicable, Ito (1957) has designed a head stage cathode follower which allows effective current limiting resistances of the order of thousands of megohms.

Analysis of results

The simple model (Fig. 2.3) of a parallel resistance and capacitance is clearly only an approximation to the complexity of actual cells. It is convenient to designate this model as that of a round cell which can be uniformly polarized by applied currents. The closest biological approach to a round cell appears to be frog ganglion cells which are without dendrites (Lenhossék, 1886) and have been treated for measurement of electrical properties as perfect spheres (Ito, 1957). An alternative ideal model is the cable (Fig. 2.15) composed of a series of similar reactive elements.

This model can be used to describe the electrical properties of long cylindrical cells such as nerve and muscle. Cells with more complicated geometry can be approximated by a combination of these models. Coombs, Eccles, & Fatt (1955*a*) and Coombs, Curtis, & Eccles (1959), for instance, developed from histological data a motoneurone of standard configuration, composed of a sphere (the soma) from which arise seven processes (the dendrites and 1 axon). Neglecting their conical origin the processes were considered to be cylinders of uniform diameter branching infrequently until they were so far from the cell that branching would not influence the effects of current applied on the soma. The cell was then treated as a combination of round cell and seven cables. A further refinement has been provided by Rall's (1957, 1962, 1965) development of mathematical formulations which enable dendritic branching to be approximated by an equivalent cylinder. Provided a cell's geometry is known therefore, excellent approximations to the specific electrical properties of its membrane can be made.

The analysis for both a round cell and a cable is based on the assumption that Ohm's Law is obeyed, i.e., that the current applied and potential obtained are linearly related. Figure 3.5

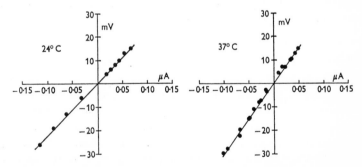

FIG. 3.5. Voltage–current relation in two cat tenuissimus muscle fibres, one at 24°C and one at 37°C, plotted from records similar to those shown in Fig. 3.6. The voltage values represent the amplitude of the electrotonic potential when a steady state is reached. Depolarization is plotted upwards (Boyd & Martin, 1959).

shows current–voltage curves for muscle fibres which support this relationship for a 30 mV hyperpolarization to near the threshold depolarization. Linear curves have also been reported for cells approximating to round cells, e.g., cat motoneurones (Coombs, Curtis, & Eccles, 1959) and lobster ganglion cells (Hagiwara,

Watanabe, & Saito, 1959). Ito (1957) found, however, that frog ganglion cells did not show this linear relationship. It is desirable therefore at any particular membrane to make current–voltage curves as a preliminary to more extensive investigation, so that constants can be calculated using values in the linear part of the current–voltage curve.

Spherical cells

For an ideal round cell which was uniformly hyper- or depolarized by the applied pulses, it would be expected that the condenser equation would apply, i.e., that

$$V = V_0 \, e^{-t/RC}$$

where V_0 is the initial voltage level before the current pulse and V is the membrane potential at the time t after the current was applied or broken. The product RC is the time constant τ_m. It will be noted that if t is made equal to RC then

$$V = V_0 \, e^{-1}.$$

Thus $\tau_m = RC$ may be measured experimentally by finding the time at which the change in potential has reached $1/e$ of its final value. From the magnitude of V, the steady potential change, the resistance (R_0) can be calculated

$$R_0 = V/I \text{ where } I \text{ is the applied current.}$$

Alternatively R_0 may be measured directly by a bridge balance method. For many purposes a knowledge of R_0 and τ_m is sufficient. For instance, a change in cell electrical properties could be investigated by measuring τ_m and R_0 in the presence and absence of the perturbing agent. The elucidation of R_m and C_m requires a knowledge of the cell surface area. This arises because R_0 is clearly the sum of the individual resistance of unit areas of membrane all in parallel, i.e.,

$$R_0 = \frac{R_m}{\text{surface area}} = R_m/\pi d^2 \text{ where } d \text{ is the cell diameter,}$$

whence R_m can be calculated and since $\tau_m = R_m C_m$ and τ_m is known, C_m may be found.

Cable

The cable differs from the round cell in that the current is not applied uniformly to the whole cell. The potential recorded by an electrode will therefore vary with the distance of the electrode from the current source. From cable theory (Hodgkin & Rushton, 1946) the potential change (V) produced by a steady current (I) across a membrane is given by

$$V = \tfrac{1}{2}I\sqrt{(r_m r_i)} \exp\{-x/\sqrt{(r_m/r_i)}\} \qquad (1)$$

where x is the distance (cm) separating the recording and current passing electrodes, r_m is the transverse membrane resistance of a unit length of membrane, and r_i is the longitudinal internal resistance of unit length of the cell interior.

As shown in Fig. 3.6A taken from the results of Boyd & Martin

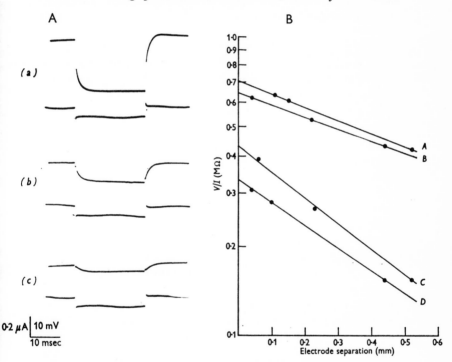

FIG. 3.6. A. Electrotonic potentials in cat tenuissimus muscle produced by current pulses with three different electrode separations. Lower record in each case is current pulse. Inter-electrode distances were: (a) 0·05 mm; (b) 0·60 mm; (c) 1·10 mm. mV scale applies to electotronic potentials, μA scale to current pulses. Normal Kreb's solution; 24°C. B. Spatial decay of electrotonic potentials in four fibres. Ordinate, amplitude of electrotonic potential, when a steady state is reached, divided by amplitude of current pulse; logarithmic scale. Abscissa, separation between current and voltage recording electrodes. Fibres A and B, 37°C; fibres C and D, 22°C (Boyd & Martin, 1959).

(1959) from cat muscle, the potentials recorded at different electrode separations (Fig. 3.6A, a, b, c) are smaller and rise more slowly the greater is the separation. When the ratio V/I is plotted against the electrode separation (Fig. 3.6B), a straight line is obtained which if extrapolated to the origin ($x=0$) would give the input resistance.

$$R_0 = \tfrac{1}{2}\sqrt{(r_m r_i)} \text{ (from eqn. (1) with } x=0). \tag{2}$$

Further, from the slope of this line the space constant (λ) of the cable may be obtained, i.e., the distance from any point on the cable over which the potential falls to $1/e$ of its value at that point. From cable theory

$$\lambda = \sqrt{(r_m/r_i)}. \tag{3}$$

From eqns. (2) and (3), r_m and r_i may be calculated. To find R_m and C_m either the cable diameter (d) must be known as for a round cell, or the internal specific resistance R_i must be known. The relationships are $R_m = \pi d r_m$ since r_m is the longitudinal transverse resistance of unit length, and πd is the circumference of the cable and $R_i = \pi (d/2)^2\, r_i$ since r_i is the longitudinal resistance of unit length and $\pi (d/2)^2$ is the area of a cross-section of the cable at right angles to its length.

If d is unknown it may be calculated provided R_i is known. R_i has not been measured directly for any cell types. For frog muscle, Bozler & Cole (1935) by impedance measurements and Katz (1948), from a knowledge of d, calculated R_i to be 260 ohm.cm at 16·5°C and 250 ohm.cm at 22°C respectively. For crustacean muscle 203 ±43 ohm.cm is reported (Henček & Zachar, 1965), also based on diameter measurements. For mammalian muscle Boyd & Martin (1959) suggest 125 ohm.cm at 37°C, this value being derived from the frog muscle results with corrections for the higher ionic concentration of mammalian muscle and the higher temperature.

C_m for a cable is derived as for a round cell from R_m and $\tau_m = R_m C_m$. τ_m for a cable is the time for the potential to rise or fall to 83% of its maximum steady value with the two electrodes as close together as possible ($x/\lambda = 0.1$, Table 1 Hodgkin & Rushton, 1946).

Single microelectrode techniques applied to cables yield $R_0 = V/I = \tfrac{1}{2}\sqrt{(r_m r_i)}$ directly (the equation with $x=0$) while τ_m may be calculated as before from the time for the potential to rise to 83% of its maximum steady value. Knowledge of d or R_i is required for further analysis. As noted by Katz and Thesleff (1957a), since

$$R_m = \pi d r_m \quad r_m = \frac{R_m}{\pi d}$$

$$R_i = \pi \left(\frac{d}{2}\right)^2 \quad r_i = \frac{R_i}{\pi (d/2)^2}$$

then
$$R_0 = \frac{1}{\pi} \cdot \left(\frac{R_m R_i}{d^3}\right)^{\frac{1}{2}}.$$

Since the ordinary cable equations are based on the assumption of an infinitely long cable, they cannot be applied to muscle fibres where the ratio of fibre length to diameter is not sufficiently high. Equations have been derived for the appropriate corrections and the original references (Fatt & Ginsborg, 1958; Kuriyama & Tomita, 1965; Vayo, 1965) should be consulted for details.

ALTERNATIVE TIME CONSTANT MEASUREMENTS

(i) *Excitability testing.* The excitability change at the make and break of a current pulse should mirror the membrane potential change and thus provide an alternative method of measuring τ_m (Frank & Fuortes, 1956; Coombs, Curtis, & Eccles, 1959; Ito & Oshima, 1965). In practice the threshold strength of a short-duration pulse is measured during and at various times after a longer rectangular current pulse. In motoneurones the membrane excitability changes show a faster time course than the membrane potential change, due presumably to accommodation (Coombs, Curtis, & Eccles, 1959).

(ii) *Strength duration and strength latency curves.* If a current pulse is applied uniformly to a round cell the membrane potential should approach its final value with the membrane time constant It is known (Katz, 1937) that

$$I_{rh}/I = 1 - \exp\left(-t/\tau_m\right)$$

where I is the current which stimulates in time t and I_{rh} is the rheobasic current (that current which is just able to excite when flowing for a long time). When $t = \tau_m$, $I = 1.58\ I_{rh}$. Thus from a plot of spike latency against current strength, it is only necessary to find the latency for a current 1.58 times the rheobasic strength. In motoneurones this method gives lower values for τ_m than the square pulse technique (Coombs, Curtis, & Eccles, 1959), due to the complications provided by accommodation, depolarization of the membrane by excitatory potentials, the generation of local responses, and the cell geometry (see Chapter 6, p. 221).

SEPARATION OF IONIC COMPONENTS OF R_m

As yet this procedure is only applicable *in vitro*. The contribution of Cl′ to membrane resistance can be deduced by replacing Cl′ with the methyl sulphate ion or other anions which appear not to penetrate muscle cell membrane (Hutter & Noble, 1960*b*). In the case of frog muscle where R_m is known to be almost completely due to K and Cl components, it is only necessary to find R_m in the presence and absence of Cl′. The K component may then be inferred.

MEASUREMENT OF SYNAPTIC POTENTIALS

Usually four parameters are considered (Fig. 3.7).

(1) Latency—the time interval between the stimulus and the beginning of the postsynaptic potential.

(2) Rise time—the time interval between the beginning of the potential and the attainment of its peak amplitude.

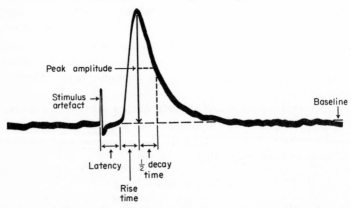

FIG. 3.7 The measurable parameters of an evoked synaptic potential.

(3) Decay time—the time interval between the peak amplitude and the decay to some selected fraction of the peak amplitude. Most commonly used are half decay time and time to decay to 1/e—the time constant in spherical cells (see also shape index, p. 261).

(4) The amplitude parameter usually measured is the peak amplitude—the vertical distance between a point on the base line and a similar point on the trace at its peak displacement (middle to middle, or top to top are commonly used). As Fig. 3.7 shows, because of noise the oscilloscope trace will have a certain 'thickness'. The noise can be considered to be distributed normally round the midpoint of the trace thickness. Thus, if a sufficient number of amplitudes are measured, middle to middle or top to top, the mean should be independent of the noise variation.

Membrane potential changes

If there is a change in the transmembrane potential (V), there will be a corresponding change in synaptic potential amplitude provided there is no compensating change in V_{tr}, the equilibrium potential for transmitter action, for from Chapter 2

$$I_{e.p.c.} = \Delta G_m(V - V_{tr}) \text{ where } I_{e.p.c.} \text{ is the synaptic current}$$

and ΔG_m is the net conductance change.

This linear relation between membrane potential and synaptic potential amplitudes was first found by Fatt & Katz (1951) at the frog neuromuscular junction and confirmed for both synaptic potential and synaptic current at the same junction by Takeuchi & Takeuchi (1959). A similar linear relationship has been found at synapses on many other cell types (mammalian motoneurones, Coombs, Eccles, & Fatt, 1955*c*; frog tonic muscles, Burke & Ginsborg, 1956*b*; giant synapse of squid stellate ganglion, Hagiwara & Tasaki, 1958; neurones of lobster cardiac ganglion, Hagiwara, Watanabe, & Saito, 1959; frog sympathetic ganglion cells, Nishi & Koketsu, 1960; ganglion cells of *Onchidium*, Kusano & Hagiwara, 1961; electroplaques of *Torpedo*, *Narcine*, *Astrocopus* and *Raia*, Grundfest & Bennett, 1961; giant cell of abdominal ganglion of *Aplysia*, Kandel & Tauc, 1965; Purkinje cell, Eccles, Llinás & Sasaki, 1966*a*).

At synapses where a linear relation between membrane potential and synaptic potential amplitude has been established it is sometimes convenient to compare synaptic potential amplitudes recorded at different resting potentials. This can be done by choosing a standard value of V appropriate to the experiment and multiplying all potential amplitudes by the factor

$$\frac{V_{standard} - V_{tr}}{V_{actual} - V_{tr}}. \tag{4}$$

For example, if working with miniature endplate potential amplitudes at the frog neuromuscular junction, the standard V might be 90 mV and V_{tr} 15 mV. The multiplication factor would then be $75/(V - 15)$ (Katz & Thesleff, 1957*a*).

Membrane potential changes may alter the time course of synaptic potentials (see p. 233). For instance, Coombs, Eccles & Fatt (1953, 1955*b*) have reported that synaptic potentials recorded intracellularly from motoneurones have a more rapid time course during hyperpolarization of the motoneurone membrane by applied current. This change was attributed to a lowering of the membrane resistance by the current. At the frog neuromuscular junction the time course of the endplate potential did not alter with variations of V.

The special role of potassium ions in the generation of the synaptic current at both excitatory and inhibitory synapses and in the determination of membrane potential means that changes in the extra- and intracellular concentration of this ion have a dual effect on synaptic potential amplitude. Not only will the amplitude change because of the membrane potential change, but because of the alteration in V_K there will be an alteration of the equilibrium potential (V_{tr}) for the synaptic potential. In these circumstances it is still possible to correct the amplitudes of synaptic potentials to a common value of V, using formula (4) provided the new V_{tr} is known. For the frog neuromuscular junction values of V_{tr} for a wide range of potassium and sodium concentrations and for a smaller range of calcium and magnesium concentrations may be found in the paper by N. Takeuchi (1963*b*).

Membrane time constant

As Fig. 3.8 shows, an increase of the membrane time constant (τ_m) can prolong the time course and increase the amplitude of synaptic potentials (Fig. 3.8D) and miniature potentials (Fig.

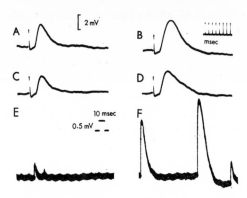

FIG. 3.8. Sub- and postsynaptic effects upon synaptic potential amplitudes and time courses. A, C, and E are control potentials. B, after 3 min exposure to 'Tensilon' 10 mg/l. D, after 5 min exposure to Liley's (1956) solution with NaNO₃ substituted for NaCl. A, B, C, D. Intracellularly recorded from the same curarized junction of the rat diaphragm in vitro at 34°C. (Hubbard, unpublished experiments.) E, F. Miniature endplate potentials recorded from rat intercostal muscles *in vitro* at 37°C. E, in Liley's solution, F 3 min later and 1 min after all anions in the solution were replaced by NO₃ (Hofmann, Fiegen, & Genther, 1962). Time and voltage markers in E apply to E and F only. Calibrations in A and B apply also to C and D.

3.8F). In the experiment illustrated, the effect upon time constant was produced by replacing with nitrate (NO_3^-) most of the Cl' of the solution bathing mammalian muscle fibres. R_m was increased, for nitrate ions penetrate the membrane less easily than Cl' and also retard the passage of Cl' (Harris, 1958). It is found that there is a linear relationship between the membrane resistance of frog muscle *in vitro* and the external NO_3^- concentration (Hutter & Padsha, 1959; Adrian, 1961; Washio & Mashima, 1963). Replacement of all or part of the Cl' in bathing solutions may thus be a useful method of increasing the amplitude of small synaptic potentials, such as m.e.p.p.s, in *in vitro* preparations. This method is particularly valuable at vertebrate neuromuscular junctions where it is probable that the permeability to Cl ions is not altered by the transmitter (Takeuchi & Takeuchi, 1960b). Replacement of Cl' by NO_3^- can also be used to assess the role played by Cl' permeability in drug effects (Parsons, Hofmann, & Feigen, 1966).

As Fig. 3.8A, B indicates, the effects of NO_3^- addition are mimicked by an anticholinesterase agent. It is, however, easy to

distinguish postsynaptic effects upon synaptic potentials from pre-
or subsynaptic actions by simply comparing an applied current
pulse and the synaptic potential under the same conditions. The
time course of such a pulse will be unaffected by anticholinesterases, or indeed by any drug affecting only the subsynaptic receptors, but will be altered in the same manner as a synaptic potential
if there is a change in membrane time constant. An example of this
technique is shown in Fig. 3.9 which illustrates the effect of temperature changes upon endplate potentials (Fig. 3.9A) and the

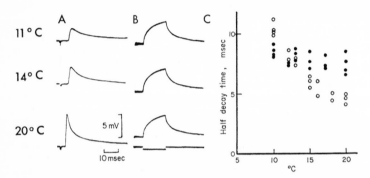

FIG. 3.9. Comparison between the effects of temperature on the
time course of the endplate potential and the membrane potential
change caused by the polarizing current. A, records of endplate
potentials at three temperatures. B, electrotonic potentials obtained
from the same muscle fibre at the same temperatures. The bottom
record is the polarizing current passed through the membrane. The
amplification was the same in all records and the voltage scale is
5 mV; time scale, 10 msec. C. Effect of temperature on the time
course of the decay of the endplate potential and that of the electrotonic potentials. Open circles: endplate potential. Full circles:
electrotonic potentials. Ordinate: half decay time of endplate
potentials and electrotonic potentials, in msec. Abscissa: temperature (Takeuchi, 1958).

electrotonic response to a current pulse (Fig. 3.9B). Clearly the
fall in temperature prolongs the decay time of the synaptic
potential (Fig. 3.9C, open circles) but has little effect upon the
time course of the electrotonic potential (Fig. 3.9C, filled circles).
It must be concluded that the temperature changes do not have
much effect upon postsynaptic electrical constants.

An example in which special postsynaptic properties affect the
synaptic potential markedly comes from frog slow muscle fibres
where the endplate potentials (also known as the small fibre

junctional potential—s.j.p.) have a hyperpolarizing phase succeeding the decline of the depolarizing phase. This can be attributed to the properties of the slow fibre membrane, since a similar hyperpolarization is found after electrical depolarizing pulses are applied to such membranes (Kuffler & Vaughan Williams, 1953*a*; Burke & Ginsborg, 1956*a*; Hess & Pilar, 1964).

MEASUREMENT OF ACTION POTENTIALS

Threshold

In tissues which possess appropriate electroresponsive electrogenic components, such as vertebrate muscle, if the postsynaptic excitatory potential exceeds a certain amplitude, characteristic of the postsynaptic membrane, an action potential will be generated. The actual magnitude of the depolarization needed depends on the pre-existing level of membrane potential. It is conventional to define the threshold level as the strength of stimulus which excites in 50% of trials. This threshold level may be measured by observation of the synaptic potential amplitude which initiates a spike potential in 50% of trials or alternatively by finding the magnitude of the applied voltage pulse which similarly excites an action potential in about 50% of trials. Figures obtained by either method should agree (see e.g., Levine, 1966*b*).

Observation of action potentials

In the many cells in which voltage clamp techniques are impracticable, valuable information about conductance changes may still be obtained from observation of certain parameters of the action potential. Figure 3.10 illustrates this technique applied to cat motoneurones before, during and after the cat was forced to breathe pure nitrogen. (Eccles, Løyning, & Oshima, 1966). Observation of the action potential amplitude (Fig. 3.10A, D SP) gives an indication of the variations of the sodium equilibrium potential V_{Na} during the experimental production of hypoxia. Again from differentiated records of the action potential (Fig. 3.10B and D, V_1, V_2) it is possible to measure with ease the rate of rise (Fig. 3.10D, V_1) and fall (Fig. 3.10D, V_2) of the spike. As Fig. 3.10 indicates, these parameters reflect the underlying sodium conductance and potassium conductance changes (ΔG_{Na} and

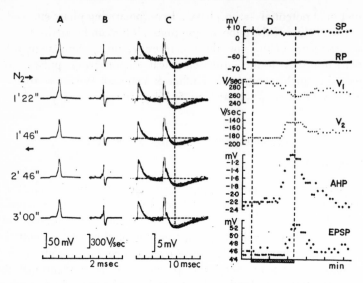

FIG. 3.10. Analysis of action potentials. This figure shows the effects of 100% nitrogen on potentials recorded intracellularly from a motoneurone. The hypoxia lasted for 2 min 18 sec. A–C. Records of the potentials recorded. The top row contains the control records and the other rows of potentials were recorded throughout the trial at the indicated times. The two rows of potentials between the arrows were recorded in the hypoxia period. A. Antidromic spike potential. Note that a monosynaptic EPSP precedes so that the firing level of the cell is reached. B. Differentiated record of the spike potential. C. Monosynaptic EPSP followed by the antidromic action potential recorded at high gain and slow sweep speed to display the after-hyperpolarization. The broken lines are the reference lines for amplitude measurements. The left set of calibrations pertains to A and B, the right set to C. D. Diagram of the changes observed in the potentials recorded (the overshoot). RP is membrane potential. The amplitude of the potential (B) is plotted as V_1 the maximum rate of rise, and V^2 the maximum rate of all of the spike. AHP shows the amplitude of the after-hyperpolarization measured at a constant latency as the broken lines in C indicate. EPSP indicates the amplitude of the synaptic potential illustrated in C (Eccles, Løyning, & Oshima, 1966).

ΔG_K). Finally the after-hyperpolarization of the spike can be measured (Fig. 3.10C, D AHP). This is a measure of the potassium equilibrium potential, V_K. The technique of action potential observation is well suited for obtaining quantitative data rapidly and easily. Similar methods have been applied to the analysis of the events following intracellular injection of ions and metabolic inhibitors into motoneurones (Coombs, Eccles, & Fatt, 1955*a*; Ito & Oshima, 1964*b*, *c*).

Voltage clamp

This method of following conductance changes is ideally suited to studying the effect of various procedures on ΔG_{Na} and ΔG_{K}. A further refinement has been added by the discovery of pharmacological agents specifically blocking one component of the conductance change so that other components may be studied in isolation (see Chapter 2, p. 60, and Chapter 6, pp. 235 and 248).

4

INVESTIGATION OF PRESYNAPTIC FUNCTION

As has already been pointed out, the chemical theory of synaptic transmission requires that upon stimulation the presynaptic element releases an appropriate amount of the chemical transmitter (neurohumour) which subsequently acts upon the postsynaptic cell. Investigation of this aspect of synaptic physiology has had two different aims. The first has been to determine transmitter release under various physiological or experimental conditions; the second has been to elucidate the mechanisms involved in the release process. Measurement of transmitter release is accordingly the topic of the first half of this chapter. It will be found that electrophysiological methods yielding quantitative measurements of a high order of accuracy are readily available for peripheral synapses and, with greater difficulty, can also be used for central nervous system synapses. While quantitative investigation of presynaptic function requires, as the *sine qua non*, quantitative assessment of transmitter release, it is at the same time desirable that data be obtained regarding the events in the nerve terminal preceding release. It must be admitted that quantitative information about these events, the topic of the second half of this chapter, is usually more difficult to obtain and interpret than release data. A note regarding terminology is appropriate here. The term 'presynaptic' is often employed to refer to all structures afferent to the synapse—with respect to a neuromuscular junction the whole motoneurone and, in turn its afferents, are 'presynaptic'. In this chapter the term will generally be used in a more restricted sense, to refer only to the nerve terminals, i.e., the structures which are most directly concerned with the secretion of neurohumours.

Investigation of presynaptic mechanisms can, of course, take several forms. The biochemistry of nerve terminals is a possible subject of study now that these structures, redesignated 'synaptosomes', can be isolated from brain (DeRobertis, 1964; Whittaker,

1965, 1966). Although undoubtedly essential for answering the fundamental question of how extrusion of transmitter is actually brought about, such studies are beyond the scope of this book. Electrophysiological techniques for the study of presynaptic function, which are dealt with here, offer the advantage of allowing extremely fine time resolution of those events which can be followed, namely, the presynaptic action potential, the effect of the transmitter substance which is released, and other postsynaptic electrical events. Fortunately, these relate directly to the function of the synapse of most direct relevance to the neurophysiologist, the transfer of signals.

The major difficulty preventing adequate electrophysiological studies of presynaptic function is the generally small size of nerve terminals. Except at the giant synapse of the squid and the avian ciliary ganglionic synapse, it is not possible to insert a microelectrode into a nerve terminal. Except at these favoured sites, therefore, only indirect investigations of nerve terminal properties are possible—thus extracellular recording must be used to record the presence of presynaptic action potentials and changes in these potentials under experimental conditions. Similarly extracellular stimulation is used to detect excitability changes in terminals from which changes in the terminal membrane potential level (polarization level) are inferred. Again it is an implicit assumption in many experiments that the presynaptic action potential is a standard or constant stimulus to the release of transmitter. In view of the observation that the amount of the transmitter released is very sensitive to any experimental alteration of the amplitude of the presynaptic action potential or applied depolarizing pulse, this would seem a hazardous assumption (Hagiwara & Tasaki, 1958; Takeuchi & Takeuchi, 1962; Katz & Miledi, 1967c) were it not for the evidence, from extracellular recording, that the nerve impulse may indeed be effectively constant (Katz & Miledi, 1965a; Braun & Schmidt, 1966; Hubbard & Willis, 1968).

While the results of extracellular recording and stimulation techniques can be interpreted in terms of the results obtained with these techniques in similar but more easily accessible tissues, there is another large body of information about presynaptic events which is interpreted in terms of a model of presynaptic transmitter synthesis, storage, and mobilization. This relates to the dependence of transmitter release upon the frequency and duration of stimulation. Currently, post-synaptic observations of transmitter outflow from terminals are interpreted in terms of a system in which a presynaptic depolarization release coupling system, which is strongly affected by the stimulus parameters, acts upon a presynaptic pool of available transmitter, the size of which varies with release on the one hand and input into it on the other hand.

It should be noted that, while by comparison with the methods for measuring release, analysis of presynaptic mechanisms may seem crude and indirect, this field of research is at present being most actively explored. As will be demonstrated, the available methods may be used to yield results of physiological and pharmacological importance.

MEASUREMENT OF TRANSMITTER RELEASE

Direct assay

The only method of assessing directly the amount of transmitter liberated by nerve terminals is to collect and measure the substance released. This method is limited, of course, to synapses where the transmitter is known and where one can be confident that all released transmitter is collected. These conditions are fulfilled for cat sympathetic ganglia (Birks & MacIntosh, 1961) which can be perfused with various solutions and continue to respond, apparently normally, to presynaptic nerve stimulation. If the perfusion fluid contains an anti-cholinesterase and an agent blocking ACh synthesis, amounts of ACh equal to those disappearing from the ganglion can be collected. It is reasonable to suppose that recovery is complete also when synthesis is not blocked, provided cholinesterase is rendered inactive (Birks & MacIntosh, 1961). Similar experiments have been done on rat phrenic nerve diaphragm preparations (Straughan, 1960; Krnjević & Mitchell, 1961; Cheymol, Bourillet & Ogura, 1962). In these cases, the assay of ACh is perforce biological because of the small amounts of ACh to be measured, but there is abundant evidence for the validity of such assays.

At synapses where transmitter action is terminated by uptake of the transmitter into the terminals it is necessary to block this local uptake by pharmacological means before transmitter output can be accurately assessed. Such drugs are not yet available for synapses where γ-amino-butyric acid (GABA) is the transmitter, and at adrenergic synapses, where uptake blocking drugs are available, it is difficult to be sure that the release process is not also affected.

The method of direct assay is difficult to operate effectively and is inherently unsuited to the analysis of rapid events. Alternative electrophysiological methods are available, which are relatively easy to use, and are suitable for analysis of rapidly changing situations. These methods depend on the statistical analysis of evoked postsynaptic potentials. Much information can also be gained by study of the spontaneous release of transmitter which is a feature of chemical synapses.

Quantum content method

It is clear that the amplitude of any synaptic potential is determined by both presynaptic and postsynaptic factors, i.e., it depends upon both the amount of transmitter which is released and the postsynaptic responsiveness to transmitter. In many cases, it is possible to distinguish unequivocally between postsynaptic and presynaptic factors, and in so doing make a quantitative assessment of transmitter release. The methods for doing so depend upon the finding that transmitter is released in multi-molecular packets or 'quanta' (del Castillo & Katz, 1954*b*, 1956*b*, 1957*c*), whose release occurs spontaneously at a low rate. This rate is enormously increased for a short period of time by a presynaptic nerve impulse. The methods which arise from this discovery have as yet mainly been applied to neuromuscular preparations because of the ease of experimental technique and the relative simplicity of interpretation of the synaptic potentials arising from one synapse alone. For this reason, most of the following discussion is concerned directly with the synapses made by motoneurone axon terminals with vertebrate striated muscle fibres. The experimental techniques and methods of analysis which have proved useful seem to be to a large extent transferable to other synapses (e.g., Kuno, 1964*a*) and it is to be hoped that their application may become general.

SPONTANEOUS RELEASE OF TRANSMITTER

In 1950 Fatt and Katz, while recording intracellularly from the frog neuromuscular synapse, detected small potentials of fairly uniform amplitude appearing apparently at random intervals (Figs. 4.1, 4.2). Their observation was fundamental, for these small potentials, termed by them 'miniature endplate potentials' were found to correspond to the basic units of transmitter dealt with by the release mechanism (del Castillo & Katz, 1956*b*). They have since been recorded from the postsynaptic cell at all nerve–muscle junctions which have been explored, whether the junction involved twitch (Fig. 4.1), slow (Fig. 4.2), or smooth muscle, or was in vertebrate or invertebrate muscle (Boyd & Martin, 1956*a*; Brooks, 1956; Liley, 1956*a*; Burke, 1957; Takeuchi, 1959; Elmqvist, Johns, & Thesleff, 1960; Ginsborg, 1960*a*; Burnstock & Holman, 1962*a*; Dudel & Orkand, 1960; Usherwood, 1963; Alnaes, Jansen & Rudjord, 1964). Similar spontaneous potentials (miniature postsynaptic potentials) have been recorded from vertebrate ganglionic synapses (Blackman, Ginsborg, & Ray, 1963*a*, Martin & Pilar, 1964*a*), vertebrate motoneurones (Katz & Miledi, 1963; Kuno, 1964*a*), and the squid giant synapse (Miledi, 1967). It is convenient to use the term miniature potentials for the spontaneous potentials at all these sites. At vertebrate neuromuscular and ganglionic synapses the miniature potentials are excitatory; at arthropod neuromuscular junctions and vertebrate spinal motoneurones both inhibitory and excitatory potentials are found (Grundfest & Reuben, 1961; Usherwood & Grundfest, 1964; Takeuchi & Takeuchi, 1966*a*; Katz & Miledi, 1963).

Pharmacological analysis was used by the first investigators of miniature potentials (Fatt & Katz, 1950, 1952) to ascertain that they were produced by multimolecular packets of transmitter. The ionophoretic application of acetylcholine (ACh), to the frog neuromuscular junction, where this substance is the transmitter, caused a smoothly graded depolarization rather than the burst of miniatures which would be expected if each miniature reflected the action of a molecule of ACh. Tubocurarine or prostigmine had graded effects on the amplitude and the time course of miniature potentials as they did on the response to ACh. Similar evidence is available for the crustacean and insect neuromuscular junction, where the transmitter is not ACh (Dudel & Kuffler, 1961*a*; Usherwood, 1963). The term 'quanta' was subsequently applied to the packages of transmitter whose postsynaptic activity is manifest as miniature potentials, when it was found that these same packages are involved in evoked postsynaptic potentials, and represent the 'basic coin' of transmitter release (see review by Katz, 1962).

The term 'quanta' has been criticized since the discovery that at the mammalian neuromuscular junction 'quanta' are not immutable, their ACh content going down if ACh synthesis is suppressed (Elmqvist and Quastel, 1965a) but it would seem improper to be more pedantic than physicists, whose quanta of electromagnetic radiation vary, in energy content, with the wavelength. The mechanism by which the nerve terminal releases quanta is apparently unaffected by reduction of the ACh content of the quanta (Elmqvist and Quastel, 1965a).

The idea that miniature potentials at the neuromuscular junction, and by analogy elsewhere, reflect the presynaptic release of transmitter, was a consequence of the theory of humoral synaptic transmission. Evidence in support of this idea therefore constituted further support for the larger theory. The finding that the frequency of miniature potentials depended on presynaptic polarization, but not postsynaptic, provided strong evidence (del Castillo & Katz, 1954d; Liley, 1956c). Further evidence was provided by degeneration experiments. Miniature potentials would be expected to disappear with nerve terminal degeneration and appear again with re-innervation. This was found to be the case at the rat neuromuscular synapse (Liley, 1956a). At the frog neuromuscular junction, miniature potentials with unusual characteristics were detected following nerve degeneration (Birks, Katz, & Miledi, 1960). These potentials are thought to have originated from Schwann cells which originally covered nerve terminals, but after degeneration of the latter were found in close proximity to the sub-synaptic membrane. In one experiment upon the rat neuromuscular synapse in which potentials were observed following degeneration, it was possible to demonstrate by electron microscopy that there were Schwann cells overlying the receptor area (Miledi & Slater, 1963).

Characteristics of miniature potentials

It is sometimes important to distinguish miniature potentials from synaptic potentials evoked by afferent nerve impulses or from potentials resulting from postsynaptic electrical activity electrotonically conducted. Methods which have been used include suppression of electrical activity by a raised concentration of Mg^{++} or Ca^{++}, or both (Katz & Miledi, 1963). A better method is the use of tetrodotoxin (Hubbard, Stenhouse, & Eccles, 1967; Blankenship,

1968; Blankenship & Kuno, 1968) a drug which blocks action potentials based upon the electroresponsive sodium permeability system, but does not affect either spontaneous release of transmitter or its postsynaptic activity (Furukawa, Sasaoka, & Hosoya, 1959; Elmqvist & Feldman, 1965; Ozeki & Grundfest, 1965). Where, as in Puffer fish muscle fibres, there exist tetrodotoxin-resistant spontaneous action potentials (Hagiwara & Takahashi, 1967), this method would obviously not be applicable.

In singly innervated cells, e.g., mammalian skeletal muscle fibres, miniature potentials may easily be distinguished from evoked postsynaptic potentials when the latter are known to be much larger; however, there exist 'giant' miniature potentials, which are multiples of miniature potentials in size, which must be classified separately from the usual miniature potentials (Liley, 1957; Elmqvist, Hofmann, Kugelberg, & Quastel, 1964) because they are not accelerated by presynaptic depolarization. They appear in the presence of tetrodotoxin (Cooke & Quastel, unpublished observations) and are therefore not likely to be due to presynaptic electrical activity.

Cursory examination of miniature potentials (Figs. 4.1 and 4.2) indicates that at any particular synapse the potentials have a particular frequency and amplitude distribution. Both give valuable information.

Amplitude

The analysis consists simply of recording the miniature potentials, measuring their amplitude and perhaps time course, and if necessary plotting the relative numbers of potentials falling into various amplitude classes, i.e., an amplitude histogram (Fig. 4.1A, C).

Of the possible combination of amplitude and time course, three patterns have been commonly found, each characteristic of a particular recording situation. It may be found, as illustrated in Fig. 4.1A, B that the potentials are all of much the same amplitude and time course. Alternatively, a wide variety of amplitudes may be found (Fig. 4.1C, D), or there may be a wide variety of amplitudes combined with a great variation in time course (Fig. 4.2A-E).

The first pattern (Fig. 4.1A, B) is that found on intracellular recording close to one synapse but remote from other synapses, e.g., the amphibian or mammalian nerve–muscle junction. Presumably all the quanta released from the terminals generate potentials

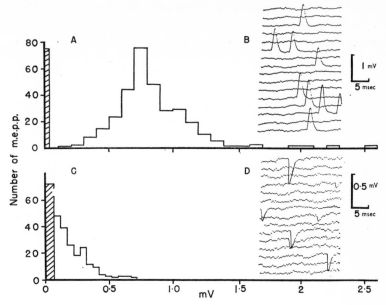

FIG. 4.1. Miniature endplate potentials (m.e.p.p.s). A, B show the amplitude distribution and sample intracellular records of m.e.p.p.s from a neuromuscular synapse in the rat diaphragm. Note in A the presence of a few m.e.p.p.s with amplitudes much greater than the mean. C, D show the amplitude distribution and sample records from the same synapse, on extracellular recording. The skew distribution of m.e.p.p. amplitudes (C) arises because an extracellular electrode records only from some fraction of the endplate area. The majority of recorded potentials are thus small and just above the noise level (hatched bar in A and C). The width of the cells in the histogram was 100 μV in A and 50 μV in C. The records (B, D) are composite and do not give an accurate representation of m.e.p.p. frequency. The temperature was 25°C. The records have been retouched (Hubbard & Schmidt, 1963).

which are recorded by the electrode. The variation in amplitude (Fig. 4.1A) reflects only the (small) variation in quantal size and variation in distance of active receptors from the site of recording, except for the small number of 'giant' potentials (Liley, 1957).

The second pattern (Fig. 4.1C, D) is found on extracellular recording at any type of synapse. There is a skew amplitude distribution (Fig. 4.1C) with the largest class of potentials merging with the baseline noise. This pattern arises because the extracellular electrode records, in effect, the local current flowing during the generation of each potential, to an extent which decreases rapidly with increasing distance from the site of generation. Even at the compact mammalian nerve–muscle junction (Fig. 4.1C) events from much of the subsynaptic region are hardly distinguishable from noise. It should be noted that the time course of these extracellular potentials is always faster than that of the corresponding intracellular potentials. As the time course of the extracellular potentials is virtually the time course of the synaptic current, it may be of use in analysis of subsynaptic events (see Chapter 5).

The third class (Fig. 4.2) is associated with multiple or distributed innervation. This type of innervation is characteristic of neurones and also occurs in the extra ocular muscles of vertebrates and quite widely in the musculature of birds and amphibians (Hess, 1961; Hess & Pilar, 1964; Kuffler & Vaughan Williams, 1953*a*, *b*; Burke & Ginsborg, 1956*a*, *b*; Ginsborg,

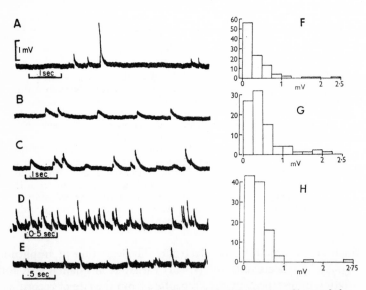

FIG. 4.2. Spontaneous potentials recorded from slow fibres of the iliofibularis muscle of the frog (*R. esculenta*). Records from four fibres A–E are shown. B and C are from the same fibre. Note the variation in size and time course of the miniature potentials. The voltage calibration in A applies also to B–E. The time scale for C applies also to B. F, G, H, show the amplitude distribution in three fibres. Ordinates, number of observations: abscissae, size of potentials (mV). F and G in normal Ringer's solution; H in Ringer's solution containing 15 mM-Mg, 0·45 mM-Ca, 10^{-6} (W/v) neostigmine bromide (Burke, 1957).

1960*a*, *b*). The difference in time course between potentials (Fig. 4.2B, C) arises because the observed potentials have been generated at widely different distances from the recording electrode and have thus widely different rise times (see Chapters 2 and 6 for the relationship between distance from site of generation and rise time). The amplitude distribution (Fig. 4.2F–H) indicates that the largest class of potentials is the smallest, i.e., those potentials generated most remotely from the recording electrode.

It is sometimes possible, if multiple innervation is suspected, to estimate the density of innervation by electrophysiological means. The method is to insert two electrodes into the same cell, separated by a known distance, and to record from them simultaneously. Fig. 4.3 shows the results of an experiment of this type in chick

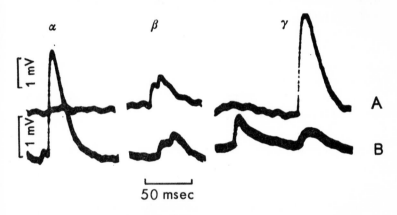

FIG. 4.3. Simultaneous records from two intracellular electrodes 1·7 mm apart and inserted in the same fibre of the anterior latissimus dorsi muscle of the chick. A and B indicate the different recording channels. The miniature potential α was recorded in channel B alone, β on A and B and γ was recorded on A and B but was largest on A (Ginsborg, 1960*a*).

muscle (Ginsborg, 1960*a*). The potential α recorded on channel B presumably originated at a point relatively close to electrode B and too distant from electrode A to be recorded by it, while the two potentials β originated between the two electrodes, being recorded by both A and B. The potential γ originated relatively close to A and distant from B. There must therefore have been at least three distinct junctional regions in the field of recording of the two electrodes.

Experimental alteration of miniature potential amplitude

Changes of miniature potential amplitude may reflect both pre- and postsynaptic factors. In practice, postsynaptic factors are much more often responsible. Clearly, alterations in amplitude follow changes in the subsynaptic action of the transmitter or changes in the postsynaptic membrane resistance or capacitance. These factors are dealt with at length in Chapter 5 in connection with the similar changes in the potentials evoked by nerve impulses.

Occasionally all sub- and postsynaptic properties appear unchanged, yet the amplitude of miniature potentials is altered. It must then be presumed that the magnitude of the quantum of transmitter is itself changed. Substances (e.g., hemicholinium No. 3) which interfere with ACh synthesis at vertebrate neuromuscular junctions are one such class. Presumably quanta contain less ACh as a result of depletion of ACh stores in the nerve terminals, and small postsynaptic potentials are generated as a result (Elmqvist & Quastel, 1965*a*). Quantal size appears to be reduced also in the disease myasthenia gravis (Elmqvist, Hofmann, Kugelberg, & Quastel, 1964).

Experimental alteration of miniature potential frequency

Because of the presynaptic origin of miniature potentials, their frequency can reflect only presynaptic events (Katz, 1962). Before attributing an observed frequency change to some experimental procedure, however, it is wise to be certain that the experimental procedure was not accompanied by other effects which could change the frequency. For instance, miniature potential frequency is powerfully affected by temperature changes (Fig. 4.4A). Similarly, m.e.p.p. frequency *in vitro* can be dramatically altered by changes in the osmotic pressure of the bathing solution (Fig. 4.4B).

If a frequency change is definitely attributable to the agent or procedure under test, it is useful to repeat the experiment in the presence of a raised $[Mg^{++}]$ or lowered $[Ca^{++}]$ in the extracellular medium. There is good evidence at nerve–muscle junctions in vertebrates and insects that the effects of depolarization or hyperpolarization of nerve terminals are reduced in these circumstances (del Castillo & Katz, 1954*d*; Liley, 1956*c*; Usherwood, 1963).

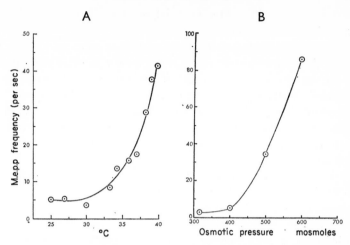

FIG. 4.4. The influence of temperature and osmotic pressure upon miniature potential frequency. The miniature potentials were intracellularly recorded from fibres in the rat diaphragm muscle *in vitro*. A. Miniature potential frequency in a single fibre at temperatures between 25 and 40°C. B. Average miniature potential frequency at various osmotic pressures produced by the addition of sucrose to the bathing solution. Each point indicates the mean frequency found at 12–25 junctions in each of two diaphragms within 5–10 min of the exhibition of the solution under test. The temperature was 34°C in all experiments (Hubbard, Jones, & Landau, unpublished experiments).

Blockade of the effect by either raised $[Mg^{++}]$ or a lowered $[Ca^{++}]$ would therefore suggest that the agent acted by changing the membrane potential of the nerve terminal.

In general, agents which affect transmitter release may affect either miniature potential frequency or quantal content alone, or act upon both. An effect on both quantal content and miniature frequency in parallel would indicate an action upon the process which couples release to polarization. An example is the increase in quantal content of synaptic potentials and increase in miniature potential frequency produced by increasing the ambient $[Ca^{++}]$ of nerve–muscle preparations (Boyd & Martin, 1956*a, b*; Jenkinson, 1957; Hubbard, 1961; Hubbard, Jones, & Landau, 1968,*a, b*). An example of an agent which affects quantal content without influencing miniature potential frequency is ACh itself, when added to the solution bathing a nerve-muscle preparation *in vitro* (Fatt & Katz, 1952; Ciani & Edwards, 1963; Hubbard, Schmidt, & Yokota, 1965). Presumably such an effect indicates an action upon the presynaptic action potential, or upon a mechanism which responds specifically to it.

Some agents produce a change in miniature potential frequency with a disproportionately small effect on the quantal content of e.p.p.s. An example is the change in miniature potential frequency produced by altering the osmotic pressure of the solution bathing a nerve-muscle preparation *in vitro* (Fig. 4.4B) which is accompanied by a much smaller increase in e.p.p. quantal content (Hubbard, Jones, & Landau, 1968c). It is difficult to interpret such an effect without postulating that the change in miniature potential frequency reflects release of transmitter through a mechanism not affected by nerve impulses.

A rather different example is the effect of lowered [Na+] on *in vitro* nerve–muscle preparations. A moderate reduction in [Na+] causes quite a large increase in miniature potential frequency in the presence of raised [K+] and a small increase in normal solution (Gage & Quastel, 1966). Its effect on end-plate potential size is small, except in the presence of very low [Ca++], in which case its effect on miniature potential frequency appears to be enhanced (Kelly, 1965). It may be concluded that an effect of lowered [Na+] facilitatory to the release mechanism is in the presence of normal [Ca++] roughly balanced by the reduction of the presynaptic action potential amplitude which would be expected in such solutions (Gage & Quastel, 1966).

Statistical characteristics of spontaneous transmitter release

Examination of a sequence of miniature potentials recorded at neuromuscular junctions reveals that the miniature potential frequency appears to vary quite markedly over short time intervals, 'bursts' of several potentials taking place at times and fairly long intervals occurring with no activity at other times. Analysis of such records has shown that the sequence of potentials conforms closely to a random or Poisson process, i.e., a stochastic process in which the probability of an event occurring is constant, over appreciable periods of time, the chance of an event occurring being unaffected by whether other similar events occur or not (Feller, 1950). The first evidence for this was the finding that histograms of interval durations fit closely an exponential distribution (Fatt & Katz, 1952). This procedure is unsuited to rapid analysis, and is very laborious. An alternative method is much simpler and shows more directly whether miniature potential occurrence follows a Poisson process. In such a process, the numbers of events in non-overlapping constant time intervals, of any duration, should follow a Poisson distribution. The probability of any given number of events occurring in a time interval Δt is given by the formula:

$$\text{Probability of } n \text{ events in time } \Delta t = \mathrm{e}^{-m}\,\frac{m^n}{n!}. \qquad (1)$$

Here m is the one parameter of the Poisson distribution and is the mean number of events occurring at time Δt. It is of course equal to $\lambda \Delta t$ where λ is the mean rate at which the events occur. It is a useful property of the Poisson distribution that the variance, calculated in the usual way, has an expected value equal to the mean.

These facts provide an easy test for the Poisson character of miniature potential occurrence (Gage & Hubbard, 1965; Elmqvist & Quastel, unpublished observations). The method consists in counting the spontaneous occurring potentials in non-overlapping time intervals of any chosen duration—say successive oscilloscope sweeps. Having counted the number in say, 100 periods, the mean per period is calculated and from this the expected number of periods with any number of miniature potentials (n) can be calculated from the Poisson generating function, formula (1). Tables of 'Poisson's Exponential Binomial Limit' are available for m between 0·001 and 100 and suitable values of n (Molina, 1942). The expected numbers can be compared with the numbers actually found, using a chi-square test.

The more usual test for conformity to a Poisson process, testing for an exponential interval distribution, is of course closely related to the above. The exponential function arises because the probability that the interval between two events be greater or equal to some time t is equal to the probability that no event occurs in the time t, which by formula (1) is equal to $\mathrm{e}^{-\lambda t}$. An exponential interval distribution is necessary but not sufficient to show a process to be Poisson. It is also *insensitive* to deviations from Poisson.

Deviations from the Poisson, or random process, are potentially of interest since they may give clues as to spontaneous alteration of the processes involved in transmitter release. Any such deviation indicates a deviation from one of the conditions necessary for a perfect Poisson process, namely,

(1) The distribution of the number of events in non-overlapping time intervals of any duration is Poisson.

(2) The process is 'stationary'—the probability of occurrence of miniature potentials does not change with time.

(3) The process is 'orderly'—events occur only one at a time.

(4) The number of events in disjoint (i.e., non-overlapping) time intervals is independent.

In fact it is commonly observed that absolute stationarity is unusual over periods of more than a few minutes, there being spontaneous fluctuations of miniature potential frequency (Gage & Quastel, 1966). Orderliness is evidently also not held to exactly. The 'giant' spontaneous potentials of about double or more normal miniature potential amplitude presumably represent responses to more than one quantum of transmitter released at a time (Liley, 1956a). Such spontaneous potentials may be as large as five times normal m.e.p.p. size, without smaller multiples being observed, and they are slowed or obliterated rather than accelerated by the addition of K^+ to the bathing medium (Elmqvist, Hofmann, Kugelberg, & Quastel, 1964). Giants might also be an indication that the quanta are not truly independent in their release, there being a tendency for events to snowball (Martin & Pilar, 1964a).

The methods of statistical analysis which could be used for detailed examination of miniature potential sequences for deviations from a Poisson process are beyond the scope of this book. Anyone interested in some further investigation should consult Cox & Lewis (1966) and would be well advised to obtain expert help.

The Poisson distribution of numbers of miniature potentials in non-overlapping periods of any definite duration has a consequence which is occasionally useful. Since in a Poisson distribution the variance is equal to the mean, the accuracy of a frequency estimate can be gauged very easily: if N miniature potentials are found in a time period x seconds, then the frequency per second can be stated to be $(N \pm \sqrt{N})/x$ (mean $\pm$ standard error of the mean). For example, if a total of 100 miniature potentials are counted in a given interval, the estimated mean frequency has a standard error of $\pm 10\%$ of the mean; if only 10 are counted, the standard error is $\pm 3 \cdot 2$.

MEASUREMENT OF EVOKED TRANSMITTER RELEASE

Quantal components of synaptic potentials

The essential evidence for the quantal nature of transmitter release by nerve impulses is the fact that synaptic potentials can be fractionated into units, identical in all respects to the spontaneous or miniature potentials, by raising the [Mg^{++}] or lowering the [Ca^{++}] of the solution bathing the synaptic region. As Fig. 4.5 shows, at a neuromuscular junction e.p.p.s become reduced until single units or small multiples are obtained on nerve stimulation. With a further reduction of the [Ca^{++}] or raising of the [Mg^{++}] the responses to stimulation are intermittent so that there are occasional failures (Fig. 4.5C).

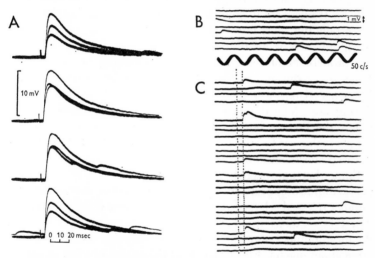

FIG. 4.5. The effect of increasing the Mg concentration upon the quantal content of e.p.p.s. A shows fluctuation of e.p.p. response at a single frog neuromuscular synapse, treated with 10 mM-Mg (Ca concentration was normal: 1·8 mM; prostigmine 10^{-6}). Intracellular recording. In each record, three superimposed responses are seen. Note the scattered spontaneous miniature potentials. B shows a frog neuromuscular synapse treated with reduced Ca (0·9 mM) and 14 mM-Mg concentration. The top part shows a few spontaneous potentials (traces separated by 1 mV steps). C (below the 50 c/s time signal) shows responses to single nerve impulses. Stimulus artefact and response latency are indicated by a pair of dotted vertical lines. The proportion of failures was very high: there are only five responses to twenty-four impulses (del Castillo & Katz, 1954*b*).

It was further shown by del Castillo & Katz (1954*a*, *b*) that when e.p.p.s had been reduced to small numbers of constituent units the number of such units in a long series of responses was distributed according to the Poisson distribution. This type of analysis while first successfully carried out at vertebrate neuro-muscular junctions (del Castillo & Katz, 1954*b*; Liley, 1956*b*; Boyd & Martin, 1956*b*) has been extended to ganglionic synapses (Blackman, Ginsborg, & Ray, 1963*b*; Martin & Pilar, 1964*a*) and to crustacean neuromuscular junctions and motoneurone synapses where ACh is not the transmitter (Dudel & Kuffler, 1961*a*; Kuno, 1964*a*).

The relation between the Poisson character of spontaneous release and that of evoked release is not difficult to see. It is known that at the nerve–muscle junction after a nerve impulse quanta are released over a small but appreciable time interval (Katz & Miledi, 1965*b*). If one were to compare the number of quanta released in corresponding short intervals after an impulse, one would expect the number to be distributed according to the Poisson process if the probability of release at the corresponding times were the same. Since the sum of any number of Poisson variates is also a Poisson variate, the result is that the number of quanta released during any defined interval following a nerve impulse should follow the Poisson law. In fact, at many synapses the period of greatest release is so brief that the postsynaptic effects of the quanta released effectively summate.

Somewhat unexpectedly, the number of quanta released by a nerve impulse appears to be a Poisson variable even when the number released is large (Martin, 1955; Elmqvist & Quastel, 1965*b*). The Poisson distribution can only be demonstrated directly when the mean number of quanta released per impulse is very low, most often about one (cf. Fig. 4.5C). That the release of a few quanta in a short period of time does not appreciably perturb the probability that others be released was already indicated by the Poisson dis-tribution of miniature potentials. That the same independence should hold when release is not depressed is not at all obvious. Indeed, it would seem likely, *a priori*, that the number of quanta available for release at any moment or in a brief time interval is not unlimited, and if the probability of release of the quanta by a nerve impulse were raised high enough, then one should obtain a *binomial* rather than a Poisson distribution. This would mean, experimentally, that the variance of e.p.p. amplitude would become smaller, relative to the mean amplitude, when quantal content (the mean number of quanta per e.p.p.) is raised. Such an effect was indeed found by del Castillo & Katz (1954*b*). Moreover, by using blockade of neuromuscular transmission by curare instead of magnesium, it is easy to show that the number of quanta released by a nerve impulse may be depressed for several seconds following a preceding impulse, and the extent of the depression depends upon the number of quanta released by the preceding impulse (Otsuka, Endo, & Nonomura, 1962; Elmqvist & Quastel, 1965*b*; Thies, 1965).

However, the relationship between postsynaptic depolarization and amount of transmitter acting can be expected to be nonlinear. Depolarization depends upon both membrane resistance and current flow. The first is reduced by the action of transmitter, and current flow, depending on membrane potential, will become less as depolarization occurs (see Chapter 2 for further discussion). Using a simple electrical model of the postsynaptic membrane, it can be deduced that $\Delta V/(E - \Delta V)$ should be linearly related to amount of transmitter acting where ΔV is the depolarization and E the difference between resting potential and the transmitter equilibrium potential (Martin, 1955). Correcting amplitudes of e.p.p.s on this basis, Martin (1955) showed that even when quantal content was high, the distribution of e.p.p. amplitudes conformed closely to that expected if numbers of quanta were distributed according to a Poisson distribution.

The Poisson character of release in these circumstances is plausibly explained if the process generating the Poisson distribution is not the actual liberation of quanta, but lies one step before this, the number of quanta at any moment available for release fluctuating according to the Poisson law. This would arise directly if only a small fraction of a pool of quanta in the nerve terminal were at any moment available for release, whether because of a particularly favourable location or because of some kind of activation. If the other quanta each had at any moment a small probability of becoming immediately available for liberation, then there would be a Poisson distributed entry of quanta into the 'immediately available store' and the number in this store would vary according to the Poisson law, no matter what the probability of the quanta leaving (Quastel & Vere-Jones, unpublished calculations; Vere-Jones, 1966). Release would be equivalent to a binomial sampling from a Poisson distribution, and therefore Poisson in character itself.

It should be emphasized at this point that synaptic potentials can be non-constant for other than statistical reasons. Alterations of quantal content occur for a variety of reasons, as well as spontaneously. Systematic changes of quantal content are especially marked early in trains of impulses, but slow changes may occur slowly throughout the duration of a long train of stimuli (del Castillo & Katz, 1954*b*, *c*; Brooks and Thies, 1962; Elmqvist & Quastel, 1965*b*). In general, trends are easily recognized as such, although fast changes are somewhat obscured by the spontaneous statistical fluctuations.

Relative estimation of transmitter release

The success of the quantal analysis of endplate potentials (del Castillo & Katz, 1956*b*) has as a consequence that small postsynaptic responses are about in proportion to the amount of transmitter acting, provided all quanta act at about the same time. Using Martin's correction, a postsynaptic response even when large may be considered a direct measure of the quantity of transmitter. Thus, the amount of transmitter generating a synaptic potential is in proportion to the amplitude of the potential, suitably corrected, provided that there is no alteration of postsynaptic sensitivity or responsiveness. Where miniature potentials are very small or absent, and the statistical properties of transmitter release therefore unknown, as at the giant synapse of the squid, it is necessary for investigators of presynaptic mechanisms to reason by analogy and assume that the postsynaptic potential is an accurate relative assay of transmitter release (Bloedel, Gage, Llinás, & Quastel, 1966).

METHODS OF ESTIMATING QUANTUM CONTENT
OF SYNAPTIC POTENTIALS

It is evident that the problem of measuring quantal content is the same as that of measuring quantal size, provided that the average amplitude of the synaptic potentials is known.

Direct method

The simplest method of determining quantal size, at the neuromuscular junction at least, is to measure the amplitude of miniature potentials. There is a wealth of information indicating that miniature potentials are identical at all times to the quantal units of e.p.p.s (del Castillo & Katz, 1954*b*; Liley, 1956*b*; Boyd & Martin, 1956*b*; Elmqvist & Quastel, 1965*a*). Since at any one junction miniature potential amplitude has a coefficient of variation of 20–25% (Fig. 4.1A), the measurement of 10–20 miniature potentials gives a fairly accurate estimate of average quantum size. It is of some importance, however, that the miniature potential amplitude be on the average considerably greater than the recording noise level; if an unknown number of the potentials are not measured because their amplitude falls below the noise level, then the average size becomes quite impossible to determine. In addition, the distribution of miniature potential amplitudes is unfortunately not quite unimodal. Most of the miniature potential amplitudes measured at a junction usually fit a normal distribution curve but, as previously mentioned, there are a significant number whose amplitude is two, three, or more times that of the modal amplitude (Fig. 4.1A). The 'giants' do not behave in the same way as other miniature potentials (Liley, 1957) and it is doubtful whether they contribute as quantal components to e.p.p.s. For this reason they should be omitted when miniature potentials are measured in order to be compared with synaptic potential amplitude for estimation of quantal content (i.e., the mean number of quanta per e.p.p.). It is also possible to mistake giants for the 'true' miniature potentials if the miniature potentials are too small to be visible as such.

The average quantal content of a series of synaptic potentials is obviously given by the relationship:

$$m = \frac{\bar{v}'}{\bar{q}'} \tag{2}$$

where $\bar{q}'$ is average quantal size and $\bar{v}'$ average synaptic potential size, both corrected for non-linearity of the postsynaptic response (see Chapter 2). It is only the necessity of correcting for non-linearity that makes this method at times give a biased result (if the correction factor is wrongly chosen) since if miniature potentials are large enough to measure accurately, and quantum content more than about one, the synaptic potentials will be so large that the correction for non-linearity becomes significant. It will be noted also that if quantum content is low, then although the formula will give accurately the average quantal content of those e.p.p.s measured, the spontaneous fluctuation of the quantal content, due to the numbers following a Poisson distribution, may well be considerable. Even if the size of the quanta and the sizes of the e.p.p.s were known exactly, the total number of quanta M in X e.p.p.s would have standard deviation $\sqrt{M}$.

In general it is quite impossible to say for any one synaptic potential how many quanta make it up, if the number is more than two, because of variation of quantum size. However $\bar{v}'$ (mean corrected synaptic potential amplitude) divided by $\bar{q}'$ (=mean miniature potential amplitude, also corrected) gives an unbiased estimate. Obviously, the greater the number of quanta in an e.p.p. (i.e., the greater 'm' is) the more closely the mean size of the quanta should approximate that of the population of quanta.

The direct method of estimating quantum content has several experimental drawbacks. It is necessary to measure many miniature potentials and synaptic potentials and the miniature potentials must be clearly measurable and therefore large. In practice, at nerve–muscle junctions the release process must be depressed (usually by adding Mg^{++} and/or removing Ca^{++} from the bathing solution). Furthermore, it is necessary to know both the resting membrane potential and the transmitter equilibrium potential. A basic assumption of the method is, of course, that the observed miniature potentials are identical with the quantal components of the evoked synaptic potentials. With multiple innervated cells this is unlikely to be true. Other methods of determining quantal content (and size) depend upon the Poisson distribution of number of quanta in synaptic potentials, and with these methods some of the inherent difficulties of the direct method are obviated. Nevertheless, the direct method is, when applicable, by far the most accurate available, and should be the method of choice.

Variance method

Because the numbers of quanta in e.p.p.s fluctuate according to the Poisson law, under constant conditions, it is possible to derive, from the variance of e.p.p. size and the mean e.p.p. amplitude, the mean number of quanta in the e.p.p.s. This arises as follows: if one measures a series of e.p.p. amplitudes and corrects each for non-linearity of the postsynaptic response, then one has a series of numbers $v_1', v_2', v_3' \ldots$ If all quanta at a junction were the same size, $\bar{q}$, then the number of quanta in each of the e.p.p.s would be

$$v'_1/\bar{q}, \ v'_2/\bar{q}, \ v'_3/\bar{q}, \ v'_4/\bar{q}, \ \ldots$$

This series would then have a Poisson distribution, for which the expected value of the variance is equal to that of the mean.

i.e. $E\{\text{var } (v'/\bar{q})\} = E\{(v'/\bar{q})\} = m$
therefore var $(v'/\bar{q}) = \bar{v}'/\bar{q}$, where $\bar{v}'$ is mean v'
but since $\bar{q}$ is constant,
var $(v'/\bar{q}) = (\text{var } v')/\bar{q}^2 = \bar{v}'/\bar{q}$
therefore, $\bar{q} = (\text{var } v')/\bar{v}'$

As a result, quantum size can be estimated as the ratio of the variance to mean of the corrected e.p.p. amplitudes.

Quanta are not, however, uniform in size, and this contributes to the total variance of the e.p.p.s. Allowance can be made for this if the variation of quantal size is known: one can assume it to be the same as that of miniature potential amplitude. If the quanta have a variance σ^2 (and therefore coefficient of variation σ/q)

$$E\{\text{var } v'\} = m(\bar{q}^2 + \sigma^2)$$

$$E[v'] = m\bar{q}$$

$$E\left\{\frac{\text{var } v'}{\bar{v}'}\right\} = \frac{\bar{q}^2 + \sigma^2}{\bar{q}} \tag{3}$$

$$\frac{\text{var } v'}{\bar{v}'} = \bar{q}\{1 + (\sigma/\bar{q})^2\}.$$

Background noise will also contribute to the estimated variance of v', therefore, a more accurate estimate of $\bar{q}\{1 + (\sigma/q)^2\}$ is

$$\frac{(\text{var } v' - \text{var due to noise})}{\bar{v}'}.$$

The contribution of noise can be taken to be the r.m.s. noise, squared, or an estimate of it may be made by making control measurements, i.e., measurements at the same time intervals as used in measuring e.p.p.s, but where there are no e.p.p.s. In the case of the neuromuscular junction the coefficient of variation of m.e.p.p.s is usually about 20–25%, and the contribution of background noise and measurement error small, provided the mean e.p.p. is about 1 mV or more. If one defines the 'apparent' $\bar{q}$ and $\bar{m}$ (q_a and m_a).

$$q_\mathrm{a} = \frac{\mathrm{var}\ v' - \mathrm{var\ (noise)}}{\bar{v}'} = \bar{q}(1 + \sigma^2/q^2)$$

$$m_\mathrm{a} = \frac{v^2}{\mathrm{var}\ v' - \mathrm{var\ (noise)}} = \frac{m}{(1 + \sigma^2/q^2)}$$

$$\bar{q} = 95\%\ q_\mathrm{a}$$

$$\bar{m} = 105\%\ m_\mathrm{a}.$$

It was pointed out previously that for these calculations it is necessary to use the values of e.p.p. amplitudes each corrected for non-linear summation of the postsynaptic response. The conversion formula for the cable-like muscle fibre is:

$$v' = \frac{v}{1 - v/V_0}$$

with V_0 equal to the resting membrane potential minus the equilibrium potential for the transmitter ($= \mathrm{RP} - 15$ mV at the neuromuscular junction, under normal conditions).

It is possible to obtain approximations for var v', and v', from values of $\bar{v}$, var v, and V_0. This saves considerable time. The method can be applied, of course, only if V_0 was constant over the same period during which the v's were recorded. The relevant formulae* are:

---

* These formulae were derived for us by Dr D. Vere-Jones, as follows:

It is convenient to define a new variable, x, equal to vC and $x' = x/1 - x$ (i.e., $x' = v'C$)

each x is equal to mean x plus a deviation (ϵ) which is either positive or negative.

$$x = \bar{x} + \epsilon$$

therefore

$$x' = \frac{\bar{x} + \epsilon}{1 - \bar{x} - \epsilon}$$

The right hand side of this expression can be expanded

$$x' = \frac{\bar{x}}{1 - \bar{x}} + \frac{\epsilon}{(1 - \bar{x})^2} + \frac{\epsilon^2}{(1 - \bar{x})^3} + \frac{\epsilon^3}{(1 - \bar{x})^4} + \cdots$$

noting that mean ϵ is 0, mean ϵ^2 is var x, and var ϵ is var x

$$x' = \frac{\bar{x}}{1 - \bar{x}} + \frac{\mathrm{var}\ x}{(1 - \bar{x})^3}$$

$$\mathrm{var}\ \bar{x}' = \frac{\mathrm{var}\ x}{(1 - \bar{x})^4} + \cdots$$

Since x' divided by $C\bar{q}$ is a Poisson variable, extra terms in the last expression may be estimated in terms of $C\bar{q}$ and the Poisson parameter m. Substitution of terms in v and C for x give the formulae:

$$\bar{v}' = \frac{\bar{v}}{1 - \bar{v}C} + \frac{\text{var } v \cdot C}{(1 - \bar{v}C)^3}$$

$$= \frac{\bar{v}}{1 - \bar{v}C}(1 + \bar{q}C)$$

$$\text{var } v' \equiv \frac{\text{var } v}{(1 - \bar{v}C)^4}(1 + 2\bar{q}C)$$

where $C = 1/V_0$.

When the variance method is applied to endplate potentials recorded from curare blocked preparations, $\bar{q}C$ is often much less than unity, and can be neglected with no appreciable loss of accuracy.

For quantum size and quantum content the formulae are:

$$q_a = \bar{q}\left(1 + \frac{\sigma^2}{\bar{q}^2}\right) \simeq \frac{\text{var } v}{\bar{v}} \cdot \frac{1}{(1 - \bar{v}C)^3}(1 + \bar{q}C)$$

$$m_a = \frac{m}{1 + \sigma^2/q^2} \simeq \frac{\bar{v}^2}{\text{var } v} \cdot (1 - \bar{v}C).$$

Where noise is at all appreciable, one should substitute (var v − var noise) for var v. A numerical example may help to show the size of the error entailed by taking $q_a = (\text{var } v)/\bar{v}$, and

$$m_a = \frac{\bar{v}^2}{\text{var } v} \quad \left(\text{i.e., } \frac{1}{(\text{Co-eff. var})^2}\right).$$

If the resting potential were 75 mV, and the mean e.p.p. 5 mV, the resulting m_a would be overestimated by about 20%. The error is in the opposite direction to that involved in taking $\bar{q}$ and $\bar{m}$ to be equal to q_a and m_a, i.e., ignoring the contribution of the variance of quantal size. In the special case when mean e.p.p. size is of the order 1–2% of V_0 the two errors roughly cancel each other.

The accuracy of the estimations, of course, depends upon the number of observations used (n). Approximately, one has for the co-efficients of variation of mean e.p.p. height, q and m

$$\text{c.v.} \quad (\bar{v}) = \frac{1}{\bar{v}} \cdot \sqrt{\frac{\text{var } v}{n}} \simeq \sqrt{\frac{1}{mn}}$$

$$\text{c.v.} \quad (\bar{q}_a) = \frac{2}{n-1}$$

$$\text{c.v.} \quad (m_a) = 2\sqrt{\frac{1}{n}\left(\frac{1}{m}+\frac{1}{2}\right)}$$

In other words, from a series of about 200 e.p.p.s one may obtain estimates of q which are within 10% of true values about two-thirds of the time, and the same is true of m, if m is not small.

Although a fairly large number of e.p.p.s are required for a reasonably accurate estimation of q and m, it is not necessary that these e.p.p.s be recorded under constant conditions. There would seem to be no objection to recording series of trains of e.p.p.s at different stimulation frequencies, and with changing environmental conditions, making estimates of 'q' and 'm' from short trains of e.p.p.s. Each of the estimates would be very inaccurate, but could be used in looking for trends or changes in either parameter during the experiment. For example, in this way it has been shown that with changing frequencies of stimulation only quantum content alters, not quantum size (Elmqvist & Quastel, 1965*b*). It was possible to use the average of all estimates of q_a at each junction to obtain values for quantum contents over a wide range of stimulation frequencies. Previously, it was shown that quantum content and size as estimated by the variance method was the same as by the direct method (Elmqvist & Quastel, 1965*a, b*).

One important requirement necessary for use of the variance method is that the variance measured and used must reflect purely the variance of e.p.p.s due to the statistical nature of the transmitter release process. It is necessary, therefore, to exclude variance related to regression of e.p.p. size, either because of changes of m or changes of quantum size. Such regression always takes place at the beginning of tetani, and for this reason the first few e.p.p.s in a train cannot be used in the estimation of quantum size or content. Regression also slowly takes place during tetani. However, the method can still be used, the contribution of regression to total variance being avoided either by doing the calculations on many small groups of e.p.p.s, or by subtracting the variance due to regression (Brooks & Thies, 1962). It is permissible also to use the variance method using groups of corresponding e.p.p.s in very short tetani, i.e., estimate q_a and m_a for the group of first e.p.p.s of similar tetani, the group of seconds, the group of thirds, etc. Here again one must guard against regression with time; in general it would seem unwise to assume that a series of corresponding e.p.p.s recorded over a time period of many minutes varied only at random.

The variance method is a very powerful one and can be applied under almost all conditions. Its accuracy is limited by the sampling error of variance, and it is more susceptible than any of the other methods to any error which may be introduced in correcting for non-linearity of the postsynaptic response. It also cannot give unbiased estimates of m and $\bar{q}$, because of variation of quantal size. Of the drawbacks of the direct method it avoids only one, the necessity of measuring miniature potentials with the assumption that quantal units are identical with the observed miniature potentials, which could be untrue at cells with many synapses.

Application of variance method to cells with more than one synapse

In a cell with more than one synaptic input the miniature potentials observed would presumably be derived from all the synapses, whereas an evoked synaptic potential could represent the release from only one or a small number of similarly located nerve terminals. Under these conditions one could not assume that the quantal components were the same size as the miniature potentials, and the variance method might be useful.

It may be pointed out that formula (3) is exact, and does not depend upon the distribution of quantum size. Moreover, the sum of Poisson variates is also Poisson. Therefore, the formula should also apply for a cell in which more than one synapse was simultaneously active, provided each released quanta according to a Poisson distribution. The variance-to-mean ratio obtained would give $\bar{q}\{1 + (\sigma/\bar{q})^2\}$. If the quanta from different synapses excited were 'seen' by the microelectrode as having different sizes, because their effects were exerted on the cell at different distances from the microelectrode, for example, then the ratio obtained would reflect a mean quantum size (plus $\sigma^2/\bar{q}$) with the sizes of different quanta weighted according to the mean outputs of each. Therefore, if in an experiment the m of all synapses stimulated altered in parallel, the variance-to-mean ratio of the synaptic potentials would remain constant, but if they were changed differently and in a way correlated with unit size, that is, if the output of either small or large quanta was changed more than that of the others, then the variance-to-mean ratio would change. A further complication, which could prevent the useful application of the method to cells with many synapses, is the great difficulty or impossibility of making the proper correction for non-linear summation if neither the geometry of the cell nor the positions of the synapses activated, are exactly known. This would be the case if one recorded from the soma of a cell, while transmitter acted along the dendrites as well as on the soma.

Method of failures

The second statistical method of estimating the quantum content of endplate potentials takes advantage of another property of the Poisson distribution. The expected proportion of times in which the variate has value x is given by $e^{-m}m^x/x!$ In particular, the chance of the value o, that is, that an e.p.p. be a 'failure', no quanta at all being released by the nerve impulse (Fig. 4.5C), is e^{-m}. Thus the mean quantum content, m, may be estimated as $\log_e$ 1/proportion of failures. Of course, this method can be used only when the postsynaptic response to individual quanta can be distinguished clearly, and under these conditions miniature potentials could be measured and quantal content estimated by the direct method. In a sense, the method is redundant, a more accurate one being available. However, the method is extremely easy to use, it being unnecessary to measure either e.p.p.s or miniature potentials except to check that unit responses could not be misjudged as 'failures', because of recording noise. In addition, the estimation of 'm' is quite independent of resting potential, transmitter equilibrium potential, or receptor sensitivity, and is without the systematic error implicit in the variance method because of the variation of quantal size. The method is not only labour saving but, under certain conditions, may well be the best available. Thus quantal content may be estimated despite an alteration of the transmitter equilibrium potential, difficult to estimate, which would make it impossible properly to correct e.p.p.s for non-linearity of the postsynaptic response. It is also appropriate when there are miniature potentials not derived from the same synapses as those stimulated (Fig. 4.6C). In this case, the alternative method is to compare the mean size of the evoked potentials with those miniature potentials whose frequency is increased for a period of several milli-seconds after each stimulus (Fig. 4.6A dots)—a method which is considerably more laborious.

The main disadvantages of this method are (1) use limited to low quantum contents, (2) necessity of quantal responses being large enough to be clearly distinguished from noise, (3) possibility

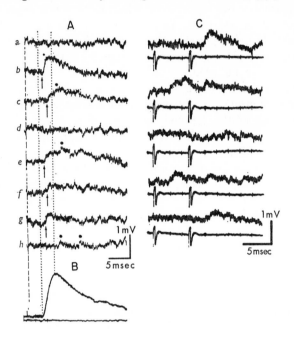

Fig. 4.6. A. Monosynaptic EPSPs in a medical gastrocnemius motoneurone of a cat produced by afferent impulses in a dissected fine filament of the medial gastrocnemius nerve at a rate of 0·5/sec. The number of afferent fibres measured in this filament was more than five. The filament was stimulated at an intensity of twice the threshold, but the input impulses were not continuously monitored. Arrows indicate the onset of the EPSP responses. Two interrupted lines show the limits of latency fluctuations of the responses which are defined by the onset and peak of the large monosynaptic EPSP evoked by stimulation of the triceps surae nerve (B). For large dots on some records, see text. C. Upper traces, monosynaptic EPSPs in a triceps surae motoneurone produced by double afferent volleys (0·5/sec) in a filament stimulated at intensities of twice threshold. The number of afferent fibres measured in this filament was more than five. Lower traces, simultaneous records of the afferent impulses from the triceps nerve. Time, 5 msec. Voltage, 1 mV for EPSPs (Kuno, 1964*a, b*).

of failures being due to failure of nerve impulse propagation rather than to the statistical nature of the release process (Krnjevic & Miledi, 1959).

The limitation to low quantum contents means that in the case of the neuromuscular junction, the method is limited to experiments in which transmitter release has been inhibited by an excess of magnesium and/or a lowered concentration of calcium, and under these conditions the effect of an agent upon transmitter release might be either greater or less than when release has not been depressed. If it is relatively simple to find out the effect of an agent on e.p.p. size in a curarized preparation then the variance method should be used for quantal content estimations. The requirement that a 'failure' must always be unambiguously recognized as such means that the method is not safely applicable to the determination of the presynaptic effect of an agent which also depresses to a considerable extent the postsynaptic response to the released transmitter.

When using the failure method one should always keep in mind the possibility of presynaptic failure of impulse conduction. When m is high, it is always quite obvious when failures are due to impulse conduction failure—they stand out against the e.p.p.s which vary relatively little, but when m is very low, of the order of 1 or less, then it may be difficult to make the distinction. To guard against impulse failure, one should check roughly the frequency of pairs and/or triplets of zero responses, since impulse conduction failures tend to occur in runs. Since the probability of a failure is e^{-m}, the probability of a pair of failures is $e^{-m} \times e^{-m} = e^{-2m}$, of triplets e^{-3m}, etc. Put another way, if in N impulses one finds n failures, then one should find about n^2/N failures followed by another failure and about n^3/N^3 triple failures, etc. A more sensitive procedure is to check the proportion of unit responses, which are usually readily recognizable as such, after obtaining an estimate of m. This should, of course, be about me^{-m}. If an agent causes failure of impulse propagation, then the method of failures is inapplicable. It would still be possible to determine whether it affected quantal content by determining whether it changed the size distribution relative to m.e.p.p. size of those e.p.p.s which did occur (expected ratio of responses of three quanta to those of two, to those of one $= m^3/6: m^2/2: m$).

The accuracy of ($\log_e 1$/proportion of failures) as an estimator of m depends mainly upon the actual number of failures found in the sample of e.p.p.s. If P is the proportion of failures, the standard deviation of m measured as $\log_e 1/P$ is $\sqrt{\{(1 - P)/NP\}}$ (Edwards & Ikeda, 1962; Martin, 1966), where N is the number of observations. Thus, the co-efficient of variation of m is about 12% if about 200 e.p.p.s are observed, and the proportion of failures is between 0·025 ($m = 3·7$) and 0·65 ($m = 0·43$), but is larger if P is outside this range.

Because the failure method does not require any correction for non-linear summation of e.p.p.s, nor that all the quanta be the same size, it would seem to be particularly suitable for use on cells with more than one synaptic input. It has been applied with some success to crustacean nerve–muscle junctions and to moto-neurone excitatory synaptic potentials (Dudel & Kuffler, 1961a; Kuno, 1964a; see also Katz & Miledi, 1963). Its main drawback is the requirement that quantum content be low enough that sufficient failures occur. In the case of the motoneurone this means that only one or a few afferent nerve fibres be stimulated, which is technically difficult (Fig. 4.6), or that an agent be applied to depress transmitter release, which cannot be done conveniently with an *in vivo* preparation.

A useful variant of the variance method

There is a variant of the variance method which can be used for calculation of quantal content when either the equilibrium potential or resting potential (i.e., V_0) is unknown, but the synaptic potentials are so large that without correction for non-linear postsynaptic response, considerable error would be incurred (Martin & Pilar, 1964a). It is absolutely necessary that the miniature potentials be large enough to be accurately measured and be identical with the quantal units of the evoked synaptic potential. One notes first

$$m = \frac{\bar{v}'}{\bar{q}'}$$

where $\bar{q}'$ is mean miniature potential amplitude, corrected as is each v for non-linearity of the postsynaptic response,

also,
$$\bar{v}' \simeq \frac{\bar{v}}{1 - \bar{v}C} (1 + \bar{q}C)$$

therefore,
$$m \simeq \frac{\{\bar{v}/(1 - \bar{v}C)\}(1 + \bar{q}C)}{\bar{q}/(1 - \bar{q}C)}.$$

Also, without appreciable error

$$m \simeq \frac{\bar{v}^2}{\text{var v}} \, (1 - \bar{v}C)^2 \left(1 + \frac{\sigma^2}{\bar{q}^2}\right)$$

squaring the first formula for m, and multiplying by the second, one obtains as a first approximation which is fairly accurate (since q^2C^2 is small)

$$m^3 = \frac{\bar{v}^4}{\bar{q}^2 \cdot \text{var } v}\left(1 + \frac{\sigma^2}{\bar{q}^2}\right)$$

$$m \simeq \left\{\frac{\bar{v}^4}{\bar{q}^2 \cdot \text{var } v}\left(1 + \frac{\sigma^2}{\bar{q}^2}\right)\right\}^{\frac{1}{3}}.$$

It will be apparent that the formula is correct or close to it (depending on the magnitude of the higher terms in the expansion on p. 133), whatever the value of the term C. The method was used by Martin & Pilar (1964*a*) in their investigation of excitatory synaptic potentials in the chick ciliary ganglion, the reason being that for technical reasons they could not accurately estimate the resting potential of the cells from which they recorded.

Extracellular additions to e.p.p. variance

There is a pitfall in the methods of estimating quantal content. Often a microelectrode in a muscle fibre picks up not only the synaptic potentials generated in that fibre, but also extracellular field potentials from neighbouring fibres (Fatt & Katz, 1951). The latter are opposite in direction to the intracellular e.p.p.s and occur at about the same time. The result is an underestimate of the mean e.p.p. amplitude, and an overestimate of the variance of e.p.p.s since the extracellular potentials also fluctuate. In short, one obtains both an overestimate of quantal size and an underestimate of quantal content. Under these circumstances, an agent which caused a purely postsynaptic change would appear to cause also a presynaptic effect, and vice versa. When there are a number of failures, i.e., when quantal content is very low, it is fairly obvious if one has this complication. When quantum contents are high, it may be very difficult to detect. One useful precaution before starting an experiment on e.p.p.s at a junction is to raise the strength of nerve stimulation gradually in the hope that the axons going to any inconvenient neighbour or neighbours are stimulated before the one going to that junction in which one is interested, and to check that e.p.p.s recorded at higher than threshold stimulation strength are no smaller than those recorded at just threshold. If an offending neighbour belongs to the same motor unit, then in a curarized preparation one may never know that the results are distorted. Not infrequently, however, the interference may appear as a peculiar flattening or notch on the e.p.p.s.

The method of failures is much more robust than the variance method when one has this problem of extracellular e.p.p.s recorded intracellularly. The fact of the interference is usually obvious, and it is often possible to use an experiment despite it, provided the quantal unit responses are sufficiently large that they will never appear as failures only because they are just balanced by the foreign inverted e.p.p.s. The direct method is of course also subject to error if the foreign e.p.p.s are large. As with the variance method this error may be far from obvious and the same precautions should be taken.

INVESTIGATION OF NERVE TERMINALS

It is usual when investigating the transmitter release process simply to infer the behaviour of nerve terminals by analogy from other structures. For example, the membrane potential of a nerve terminal cannot usually be measured directly and the effects on it of changing the potassium ion concentration can only be inferred from studies of other tissues. Again it is possible to release transmitter from motor nerve endings by applying depolarizing current pulses, but the relationship between these and the depolarizations they cause lies open to question. Because of these limitations, it is often necessary to rely on qualitative rather than quantitative reasoning.

Transmitter synthesis, storage, and mobilization

Transmitter stores

Fig. 4.7 indicates the scheme of synthesis and storage of ACh postulated on electrophysiological evidence at nerve–muscle and ganglionic junctions (Elmqvist & Quastel, 1965*b*). From the limited evidence available, it seems probable that similar storage mechanisms operate at other synapses (Hubbard, 1963). The size

FIG. 4.7. A schematic diagram of the synthesis and storage of transmitters.

of the mobilization and immediately available stores can in principle be measured at any synapse where synaptic potentials can be measured. This is not true of the total presynaptic store which is at present measured by blocking transmitter synthesis and measuring the amount of transmitter which can be released thereafter. Obviously the transmitter and its metabolism must be known and the method has accordingly only been applied to cholinergic synapses.

Measurement of presynaptic ACh store

As indicated in Fig. 4.8, ACh is formed from acetyl-coenzyme A and choline under the influence of the enzyme choline acetylase. ACh is broken down to acetate and choline by the enzyme acetylcholinesterase, and the choline moiety is reabsorbed. The drug hemicholinium No. 3 ($\alpha\alpha$-dimethyl ethanolamine 4,4′ biacetophenenone, 'HC-3') blocks ACh synthesis in intact nervous tissue but not in homogenates. Apparently the drug does not interfere with choline acetylase action directly, but probably interferes with choline transport into nerve terminals (MacIntosh, Birks, & Sastry, 1956; Schueler, 1960; MacIntosh, 1961). At mammalian neuromuscular synapses, *in vitro*, it has been found that e.p.p.s and miniature potentials run down in amplitude to apparent extinction when stimulation is prolonged in the presence of 2×10^{-7} g/ml of HC-3 (Elmqvist, *et al.*, 1964; Elmqvist & Quastel, 1965*a*).

There is evidence that HC-3 at this concentration completely blocks synthesis (Birks & MacIntosh, 1961); the amount of ACh in a nerve terminal can therefore be determined as the total amount that can be released after synthesis is blocked by HC-3. At nerve–muscular junctions this amount can be estimated as the

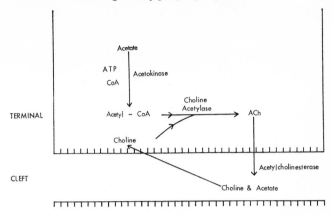

FIG. 4.8. A schematic summary of the metabolism of ACh. In the terminal, the high energy compound acetyl-CoA is formed from ATP, coenzyme A, and acetate under the influence of the enzyme acetokinase. Acetyl-CoA is combined with choline by the enzyme choline acetylase to form ACh. The ACh is liberated into the synaptic cleft and broken down to choline and acetate fragments by the enzyme acetylcholinesterase (AChE). The choline is then reabsorbed by the nerve terminal. ACh metabolism is thus dependent on a supply of energy (ATP) and the circulation of choline.

sum of all the e.p.p.s and miniature potentials elicited by prolonged repetitive stimulation until such time as the e.p.p.s vanish. Alternatively, miniature potentials released by raising the potassium concentration of the bathing medium can be recorded. By plotting the amplitude of e.p.p.s or miniature potentials against the sum of amplitudes of all foregoing e.p.p.s or miniature potentials, and by extrapolating the resulting curve to zero e.p.p. or miniature potential amplitude, it is possible to obtain an estimate of total releasable transmitter (Fig. 4.9). The result is best expressed in terms of the initial quantum size; it is then independent of differences of postsynaptic sensitivity due to muscle fibre dimensions or membrane potential (Katz & Thesleff, 1957*a*), or the presence of postsynaptic depressing substances such as Mg^{++}, K^+, tubocurarine, or the HC-3 itself. Such store estimates appear to be quite independent of how rapidly the nerve terminals are emptied, (Elmqvist & Quastel, 1965*a*), which supports the assumption of complete blockade of transmitter synthesis.

Examples of the results of determination of presynaptic ACh stores in the rat diaphragm-phrenic nerve preparation *in vitro* are shown in Fig. 4.9 (Elmqvist & Quastel, 1965*a*). In the experiment

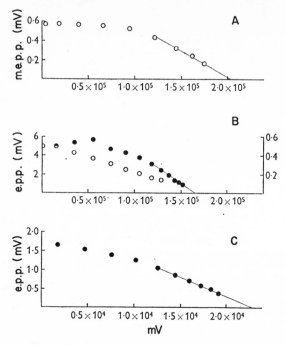

FIG. 4.9. Measurement of the presynaptic store. E.p.p. and miniature potential amplitude plotted against the sum of e.p.p.s. and
miniature potentials previously recorded. A. Miniature potentials
released by KCl (20 mM) in the presence of HC-3 4×10^{-6} M.
B. Indirect stimulation (10·5/sec) in the presence of 15 mM Ca^{++},
3 mM Mg^{++}, and 4×10^{-6} M HC-3. C. Indirect stimulation
(1·1/sec) in the presence of 6×10^{-7} g/ml. dTC and 10^{-5} M HC-3.
The terminal parts of the curves have been extrapolated to the
abscissae by eye (Elmqvist & Quastel, 1965a).

illustrated in Fig. 4.9A, the miniature potential frequency was
raised by adding 20 mM KCl to the solution bathing the muscle.
The extrapolation of miniature potential size gives a total initial
store corresponding to $2·1 \times 10^5$ mV or 370,000 times the amount
in a single quantum of initial size. The extrapolation of e.p.p.
amplitudes is equally valid provided their diminution can be
attributed to change in quantum size. This is generally the case in
experiments using Mg to block neuromuscular transmission (Fig.
4.9B), or, if tubocurarine is used (Fig. 4.9C), when stimulation is
at a frequency of less than 5/sec. Because of the difficulties involved
in measuring quantum size when miniature potentials are close to
noise level, or quantum content becomes highly variable, curarized

preparations are usually preferable. In Fig. 4.9B, the results from a Mg-blocked preparation indicate an initial store of 1.7×10^5 mV, which corresponds to 330,000 times the amount in a quantum initially. In the experiment shown in Fig. 4.9C, in which tubo-curarine 10^{-6} g/ml was used to block transmission, the quantum content derived from the coefficient of variation of the e.p.p.s appeared to be steady throughout the experiment at about 120 quanta per impulse. The total initial store 2.3×10^4 mV therefore corresponded to 170,000 initial quanta. In rat phrenic nerve terminals, the average store was found to be $270,000 \pm 70,000$ quanta (mean of 14 determinations $\pm$ S.D.). Similar results have been obtained at the human neuromuscular synapse (Elmqvist *et al.*, 1964; Elmqvist & Quastel, 1965*b*).

Transmitter synthesis

It is perhaps redundant to point out that investigation of the effect of an agent on transmitter synthesis is by exactly the same method as that used for investigation of the store. Partial blockade of synthesis would be indicated by a final plateau of synaptic potential size.

The immediately available store and mobilization

The presynaptic store as measured above (some 270,000 quanta of ACh in phrenic motor nerve terminals) is large compared with the number of quanta (100–300) normally released by a nerve impulse (Martin, 1955; Liley, 1956*b*; Boyd & Martin, 1956*b*; Takeuchi & Takeuchi, 1960*a*; Elmqvist & Quastel, 1965*b*). Investigation of the variation of quantum content with stimulation parameters has shown that not all of the presynaptic store appears to be immediately available for release by nerve impulses. It has been necessary to postulate a number of transmitter stores, the contents of which differ in their availability for release.

The basic observation which has led to the concept of an immediately available store is illustrated in Fig. 4.10A, B. It is that, at many synapses, after one synaptic potential (in this case an e.p.p. elicited by nerve stimulation) further stimuli elicit potentials which are smaller in amplitude (because of a smaller quantal content) for periods up to 10 seconds (Liley & North, 1953; Lundberg & Quilisch, 1953*a*, *b*; Takeuchi, 1958; Curtis & Eccles, 1960; Eccles, Oscarsson, & Willis, 1961; Thies,

1965; Elmqvist & Quastel, 1965*b*). At nerve–muscle junctions it can be shown that the size of this depression of the second response is directly correlated with the number of quanta released by the first impulse (Fig. 4.10C). If, for instance, this number is drastically reduced (e.g., by increasing the $MgCl_2$ content of the bathing medium, then the depression may disappear and the second response have a larger quantal content than the first for intervals of up to 200 msec (del Castillo & Katz, 1954*b*; Hubbard, 1959, 1963). Conversely, if the quantal content of the first e.p.p. is increased by, for example, increasing the $CaCl_2$ concentration

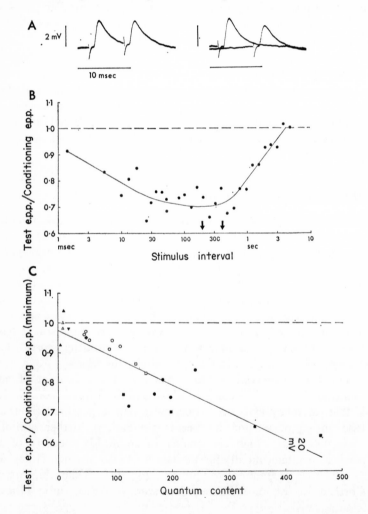

of the bathing medium, this depression is increased in magnitude but not in duration (Lundberg & Quilisch, 1953*b*; Takeuchi, 1958; Thies, 1965). Variation of depression also occurs spontaneously, and shows a correlation with the spontaneous variation of the height of the previous e.p.p. (Elmqvist & Quastel, 1965*b*). The simplest explanation of these findings is that the release of a large number of quanta entails the depletion of some factor needed for subsequent responses. In all probability this is simply the emptying of a store of immediately available preformed quanta of transmitter, but depletion of anything required for transmitter release would give the same result.

An extension to the concept of an immediately available store arises from experiments (Fig. 4.11) in which synaptic potentials are elicited by repetitive stimulation at various rates. At the curarized mammalian neuromuscular junction for instance, at all rates above 5–10/sec, the first endplate potential detected is usually the largest and the amplitude of later responses declines progressively ('early tetanic rundown') to a relative plateau, reached after half a dozen impulses (Liley & North, 1953; Hubbard, 1963; Elmqvist & Quastel, 1965*b*). Early tetanic rundown is ascribed to a progressive depletion by the repeated stimuli of the 'immediately available store'. The quantum content of the e.p.p.s can be said not to fall to zero only because the 'immediately available store' is sustained by a 'repletion' or 'mobilization' process.

FIG. 4.10. Depression of intracellularly-recorded test e.p.p.s following conditioning e.p.p.s at various intervals in a guinea pig nerve–muscle preparation *in vitro*. A. Two sample records at stimulus intervals of 7 msec and 313 msec (superimposed, with 285 msec of baseline omitted) from a curarized preparation at 37°C; lengths of bars show 2·0 mV and 10·0 msec for both records. B. Relative amplitude of test e.p.p.s (ordinate) are plotted against stimulus intervals (abscissa, log scale). Ten pairs of e.p.p. amplitudes were used to determine each point. C. Relationship between maximum depression (minimum recovery) and initial release of ACh. Relative amplitudes of test e.p.p.s at intervals of 195–400 msec (ordinate, arrows in Fig. 4B) are plotted against mean quantum content of conditioning e.p.p.s (abscissa) for 23 tests in twelve fibres of eight muscle preparations. Values of quantum content were calculated from amplitudes of 90 to 200 conditioning e.p.p.s taken at a single interval or at ten to twenty intervals. Open symbols for 22–23°C; filled symbols for 34–38°C. ○: curarized preparation, ▲: bathing solution enriched with 8 mM magnesium ion, ■ enriched with 7·2 mM calcium ion, ◆ calcium ion lowered to 0·75 mM, ▼ calcium ion lowered to 0·45 mM (Thies, 1965).

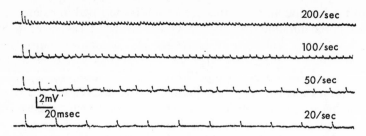

FIG. 4.11. The effects of repetitive stimulation upon endplate potential (e.p.p.) amplitude in a curarized rat diaphragm preparation. Note that the e.p.p. amplitude is largest at the beginning of stimulation and falls during stimulation to a plateau level. The level of this plateau is greater the lower the frequency of stimulation. Even in this plateau phase e.p.p.s show some variation in amplitude, due to the Poisson character of release. This variability enables quantal content to be determined by the 'variance' method. The illustrations are of intracellular records all from the same synapse at the indicated frequency of stimulation. The temperature of the bathing Liley's. solution was $37°C$ and the curare concentration $2·10^{-6}$ g/ml (Hubbard, unpublished observations).

Fractional release

A corollary of the concept of an immediately available store is the concept that an impulse releases only a fraction of this store (Liley & North, 1953). It has become customary to denote this fraction as p (since on the average it is equal to the probability of release of the constituent quanta) and the number of quanta in the store as n. Clearly then an impulse releases on the average np quanta, this number depending on the values of n and p at the relevant time. Clearly, also $np = m$, where m is the quantum content of a response previously determined. At the vertebrate nerve–muscle junction estimates of n normally lie between 300 and 1000 while p ranges between 0·14 and 0·46 (Elmqvist & Quastel, 1965b; Martin, 1966), the value varying widely from one junction to another.

Measurement of n and p

If the amplitudes of e.p.p.s during a tetanus are measured, it is found that except for the first response the amplitudes of successive responses fall roughly geometrically towards the plateau size (Fig. 4.11). By a simple graphical method it is possible to arrive at estimates of the immediately available store (n) and the rate of its depletion because of the release caused by each impulse. This rate is the same as the 'fractional release' or p. This is done by plotting the amplitudes of each e.p.p. in the series against the sum of previous e.p.p.s in the series and extrapolating the more or less straight line formed by the first few points to the abscissa. The intersect gives the amount of transmitter which would have had to be released for the e.p.p.s to fall to zero amplitude had there been no mobilization, and hence gives an estimate of the 'immediately available store' (n). This can be expressed in terms of number of quanta after division by q, the quantal size. Now, the mean quantal content of the first e.p.p. of each train (m) being known, p may be calculated from

$$p = \frac{m}{n}.$$

It is not necessary to the estimation of n and p that the sizes of the e.p.p.s or the estimates of immediately available stores be calculated in terms of quantal units, if the object of an experiment is simply to compare store estimates under different conditions which are known not to affect quantum size (pre- or postsynaptic-ally). It should also be noted that there remains the possibility that at some synapses, including perhaps the non-curarized neuromuscular junction, early tetanic rundown of synaptic potential amplitude may be partly a reflection of diminished sensitivity of postsynaptic receptors because of their desensitiza-tion by released transmitter (see Chapter 5). Under these circum-stances, the synaptic potentials size would mirror quantum size rather than quantum content. Estimation of quantum size by the variance method, if applicable, would soon show if this were the case. The measurement of n by Elmqvist & Quastel's (1965*b*) method is only approximate since it omits the partial repletion of the immediately available store which the mobilizing process would produce between the first few e.p.p.s. It is likely, however, that this is not serious, for it is frequently observed that e.p.p.s in a tetanus rundown to below the level at which they are sub-sequently sustained, suggesting that the mobilization process is somewhat delayed (Elmqvist & Quastel, 1965*b*). Liley & North's (1953) method, in contrast, overcompensates for the effects of mobilization by adding in the value of the tetanic tail. Comparison of the two methods (Hubbard, Jones, & Landau, unpublished observations) shows that they give similar qualitative results but that, as expected, estimates of n are generally higher with the Liley

F

& North (1953) method. Both methods are open to a more serious objection which is that the fractional release (*p*) of transmitter increases progressively with each impulse in a tetanus. Certainly this seems to happen in magnesium-depressed preparations. Usually this increase would seem to be small except between the first two impulses and we have suggested, therefore, that the amplitude of the first e.p.p. should not be included when the regression curve is fitted if the second e.p.p. is greater than 85% of the first. For the methods to be applied it is obviously necessary that the early tetanic rundown be prominent. In general, the methods are best applied to averages of several replicate tetani, since the statistical variation of height in each e.p.p. (which makes estimation of quantum content possible) also tends to obscure the pattern of the early tetanic rundown.

Use of pairs

A very simple method of finding variations in *p* is easy to use and gives quite valid results provided one can be sure that early tetanic rundown is not due to receptor desensitization, which has been established for the curarized neuromuscular junction (Otsuka, Endo, & Nonomura, 1962). This is simply to note the ratio of the sizes of e.p.p.s in pairs about one second apart (avoiding the phase of potentiation but still at nearly maximum depression), repeated no more than four times per minute. Fig. 4.12 illustrates

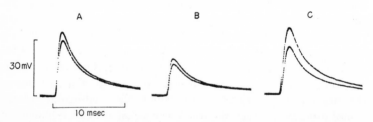

FIG. 4.12. Fractional release measured by assay of neuromuscular depression in an *in vitro* frog nerve muscle preparation. Double stimuli at an interval of 1 sec were applied to the nerve every 10 sec. In each record, the first (larger) and the second (smaller) e.p.p.s are superimposed. Modified Ringer solution with 12·7 mM $CaCl_2$ was used. A. In *d*-tubocurarine, 2×10^{-6} g/ml; B, in *d*-tubocurarine, 4×10^{-6} g/ml; C, 2 min after adding phenol, 6×10^{-5} g/ml, the concentration of *d*-tubocurarine being 4×10^{-6} g/ml. Note that the degree of depression of the second e.p.p. was not altered by changing the concentration of *d*-tubocurarine from 2×10^{-6} to 4×10^{-6} g/ml, but was greatly increased (C) in the presence of 6×10^{-5} g/ml phenol (Otsuka & Nonomura, 1963).

the application of this method to determine the effect of curare and of phenol upon fractional release from the store in frog motor nerve terminals. It is clear that when the curare concentration was increased (Fig. 4.12B), the e.p.p. evoked was smaller but the depression of the second response was of the same relative magnitude as the control experiment (cf. Fig. 4.12A, B). This is to be expected if curare acts purely postsynaptically and does not alter the available store or the fractional release from it. In contrast, phenol increased e.p.p. amplitudes and also increased the depression of the second response (Fig. 4.12C). The increase of depression indicates that the first impulse released more quanta from the store than it did in the absence of phenol. The values of p calculated from pairs are in close agreement with p values calculated from the analysis of tetani (Hubbard, Jones, & Landau, unpublished observations). This simpler method suffers, however, from the high sampling error of the ratio (second response/first response) due to the spontaneous variations of e.p.p. size which are related to the statistical nature of the release process. Unless a change of fractional release is quite large, it may easily escape recognition. Experimentally it is no more difficult to use repeated short tetani instead of pairs and, in so doing, obtain considerably more information. Admittedly much more labour is required.

The use of this method which allows from the same data the calculation of m, q, n, p, and mobilization rate is illustrated in Fig. 4.13, which depicts these parameters measured at a curarized neuromuscular junction, the rat diaphragm phrenic nerve preparation *in vitro*. In the experiment the preparation was initially bathed in Liley's solution which contains 5 mM KCl. It was then exposed to a solution with 15 mM KCl. During the whole experiment e.p.p.s were elicited every minute by 40 stimuli at 100/sec and, as Fig. 4.13A (con) shows, have the typical form of a tetanic train of e.p.p.s in a curarized preparation. The first is the largest, and the amplitudes of later e.p.p.s fall approximately exponentially to reach a fluctuating plateau of amplitude.

Upon raising the bathing [K] from 5 to 15 mM the membrane potential of the muscle fibre fell (Fig. 4.13B). Despite this fall, however, the amplitude of e.p.p.s in the train markedly increased (Fig. 4.13A, 7 min, 28 min). The increase in amplitude had a prolonged time course and the e.p.p.s were still increasing in size after 28 minutes exposure. Upon changing back to the 5 mM K solution the e.p.p. amplitudes fell rapidly (cf. Fig. 4.13A con, 3 min).

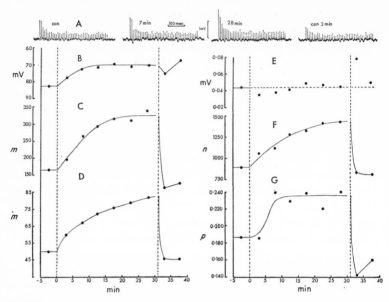

FIG. 4.13. Use of intracellularly recorded trains of e.p.p.s to find quantal content (*m*), mobilization rate (d*m*), fractional release (*p*), and presynaptic store (*n*) at a nerve–muscle junction. A. Sample trains of e.p.p.s evoked by 40 stimuli at 100/sec each min before (con), and at various times after exposing a phrenic nerve diaphragm preparation *in vitro* to a solution with 15 mM KCl instead of the control 5 mM KCl. B. Muscle fibre membrane potential. C. Quantal content (*m*) of the first member of the train. Points are averages of 5 min periods and are placed in the centre of the relevant period. D. Mean quantal content of the last 20 e.p.p.s of the train. Points are 5 min averages as in C. E. Quantal size corrected for the membrane potential changes shown in B. F. and G. Presynaptic store and fractional release respectively. Each point is an average of the 5 values for the 5 min period. Vertical broken lines indicate exhibition and removal of the test solution. Temperature 34°C (Hubbard, Jones, & Landau, unpublished observations).

By analysis of variance of the e.p.p.s of Fig. 4.13A and other records (not shown) of similar e.p.p. trains elicited at one-minute intervals throughout the experiment, the mean quantal content of the various members of the train could be estimated. Thus Fig. 4.13C shows the mean quantal content (*m*) of the first e.p.p. of the trains. Each point is an estimate obtained from five samples and is placed in the middle of the relevant time period. Clearly there was a progressive increase in *m* over the period of exposure to 15 mM K. Similarly the later members of the train show an increase in quantal content. Fig. 4.13D, for instance, shows the mean quantal content estimated from the variance of the last 20 e.p.p.s in five successive trains (so that each point is based on 100 e.p.p.s), that is, the mean quantal content of the tetanic tail. Again there was a progressive increase in quantal content throughout the 30-minute period of observation.

Postsynaptic factors are excluded as a cause of this increase by the finding that the quantal size (Fig. 4.13E) was unchanged throughout the experiment (the quantal size was of course corrected for membrane potential changes).

From the quantal contents of the successive members of the train n was calculated. The result (Fig. 4.13F) calculated according to the methods of Elmqvist & Quastel (1965b) was that the store progressively increased during the exhibition of the raised K. In contrast fractional release (p) increased rapidly in the first 5 minutes after exhibition of 15 mM K and thereafter showed little change (Fig. 4.13G).

Clearly the prolonged effects of K upon transmitter release were exerted through a maintained increase in p together with a progressive increase in n, the available store. This progressive increase in n (Fig. 4.13F) presumably can be correlated with the progressive increase in the quantal content of the e.p.p.s of the tail of the tetanus (Fig. 4.13D) which indicates a progressive increase in the mobilization of transmitter. If mobilization is measured as quantal release/min, the results of Fig. 4.13D indicate a 50% increase in this rate after 30 minutes exposure to a solution with 15 mM K. It should be noted that for calculating the parameters illustrated in Fig. 4.13 a computer program was devised, particularly so that the various regressions could be computed automatically. The subjective nature of graphical estimation of these regressions, based as they often are on only 5–6 points, makes some such automatic processing highly desirable.

Mobilization

The height at which e.p.p.s are sustained immediately following the early tetanic rundown (Fig. 4.13) is by definition a measure of the rate of 'mobilization' into the 'immediately available store'. This rate may be calculated as in the experiment illustrated (Fig. 4.13D) as the plateau e.p.p. size divided by the time between impulses. As Fig. 4.11 indicates, the rate seems to be dependent upon the rate of stimulation. Fractional release is also important, for increasing the [Ca] in the solution bathing *in vitro* nerve–muscle preparations, which is known to increase fractional release (Elmqvist & Quastel, 1965*b*), also increases mobilization at stimulus frequencies below 100/sec. Roughly it would appear that normally there is a maximum mobilization rate which is attained at about 100 impulses/sec (unless fractional release is depressed, e.g. by means of magnesium), and that the effect of an increased fractional release is to make the mobilization rate at low frequencies of stimulation approach more closely to the maximum. Although depletion of the immediately available store may well be the actual stimulus of mobilization into it, this is as yet uncertain; it would seem that the frequency of stimulation as such also plays some part (Elmqvist & Quastel, 1965*b*).

As yet there has been very little investigation of the mobilization process at any synapse, despite its great physiological importance in permitting the sustained release of transmitter. The only experimental agents which have been shown to affect it, apart from an action secondary to an effect on fractional release (like that of calcium ions), are hyperpolarizing and depolarizing currents and exposure to an increased extracellular potassium concentration (Hubbard & Willis, 1962, 1968; Parsons, Hofmann, & Feigen, 1965; Hubbard *et al.*, unpublished observations).

The dependence upon stimulus frequency of the plateau heights of e.p.p.s after early tetanic rundown (Fig. 4.11) is to a large extent a measure of fractional release of transmitter, since the higher the fractional release the more the mobilization per unit time approaches its maximum. At the lower rates of stimulation an increase in frequency dependence strongly suggests an increased fractional release. Such an experiment may be quite easy to perform indirectly. For example, one can examine the effect of an agent upon the frequency dependence of strength of contraction of a lightly curarized muscle stimulated indirectly (Blackman, 1963). However, such an experiment is inherently ambiguous in its interpretation, since a reduction of the mobilization response to depletion of the immediately available store would result in the same visible effect.

In the investigation of how an agent or experimental treatment modifies transmitter release it must always be recognized that mobilization rate and fractional release influence the quantum content of synaptic potentials, their relative importance depending upon the particular conditions of an experiment. During repetitive stimulation, for example, release may at first be limited by the mobilization process, but if fractional release be depressed the release will become limited by this. For instance, an agent might depress the potentiation of fractional release which occurs during high-frequency stimulation. This could be mistaken for an inhibition of the mobilization process since the effect would appear as a reduction of the plateau phase of synaptic potential amplitude. If the test were repeated at several stimulation frequencies, so as to be sure that mobilization reached its maximum under both test and control conditions, effects on fractional release and mobilization could be separated.

Mobilization store

With prolonged tetani at frequencies of more than about 5/sec, mobilization does not remain at its initial level but falls slowly and progressively, apparently to be maintained eventually at a level which is much lower than that found at first (del Castillo & Katz, 1954c; Brooks & Thies, 1962; Elmqvist & Quastel, 1965b). If this fall is also ascribed to depletion of a presynaptic store, it is possible to arrive at a figure for a 'mobilization store'. Elmqvist & Quastel (1965b) found this store was about 50–100 times larger than the immediately available store. The anatomical substrate of the mobilization store is unknown; certainly it appears to be only a fraction of the total amount of transmitter normally stored in a nerve terminal. Its determination is not easy, since it requires the recording of large numbers of synaptic potentials over a period of several minutes. It is difficult to choose for any junction just that frequency of stimulation at which mobilization will not be maintained, but will also not fall so low that synaptic potentials become so small as to be unmeasurable before they reach their final plateau.

The rate at which mobilization can be maintained indefinitely should be of some interest physiologically and pharmacologically. Presumably it represents the rate at which transmitter can be put into a form in which it can be mobilized and then released. Experimental modification might well give clues regarding the mechanisms involved at this level of the transmission process. As yet this has not been attempted, but the experimental techniques involved seem to be rather easy. One need only stimulate indirectly at about 10/sec or more for a few minutes, enter a cell with microelectrode and, while continuing stimulation, attempt the modification. It is important to recognize, however, that a change of fractional release or mobilization would have at least a temporary effect on synaptic potential amplitude. The quantal contents of synaptic potentials would be rather small. At the nerve–muscle junction, for instance, only a small quantity of curare would be necessary to suppress muscle contraction, and quantum contents of e.p.p.s could be determined by the direct rather than the variance method. Indeed it would be rather important that miniature potentials be visible since their frequency tends to go up enormously during prolonged tetani, and release of transmitter between impulses accounts for a very appreciable fraction of the total transmitter release.

Since the functional separation of transmitter stores in a nerve terminal is postulated solely on the basis of release data, it is possible that they should be regarded as convenient fictions which help in providing a mental picture of presynaptic events rather than as actual entities. As pointed out by Elmqvist & Quastel (1965b) all the output data on which the scheme is based could be explained in other ways. For instance, while it appears plausible to correlate the postulated stores with the vesicles found in motor-nerve terminals at different distances from release sites (Hubbard & Kwanbunbumpen, 1968), there could well be analogous stores of a membrane constituent important to the release process. Another point to be enphasized is that a continuum of intra-cellular stores, rather than a sharp separation, is in no way contradicted by existing experimental results which are insufficient to distinguish between several stores with transmitter moving from one to the other and the more likely alternative of rather slow diffusion of material in the nerve terminals towards the site of release.

Electrical events in nerve terminals

The action potential in nerve terminals

At the squid giant synapse (Hagiwara & Tasaki, 1958) and in the chick ciliary ganglion (Martin & Pilar, 1963b, 1964b) it is possible to record from both the pre- and postsynaptic elements of the synapse. At these synapses it appears that the action potential in the nerve terminal is similar in its characteristics to action potentials elsewhere. Fig. 4.14 shows intracellularly recorded action potentials from pre- and postsynaptic giant fibres in the

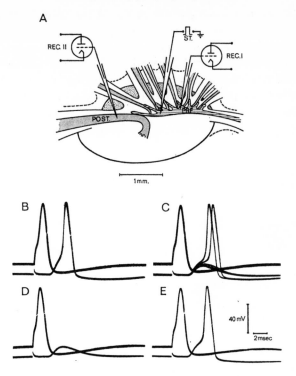

FIG. 4.14. A, Schematic diagram showing the squid giant synapse and typical placement of the electrodes. B, C, D, and E, records of potentials (positive upwards) in presynaptic axon (upper trace) and postsynaptic axon (lower trace) before tetrodotoxin. B shows a presynaptic action potential, EPSP and postsynaptic action potential, elicited 30 seconds after a preceding stimulus. C shows superimposed records during stimulation at 1/sec. D. 2 seconds later. E. 30 seconds later. Voltage calibration: 40 mV for both traces. Time Calibration: 2 msec (Bloedel, *et al.*, 1966).

squid stellate ganglion (Bloedel, Gage, Llinás, & Quastel, 1966) and the presynaptic action potential, normal in amplitude, preceding an excitatory postsynaptic potential which has been reduced in size because of repetitive stimulation of the presynaptic axon.

At other synapses recording of presynaptic action potentials is perforce extracellular, and information regarding their absolute magnitude and time course is lost. The form of the potential to be expected when recording extracellularly near the terminal from conducting fibres was described by Brooks & Eccles (1947) and potentials of this form are indeed found (Hubbard & Schmidt, 1963; Katz & Miledi, 1965a; Braun & Schmidt, 1966). At the beginning of the terminal, due presumably to the sudden reduction in outward current density when the wave front enters the non-myelinated terminal expansion, the spike is relatively large with little or no initial positivity (Fig. 4.15A). In a long terminal

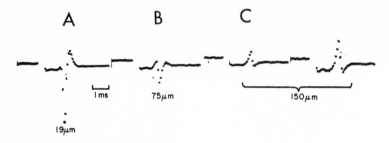

FIG. 4.15. The conformation of spike potentials in the vicinity of nerve terminals. All records are from unmyelinated fine terminal branches of motor nerves in the frog sartorius muscle. A. Near the transition from myelinated to unmyelinated nerve. B. Midway between the transition and the ultimate terminal. C. Close to the terminal. All distances represent distance along the terminal from the end of the 'parent' myelinated segment. In C the second record is at a higher gain than the other records. The records are dotted because they were recorded from an averaging computer operating in 80 μsec steps (Katz & Miledi, 1965a).

like that of frog nerve–muscle junction, the impulse may be recorded at a point midway between the termination and the beginning of the terminal. As Fig. 4.15B shows, it then has the familiar triphasic (positive-negative-positive) shape normally associated with an extracellularly recorded impulse. Near the terminal end the nerve spike again becomes diphasic but is now positive-negative (Fig. 4.15C) and relatively much smaller, presumably because of the lessening terminal fibre diameter, than at the point of branching (Fig. 4.15A). If the ultimate terminals do not conduct impulses, the diphasic wave becomes monophasic and positive (Fig. 4.16B), as Dudel (1965a) has demonstrated at the crustacean motor-nerve terminal.

To record the presynaptic action potentials in this way, it is essential that the recording electrode be close to the nerve terminal (Fig. 4.17). At neuromuscular junctions proximity to the endplate may be judged by whether it is possible to record extracellular

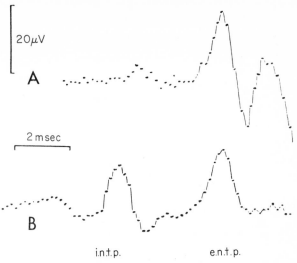

i.n.t.p.   e.n.t.p.

FIG. 4.16. Recording of presynaptic action potentials in excitatory
and inhibitory nerve fibres at a crayfish nerve–muscle junction. A.
Stimulation of the excitatory nerve at 5/sec leads to a diphasic excitatory nerve terminal potential (e.n.t.p.). At the right end of the
trace the negative excitatory postsynaptic potential starts; its
amplitude is 75 μV. B. Excitatory transmission is inhibited by a
group of 5 stimuli at 100/sec set to precede each excitatory
stimulus, the last of the resulting inhibitory nerve terminal potentials (i.n.t.p.) is visible in the beginning of the trace. The inhibited
excitatory nerve terminal potential is monophasic and positive,
the excitatory postsynaptic potential is completely blocked. Each
trace is the sum of 1000 individual records and the points delivered
by the averaging computer are connected manually for better illustration (Dudel, 1965a).

m.e.p.p.s (Fig. 4.17B), which can be done only within a few
microns of the junctional region (del Castillo & Katz, 1956a;
Hubbard & Schmidt, 1963).

There are several ways in which observation of the amplitude
of presynaptic spike potentials can be of analytical value. Firstly,
a nerve impulse must reach the vicinity of the terminals for transmitter release to take place. By observing the presynaptic potential
it is, therefore, possible to distinguish between presynaptic nerve
block and presynaptic failure of transmitter release. Mg^{++} ions,
for instance, appear to block transmitter release without changing
the presynaptic spike potential (Hubbard & Schmidt, 1963; Katz
& Miledi, 1965c). In contrast at the crayfish nerve terminal, if inhibitory nerve impulses (Fig. 4.16B, i.n.t.p.) precede an excitatory

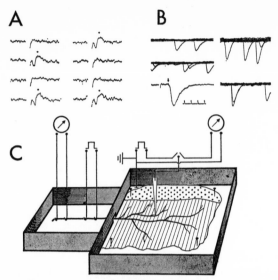

FIG. 4.17. Localization and stimulation of nerve terminals in the rat diaphragm phrenic nerve preparation *in vitro*. A. Successive oscilloscope traces recorded during threshold terminal stimulation at 1 sec intervals. Antidromic responses (successes) recorded from the phrenic nerve in oil are marked with a dot. The break in the sweep is due to the stimulus artefact. The percentage of failures in this series was 50%. B. Records of extracellular miniature endplate potentials and an endplate potential (first column, third record) obtained in the vicinity of nerve terminals. Note the presynaptic spike potential (arrow) preceding the e.p.p. set up by phrenic nerve stimulation (1 msec timer). C. Schematic diagram of recording and stimulating circuits (Gage & Hubbard, 1966*a*).

nerve impulse (Fig. 4.16A, B, e.n.t.p.), the excitatory nerve impulse changes in form from a diphasic (positive-negative) potential (Fig. 4.16A) to a monophasic (positive) potential (Fig. 4.16B) indicating that the inhibition is presynaptic and produced by a blockage of propagation of the excitatory nerve impulse in the terminal region.

Secondly, transmitter release appears to be related to the total amplitude of the action potential (Hagiwara & Tasaki, 1958; Takeuchi & Takeuchi, 1962; Katz & Miledi, 1965*d*). It is, therefore, often of some importance to determine, using extracellular recording, whether a procedure affecting transmitter release acts by altering the presynaptic spike potential. For example, in isolated nerve–muscle preparation an increase in the bathing [Mg^{++}]

decreases the release of transmitter by nerve impulses while an increase in the bathing Ca^{++} increases the release of transmitter. Observation of the presynaptic spike amplitude indicates no consistent parallel changes. It may, therefore, be concluded that Mg^{++} and Ca^{++} act directly on the release mechanism (Hubbard & Schmidt, 1963; Katz & Miledi, 1965*c*). This method can also be of great value in physiological and pharmacological research. For instance as Fig. 4.18 indicates, 2×10^{-5} g/ml of γ-aminobutyric

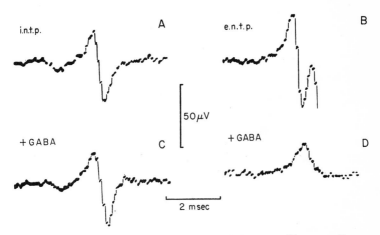

FIG. 4.18. Drug actions on nerve terminals integrated by recording of terminal action potentials. In the figure the effect of GABA on the inhibitory nerve terminal potential and on the excitatory nerve terminal potential recorded in the same electrode position is compared. A and B are control inhibitory nerve terminal potentials and excitatory nerve terminal potentials. In C the inhibitory nerve terminal potential is not affected by GABA at a concentration of 2×10^{-5} g/ml, while in D the excitatory nerve terminal potential is made positive by the same GABA concentration. Each record is the sum of 400 repetitive potential records using an averaging computer (Dudel, 1965*b*).

acid (GABA) does not affect the form of the inhibitory spike potential at crayfish motor-nerve terminals (Fig. 4.18A, C) but in the presence of the same concentration of the drug the excitatory nerve potential is changed from a diphasic to a monophasic form (Fig. 4.18B, D). GABA thus has an action identical with that produced by stimulating the inhibitory nerve (Fig. 4.16), and in contrast to Ca^{++} or Mg^{++} acts by affecting the presynaptic action potential.

Synaptic delay

When recording the spike potential in nerve terminals, the post-synaptic potential will of necessity also be recorded and therefore the synaptic delay can be measured. As Fig. 4.19 indicates, the synaptic delay may be defined as the interval between the negative peak of the presynaptic spike and the beginning of the focal extra-cellularly recorded synaptic potential. Effectively the interval is

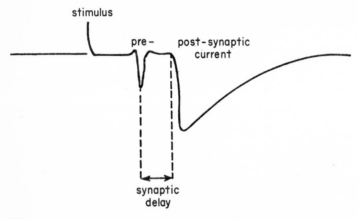

FIG. 4.19. Measurement of synaptic delay. The diagram shows the focal response extracellularly recorded at an endplate spot in a frog sartorius nerve–muscle preparation (downward deflections indicate negativity at the external electrode (Katz & Miledi, 1965*b*).

measured between the time of maximum local inward current through the axon membrane and the start of the local inward current through the postsynaptic membrane. Measurements of minimum synaptic delay made from records of the type illustrated in Fig. 4.19 indicate that the minimum synaptic delay at the rat nerve–muscle junction is 0·217±0·004 msec (average of 35 junctions at 34–36°C (Hubbard & Schmidt, 1963) while at the frog nerve–muscle junctions the minimum delay is 0·54 msec at 17·5°C (Katz & Miledi, 1965*b*). With this type of measurement there is no time lag due to conduction of the impulse in the terminal and the delay represents only the interval between the depolarization of the terminal and the release of transmitter together with the time taken by the diffusion of the transmitter across the synaptic cleft and its reaction with subsynaptic receptors, which causes an increase in the subsynaptic membrane conductance.

In fact, estimates of the diffusion time at the frog nerve–muscle junction indicate that 50 μsec is the maximum which could be expected (Katz & Miledi, 1965*b*). At the same nerve–muscle junction the reaction of ACh with the receptor and the ensuing conductance change consumes less than 100 μsec (Katz & Miledi, 1965*b*; Nastuk, Manthey, & Gissen, 1966). The lower record in Fig. 4.20 shows the depolarization of frog muscle membrane

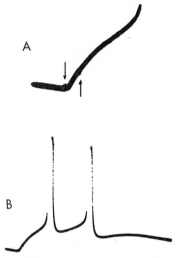

FIG. 4.20. The speed of the receptor–transmitter combination at a cholinergic synapse. The intracellular records from a frog nerve–muscle junction show depolarization of the postjunctional membrane produced by high-speed iontophoretic application of acetylcholine. The depolarization was sufficient to trigger the discharge of two action potentials. A. Enlarged view of the onset of depolarization produced in B. Arrows mark the start and end of the iontophoretic pulse which was 1·2 msec in duration (Nastuk, Manthey, & Gissen, 1966).

produced by the high-speed iontophoretic application of ACh. The depolarization was sufficient to trigger two action potentials. In the upper trace which is an enlarged record of onset of depolarization, it is evident that the depolarization began soon after the onset of the pulse (arrow in Fig. 4.20A), which lasted only 1·2 msec. It must therefore be concluded, and herein lies the main interest of measuring synaptic delays, that the delay recorded in

Fig. 4.19 is largely due to presynaptic events. It is to be expected that observation of synaptic delay will prove useful in the elucidation of the release mechanism and of the mode of action of agents affecting release.

In using the synaptic delay as an analytical tool it is useful to remember that the delay has a high temperature coefficient (Samojloff, 1925; Katz & Miledi, 1965*d*). Furthermore, while the previous discussion has been based on the minimum synaptic delay, it is easy to show (Fig. 4.21) that if the quantal content of responses is

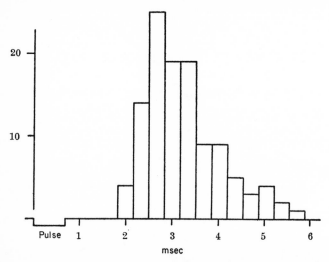

FIG. 4.21. The dispersion of synaptic delays in a cooled frog nerve–muscle preparation. The histogram indicates the latency distribution of e.p.p.s evoked by constant current pulses of 0·68 msec duration (Pulse) applied to nerve terminals in a frog sartorius muscle *in vitro*. The bathing solution contained tetrodotoxin 4×10^{-6} g/ml. Temperature 4·5°C. Ordinate: number of observed responses. Abscissa: time interval between the start of the depolarizing pulse and the start of e.p.p.s (Katz & Miledi, 1965*e*).

reduced to a low level, all quanta are not released simultaneously but there is a spread of delays which like the minimum delay are much increased by lowering the temperature of the preparation. Similar spread in time of quantal components of motoneurone excitatory postsynaptic potentials has been observed by Kuno (1964*a*) and doubtless occurs at all chemical synapses. At the many central synapses where long-lasting transmitter action, is of great functional importance (e.g., Eccles, 1964, pp. 160–64), it is possible that this prolonged action is brought about either by prolongation of the transmitter release process or by prolonged postsynaptic action of transmitter already released. Investigation of the quantal components at such synapses could determine which of these mechanisms is involved. The existence of synaptic delay is, of course, also of great importance to the function of cell assemblages. Its importance to the analysis of cell 'hookup' cannot be exaggerated.

A simpler method of measuring synaptic delay is to measure the time between the stimulus and the onset of the intracellularly recorded synaptic potential. When the quantal content of responses is low the dispersion of their latencies is obvious with this method (Eccles & Liley, 1959) but it suffers from the disadvantage that the time measured includes an unknown fraction of utilization time (time between onset of stimulation and setting up of propagated response) at the site of stimulation, and conduction time, as the nerve impulse propagates from the site of stimulation to the terminal.

Application of current to nerve terminals

Polarization of nerve terminals by applied current has been used in two ways. Firstly, to study the excitability of nerve terminals and hence, indirectly, to obtain information regarding the membrane potential of fine nerve endings. Secondly, and of more fundamental interest, to study the effect of polarization of the presynaptic membrane upon transmitter release. Except at the squid giant synapse such studies have of necessity been indirect, the polarization caused by any given current remaining unknown.

Excitability studies

These supplement recordings of the presynaptic action potential to give an indication of membrane potential changes under certain conditions. They are not applicable to all synapses. The crustacean neuromuscular junction, for example, appears not to be excitable by electrical stimuli (Dudel & Kuffler, 1961b). At synapses such as the vertebrate neuromuscular, and in the spinal cord, antidromic impulses can be evoked by application of current pulses. These can be recorded (Fig. 4.17A) and their threshold used as an index of terminal excitability. At neuromuscular junctions these antidromic impulses are single and all-or-nothing;

threshold can be assessed simply by recording the amplitude of the stimulating pulse necessary for evoking an impulse in the particular terminal being studied (Hubbard & Schmidt, 1963). In the spinal cord, as Fig. 4.22 shows, an electrode will stimulate a population of endings and therefore a stimulating pulse will invoke a compound antidromic potential, the size of which

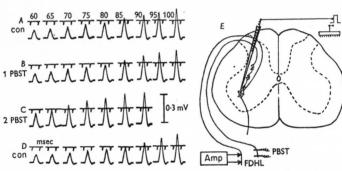

FIG. 4.22. Testing the excitability of nerve terminals in the cat spinal cord. A relatively coarse microelectrode filled with 4 M-NaCl and with a resistance of about 1 MΩ was inserted into the motor nucleus of the flexor digitorium longus and flexor hallucis longus and single pulses of 0·15 msec duration were applied by a Grass Stimulator with Isolation Unit, the electrode being negative to the indifferent electrode. Since the L6, L7, and S1 ventral roots had been cut, the spikes recorded at a brief latency (2·0 msec) in the flexor digitorium longus and flexor hallucis longus nerve (A–D) must have been due to impulses in large muscle afferents directly stimulated by the pulses. The voltages giving the current pulses were increased from 60 to 100 V, as shown by labels above the respective columns. A and D give control responses for these various stimuli, while B and C show spike potentials produced by the same stimuli, but after conditioning by one or two volleys in the posterior biceps semitendinosus nerve, 14 msec earlier. In C the 2 posterior biceps semitendinosus volleys were 3·5 msec apart. Note same time and potential scales for all records. Each spike was formed by the superposition of about five faint traces repeated at an interval of 1 sec. A diagrammatic illustration of the experimental arrangements is shown in E (Eccles, Magni, & Willis, 1962).

depends upon the pulse amplitude and the excitability of the population of terminals (Wall, 1958). In the experiment illustrated the depolarization of nerve terminals associated with presynaptic inhibition was detected by the increased excitability of the terminals (Eccles, Magni, & Willis, 1962). Because of the increased excitability, a compound action potential larger than in the control situation (Fig. 4.22A, D) was set up by each size of current pulse (Fig. 4.22B, C). Greater precision was attained in these experiments by using a range of currents in each stage so that the amounts of current needed to produce similar sizes of compound antidromic potentials could be compared.

In interpreting results of stimulation experiments it must be remembered that excitability changes need not necessarily reflect changes in membrane potential. For instance, any procedure which inactivates the sodium conductance mechanism will raise the threshold for impulse initiation, quite apart from any effect the procedure may have on membrane potential. Examples of inactivating agents include increased Ca^{++} and Mg^{++} concentrations in the bathing medium (Frankenhaeuser & Hodgkin, 1957), prolonged depolarization (Hodgkin & Huxley, 1952a) such as would be produced by maintained current or raised extracellular K concentrations, and many local anaesthetics such as cocaine and procaine (reviewed by Shanes, 1958). Alteration of membrane resistance would also affect excitability (see Chapter 2). There is good evidence, however, from muscle and peripheral nerve, that increased excitability accompanies membrane depolarization and decreased excitability membrane hyperpolarization, other things being equal (Jenerick & Gerard, 1953; Lorente de Nó, 1947b). The method is therefore useful provided conditions are sufficiently well controlled.

Methods of extracellular application of polarizing currents

Artificial variation of the presynaptic membrane potential by means of applied direct current can be usefully employed in association with either recording from or stimulation of nerve terminals (see e.g., Hubbard & Schmidt, 1963; Gage & Hubbard, 1966a). Similar current-passing techniques have also been applied to the cat spinal cord (Eccles, Kostyuk, & Schmidt, 1962). If terminals are polarized in conjunction with the recording of postsynaptic potentials, the principal technical difficulty is to confine the focus of current to the nerve terminal while avoiding secondary effects due to passage of current through postsynaptic structures. Suitable circuits which overcome these difficulties at the nerve–muscle junction have been described by del Castillo & Katz (1954d) and Hubbard & Willis (1962), (Fig. 4.23A, B). It should be noted that both methods are satisfactory if only miniature potentials are to be recorded. If e.p.p.s are also to be recorded, method A is to be preferred, as with method B there is a tendency

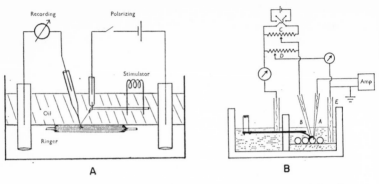

FIG. 4.23. Method of polarizing the nerve terminals of *in vitro* preparations. A, the method of del Castillo & Katz (1954*d*). The muscle lies at an oil-Ringer interface so that current passes through the nerve at the interface. B, The method of Hubbard & Willis (1962), employed for polarizing the presynaptic terminals of the rate neuromuscular junction. The muscle (represented by circles) was placed in the right-hand side of the divided recording chamber. The nerve passed beneath the partition into the left compartment where it was mounted upon stimulating electrodes. A fine microelectrode (*A*) was used to record intracellular potentials from muscle fibres. Polarizing currents were passed between a micro-pipette (*B*) placed near an endplate region and an electrode in contact with the nerve in the paraffin pool in the left compartment. The source of current was a battery connected to a variable resistance through a reversible switch (*C*). A bridge circuit was established by shunting the polarizing circuit with a potentiometer (*D*) with the sliding contact connected to earth (*E*). Currents were monitored by micro-ammeters as shown.

for impulse transmission to be blocked at the oil-Ringer interface.

Fig. 4.24 illustrates the use of polarizing techniques in conjunction with nerve terminal testing at motor-nerve terminals in the rat diaphragm. In this experiment the origin of the post-tetanic hyperpolarization of nerve terminals was being determined. Before the tetanus the stimulus strength was determined at which only a percentage of stimuli applied to terminals at one-second intervals elicited an antidromic response. For convenience the percentage of failures in 20-second periods is plotted. In the control experiment (Fig. 4.24A) after tetanic stimuli at 100/sec for 10 seconds the same stimuli were ineffective for nearly 40 seconds (Fig. 4.24A-arrow) and then antidromic potentials were again evoked in about the pretetanic proportion. As Fig. 4.24B indicates, the duration of the post-tetanic depression of excitability was prolonged by depolarizing currents while hyperpolarizing

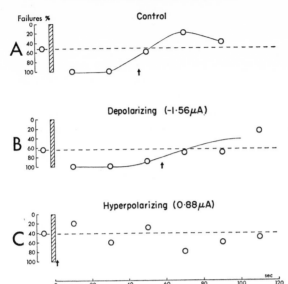

FIG. 4.24. Use of polarization combined with stimulation of nerve terminals. The figure illustrates the effect of polarizing currents upon post-tetanic excitability of motor nerve terminals in the phrenic nerve-rat diaphragm *in vitro*. A. Control. B. After application of a 1·56 μA depolarizing current to the terminal through a second microelectrode. C. After application of a 0·88 μA hyperpolarizing current to the same terminal. Ordinates: Percentage of threshold stimuli applied to the nerve terminals at a rate of 1/sec which did not evoke an antidromic action potential (% failures). Interrupted horizontal line represents the percentage of failures in the observation period (20–40 sec) before the tetanus. The vertical hatched block indicates a standard tetanus of 1000 stimuli at 100/sec applied to the phrenic nerve. In the post-tetanic period, the circles represent the percentage of failures in consecutive 20-sec periods after the tetanus, stimulation being at 1/sec and the same strength as before the tetanus. Abscissae: Time (sec) measured from the end of the tetanus. The circles are placed in the centre of the 20-sec periods over which the percentage of failures was calculated. The arrows mark the time at which the first post-tetanic antidromic response occurred (Gage & Hubbard, 1965).

currents could abolish the excitability change (Fig. 4.24C) or even, as other experiments showed, reverse the change to an exaltation of excitability (Gage & Hubbard, 1966a). This was strong evidence for the generation of the post-tetanic excitability change by a mechanism with an equilibrium potential.

Transmitter release by presynaptic polarization

The methods described above have also been used to evoke release of transmitter by depolarizing the nerve terminal membrane. Results of such experiments have indicated that long-lasting depolarization (several msec) evokes an increase of m.e.p.p. frequency, the logarithm of the release rate being in proportion to the current applied (del Castillo & Katz, 1954d; Liley, 1956c).

More recently, Katz & Miledi (1966) have made use of local application of current pulses from an electrode which is placed on a nerve terminal (in frog muscle where nerve terminals are long). Positioning of the electrode is done under a compound microscope and the position checked by recording of extracellular m.e.p.p.s. The electrode placement relative to the nerve terminal is like that used by Huxley & Taylor (1958) to apply local depolarization to activate the contractile system of muscle fibres via the sarcoplasmic reticulum. Under such conditions brief current pulses give almost equally brief polarization of the underlying structure. The time course, though not the extent, of the nerve terminal depolarization may be gauged from the muscle fibre depolarization which takes place at the same time. This shows an effective time constant for the rise and decay of a fraction of a millisecond, and currents needed to evoke release of transmitter may actually reverse the membrane potential of the muscle fibre and, presumably, the nerve terminal. This technique depends also on the use of an agent to block the presynaptic action potential, since such pulses will otherwise evoke action potentials which are propagated and cause transmitter release along the whole length of the nerve terminal, i.e., presynaptic polarization escapes from control of the experimenter if the action potential mechanism is intact.

Probably the most specific drug for preventing this mishap is the puffer fish poison, tetrodotoxin, which abolishes action potentials in nerve and striated muscle by preventing the rise in sodium conductance which otherwise occurs with membrane depolarization (Mosher, Fuhrman, Buchwald, & Fischer, 1964; Narahashi, Moore, & Scott, 1964) without affecting the transmitter release mechanism at synaptic junctions (Elmqvist & Feldman, 1965; Bloedel, Gage, Llinás & Quastel, 1966, 1967; Katz & Miledi, 1966, 1967b; Grundfest, 1966; Ozeki, Freeman, & Grundfest, 1966a; Kusano, Livengood & Werman, 1967). The method is therefore valuable in studying the relation between transmitter release and the intensity and duration of presynaptic polarization (Bloedel *et al.*, 1966, 1967; Katz & Miledi, 1967*a*, *b*, *c*) and the time course of transmitter release following a brief depolarizing pulse. As shown in Fig. 4.21, there is both a spread in the delay of appearance of quantal components following such a pulse as well as a minimum delay (Katz & Miledi, 1965*b*).

Another promising use of tetrodotoxin depends on the fact that the electrical activity of vertebrate smooth muscle is not affected by tetrodotoxin (Toida & Osa, 1965; Bulbring & Tomita, 1966). The poison may thus be used to distinguish between agents acting directly on smooth muscle and agents acting on smooth muscle indirectly by stimulation of intramural nerves. Such indirect actions will be blocked by tetrodotoxin (Gershon, 1967).

5

ANALYSIS OF SUBSYNAPTIC EVENTS

It is the purpose of this chapter to deal with the investigation of the immediate effects of transmitter that has been released. The scheme in Fig. 5.1 shows the action and fate of the transmitter

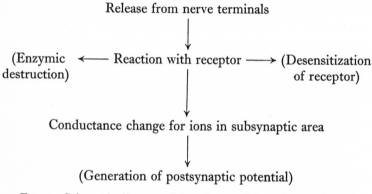

Release from nerve terminals

(Enzymic destruction) ← Reaction with receptor → (Desensitization of receptor)

Conductance change for ions in subsynaptic area

(Generation of postsynaptic potential)

FIG. 5.1 Schematic diagram of the effects and fate of transmitters. Brackets imply that the bracketed item is not always a concomitant of transmitter action.

(acetylcholine) at the neuromuscular junction, and somewhat by analogy, at most other synapses. The brackets placed around enzymic destruction, desensitization, and generation of post-synaptic potentials are to indicate that these may not occur at every synapse. Enzymic destruction probably takes place only at synapses where rapid termination of transmitter action is important. Desensitization of receptor—a reduction of postsynaptic sensitivity to transmitter if there is prolonged exposure to it—certainly occurs at the neuromuscular junction (Katz & Thesleff, 1957*b*) but is unlikely to be of much, or any, functional significance even here. It is likely that at many synapses, such as adrenergic ones, released transmitter is later taken up again by nerve terminals and stored for future use. A potential change is not always a necessary feature of transmitter action—inhibition may be effected by a conductance change only (see Chapter 2). Even a conductance change may not always be involved; a chemotransmitter may in some cases act upon the metabolic activity of the postsynaptic cell. For instance some recent evidence suggests that at soma synapses transmitter action may cause hyperpolarization by stimulation of (Na^+) extrusion rather than by a conductance change (see Chapter 2).

Whatever the mechanism of transmitter action, it is presently considered that in all cases it is mediated as a result of the combination of transmitter substance with a specific receptor. Only in this way can one explain the different actions of transmitter depending upon the target cell, for example, the difference in ACh action depending on whether it acts at the skeletal myoneural junction or on the sino-auricular node of the heart. The concept of specific receptor was put forward by Paul Ehrlich (quoted in Albert, 1965) who envisaged receptors as chemically defined areas of large molecules which combined with an active substance by virtue of their chemically complementary nature. This concept has two corollaries of great significance in the analysis of synaptic mechanisms. One is that it is possible in principle to determine the chemical properties of the receptor by determining how it interacts with a variety of substances. The second is that at synapses where the transmitter is unknown any candidate for the role of transmitter must be shown to be acting on the same receptor as the endogenous transmitter.

It should be obvious that to say a cell is chemosensitive means not only that it has receptors which interact with a substance, but that some sort of functional action then takes place. There is, in general, no reason to assume that only cells which react to an active substance contain receptors for it, that is, it is possible that many drugs may interact with or be bound to membrane components without this combination having any physiological effect. For this reason, mere isolation of a cell component which binds a drug does not mean a physiological receptor has been isolated.

For these reasons, it is usually neither desirable nor practical to study in any direct way the combination of transmitter or drug with post-junctional receptor. In general, evidence regarding these basic phenomena must be indirect. The effect of transmitter substances, or compounds which act similarly, at a synapse can be measured more or less directly by:

(1) change of function of the postsynaptic cell - action potential frequency or muscle contraction.

(2) change of membrane potential or current flow.

(3) change of membrane conductance.

The more direct the measurement, the more difficult it is.

ELEMENTARY KINETICS

It was found (Clark, 1933) that the effects of potent drugs on cells were reversible, and the number of receptor molecules seemed to be much less, generally, than the number of drug molecules in the vicinity. The finding of a hyperbolic relation between the concentration of drugs such as ACh, nicotine, and adrenaline and their effects on biological tissues (see, e.g., Fig. 5.6A, p. 187) led Clark to suggest that drug action could be quantitatively described by the equations derived by Langmuir (1916) for the absorption of gas molecules by catalysts. These equations are also formally identical to those relating enzyme and substrate interaction to the velocity of a chemical reaction since they are derived on the basis of identical assumptions (Ariens *et al.*, 1956).

If the free receptor concetration (or number per unit area) is denoted [R] and the substrate (or in pharmacological terms, the agonist concentration) is [A], and the interaction with receptor is reversible, i.e., $[A] + [R] \rightleftharpoons [AR]$, then at equilibrium,

$$[A]\,[R] = K_a[AR] \tag{1}$$

where K_a is the dissociation constant of the agonist–receptor combination, the concentration of the latter being [AR]. Now, in most cases it can be assumed that the concentration of agonist is not appreciably altered because of the (small) number of molecules which combine with R. Denoting the total number of receptor molecules by R_t, $R_t = [R] + [AR]$. Substituting for [R] from (1) we get

$$R_t = K_a[AR]/[A] + [AR] = [AR]\,(K_a/[A] + 1)$$

and $$[AR] = R_t/(1 + K_a/[A]) \tag{2}$$

and   in reciprocal form

$$1/[AR] = (1 + K_a/[A])/R_t.$$

That is the reciprocal of the [AR] is linearly related to the recipricol of the agonist concentration ([A]).

Again, if two molecules of agonist combine with receptor

$$[A] [R] = K_a[AR] \tag{4}$$

and
$$[A] [AR] = K_b[A_2R] \tag{5}$$

Assuming as before that the total [A] is not appreciably altered

then
$$R_t = [A_2R] + [AR] + [R]$$

substituting for [AR] from (5) and for [R] from (4) we get

$$R_t = [A_2R] + K_b[A_2R]/[A] + K_aK_b[A_2R]/[A]^2$$

whence
$$[A_2R] = R_t/(1 + K_b/[A] + K_aK_b/[A]^2)$$

and reciprocally

$$1/[A_2R] = (1 + K_b/[A] + K_aK_b/[A]^2)/R_t.$$

The plot of the reciprocal of the concentration of the active complex versus the reciprocal of the receptor concentration thus gives a parabola. Polynomials of n degree result if n molecules of agonist are involved per receptor molecule.

In the case of the interaction between an enzyme and its substrate it can be assumed that the velocity of the resulting reaction is proportional to the concentration of the enzyme substrate combination, i.e.,

$$v = a[AR] \tag{6}$$

when v is the reaction velocity. The maximum reaction rate obtainable (V), would occur when [AR] is equal to R_t, i.e., when all receptor (e.g., enzyme) is in the combined form then

$$V = a R_t. \tag{7}$$

Then from (6) and (7)

$$v/V = [AR]/R_t \tag{8}$$

and from (2)
$$[AR] = R_t/(1 + K_a/[A])$$

substituting in (8)
$$v/V = 1/(1 + K_a/[A])$$

and
$$v = V/(1 + K_a/[A]) \tag{9}$$

whence
$$1/v = \frac{1}{V}(1 + K_a/[A]).$$

$$= K_a/VA + 2/V \tag{10}$$

Figure 5.2 shows the hyperbola relating v and [A] (eqn. (9))

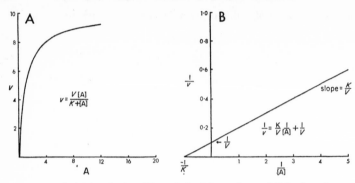

FIG. 5.2. Initial velocity (A) and double reciprocal (B) plots for a one-substrate reaction (Morrison, 1965).

and the straight line (eqn. (10)) resulting from the plot of $1/v$ versus $1/A$ (as suggested by Lineweaver & Burk, 1934). The intercept on the ordinate gives $1/V$, the intercept on the abscissa gives $-1/K_a$. The same should be true for an agonist-receptor response, *provided the measured response is directly proportional to* [AR]. The same type of plots will be obtained irrespective of the number of agonists (or substrates) provided only one is varied at a time.

With multimolecular reactions there should be, of course, a polynomial rather than straight line on the reciprocal plot. If one assumes that the concentrations of intermediately combined forms of receptor are negligible, compared to free ([R]) and active forms ([A_nR]), then the equation reduces to

$$[A_nR] = R_t/(1 + K_{a-n}/[A]^n)$$

and

$$1/v = 1/V(1 + K_{a-n}[A]^n).$$

Thus, a plot of $1/v$ versus $[A]^n$ should give a straight line, and n may be determined by finding the value of n which gives this linear result (Cavanaugh & Hearon, 1954).

Affinity and intrinsic activity

In the above formulation, with the assumption that measured response is a single linear function of the amount of agonist–receptor combination, two parameters only control the activity of an agonist. One is its affinity for the receptor, measured as an affinity constant, $1/K_a$, the reciprocal of the dissociation constant of the drug-receptor complex. The other is intrinsic activity, the constant determining the effect per unit of the drug-receptor complex (Ariens *et al.*, 1956). Relative activity of agonists can be determined from V, the reaction velocity when the receptors are saturated with the drug. In the Lineweaver–Burk plot (Fig. 5.2B) $1/V$ is the intercept of the straight line with the ordinate. This intercept for any particular substance is then a measure of its intrinsic activity. In practice, intrinsic activity is usually expressed as a function of the intrinsic activity of a reference compound, the activity of this compound being given the value one. Further information on these concepts can be found in Ariens (1964).

Antagonists

Pharmacological antagonists can be divided into two classes, (1) inhibitors which act on the same receptor as the agonist and (2) substances which oppose the action of an agonist in some other way, usually by interacting with another receptor.

Inhibitors can be divided into two groups, competitive and non-competitive, on the basis of reaction kinetics. Competitive inhibitors can be defined as those which act by combination with the same receptor site as the agonist, thus,

$$\left.\begin{array}{l} [A] + [R] \rightleftharpoons [AR] \\ [I] + [R] \rightleftharpoons [IR] \end{array}\right\}$$

$$\left.\begin{array}{l} [A]\,[R] = K_a[AR] \\ [I]\,[R] = K_I\,[IR] \end{array}\right\}$$

$R_t = [R] + [AR] + [IR]$ and substituting for $[R]$ and $[IR]$

$$= [AR] + \frac{K_a}{[A]}\,[AR] + \frac{[I]}{K_I} \cdot \frac{K_a}{[A]}\,[AR]$$

$$[AR] = \frac{R_t}{1 + \dfrac{K_a}{A}\left(1 + \dfrac{I}{K_I}\right)} \tag{11}$$

and

$$1/[AR] = \left\{1 + \frac{K_a}{[A]}\left(1 + \frac{[I]}{K_I}\right)\right\}\bigg/ K_t. \tag{12}$$

Equations (11) and (12) are the same as eqns. (2) and (3) except that $K_a/[A]$ is multiplied by $(1 + I/K_I)$. Thus, the action of a competitive inhibitor is to reduce the apparent affinity of agonist and receptor.

If the inhibitor combines with a site other than that site which interacts with the agonist, and its affinity for the site is the same whether agonist is combined or not, then it is a non-competitive inhibitor. One has the following equations:

$$[R]\,[A] = K_a[AR]$$
$$[AR]\,[I] = K_I\,[ARI]$$
$$[R]\,[I] = K_I[RI]$$

$$R_t = [AR] + [R] + [ARI] + [RI]$$

whence by substitution

$$R_t = [AR] + \frac{K_a}{[A]}\,[AR] + \frac{[I]}{K_I}\,[AR] + \frac{[I]}{K_I}\cdot\frac{K_a}{[A]}\,[AR]$$

$$[AR] = \frac{R_t}{\left(1 + \dfrac{K_a}{[A]}\right)\left(1 + \dfrac{[I]}{K_I}\right)} \tag{13}$$

$$1/[AR] = \frac{1}{R_t}\left(1 + \frac{K_a}{[A]}\right)\left(1 + \frac{[I]}{K_I}\right). \tag{14}$$

This is simple non-competitive inhibition, and eqns. (13) and (14) are identical to eqns. (2) and (3) save that R_t is replaced by $R_t/(1 + [I]/K_I)$. A non-competitive inhibitor thus appears to reduce the intrinsic activity of the agonist, without changing the affinity. If the affinity of inhibitor for receptor is changed, depending on whether agonist is or is not present (a so-called 'allosteric' effect) then the equations must be modified:

$$[AR] = R_t \Big/ \left\{ 1 + \frac{K_a}{[A]}\left(1 + \frac{[I]}{K_I}\right) + \frac{[I]}{K_{ARI}} \right\} \tag{15}$$

$$1/[AR] = \frac{1}{R_t}\cdot\left\{ 1 + \frac{K_a}{[A]}\left(1 + \frac{[I]}{K_I} + \frac{[I]}{K_{ARI}}\right) \right\}. \tag{16}$$

These reduce to eqns. (13) and (14) if $K_{ARI} = K_I$, and to eqns. (10) and (11) if K_{ARI} is very large, and in this case the action appears exactly the same as single competition, although a different site of combination has been assumed. That is, if an inhibitor combines with receptor, but not with the agonist–receptor combination, it may be *impossible* to determine whether it combines with receptor at the same site as the agonist, or a different one. Another possibility is that K_{ARI} is much greater than K_I, in which case eqn. (15) simplifies to:

$$[AR] = R_t \Big/ \left(1 + \frac{K_a}{[A]} + \frac{[I]}{K_{ARI}} \right).$$

There is no reason why I, the inhibitor, should not be the same as the agonist. This expression describes the phenomenon of enzyme inhibition by excess of substrate.

Allosteric effects

Competitive inhibition is characterized by an apparent change of K_a. An actual change of affinity of the receptor for agonist, by an agent (called an 'allosteric' effect), would of course result in families of straight lines relating $1/v$ to $1/[A]$ (provided v was proportional to [AR]), with intercepts at the same point on the ordinate, i.e., the same picture as obtained with competitive inhibitor. To distinguish these possibilities, it is important to note that competitive inhibition is further characterized by the fact that, for equal responses (i.e., equal [AR]), the denominator in the right-hand side in eqn. (12) is always the same, i.e.,

$$1 + \frac{K_a}{[A]} \left(1 + \frac{[I]}{K_I} \right) = C$$

where C is a constant that increases with diminishing response chosen. Thus,

$$[A] = \frac{K_a}{C - 1} \left(1 + \frac{[I]}{K_I} \right), \qquad (17)$$

that is, a plot of agonist concentration versus inhibitor concentration such that the combination yields any arbitrary response yields a straight line with intercept on the ordinate equal to $K_a/(C-1)$ and intercept on the abscissa equal to $-K_I$. Such a relationship would not be expected in the case of the allosteric effect. Taking a family of such lines, one should find in the case of competition that the ratio of the intercept on the ordinate, $Ka/(C-1)$, to the slope, $\{K_a/(C-1)\} \cdot \{1/K_I\}$, always yields the same value (K_I). This method was employed by Jenkinson (1960) to determine the affinity of the ACh receptor for *d*-tubocurarine.

APPLICATIONS OF KINETIC EQUATIONS

The major difficulty in applying the kinetic theory outlined to drug actions is that there is generally no reason to assume that any measured response is related in any specific simple way to the concentration or amount of drug–receptor complex. It is usual to hope for the best and assume that if a plot of the inverse of the response shows a linear relation with the inverse of agonist concentration, then it does so because it reflects agonist–receptor complex concentration. In some cases it is possible to make curves fit by choosing the right relation between response and (presumed) active complex. For example, there appears to be a threshold concentration of ACh necessary for contraction of the frog rectus (Fig. 5.3A). Curves of ACh concentration vs. contraction can be extrapolated below the abscissa. If one assumes that response is proportional to $[AR] - [AR]_0$, where $[AR]_0$ is the 'threshold'

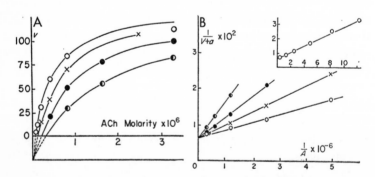

Fig. 5.3. ACh dose-response curves and the effect of the competitive inhibitor dihydro-β-erythroidine. A. Ordinate shows rate of contraction (v) of frog rectus muscle (height of contraction in 1 mm, on an arbitrary scale). The dotted segments are the extrapolations used to evaluate the constant a. Open circles, no inhibitor; crosses, dihydro-β-erythroidine 0.7×10^{-8} M; full circles, 1.9×10^{-8} M; half-filled circles, 4.7×10^{-8} M. B. The data in A plotted as reciprocals. The symbols are the same as those used in A. The inset shows the entire curve in the absence of inhibitor (Kirschner & Stone, 1951).

amount of agonist–receptor complex, then, in the presence of an inhibitor

$$v = C([AR] - [AR]_0)$$

$$= \frac{C \cdot [R_t]}{1 + \dfrac{K_a}{[A]}\left(1 + \dfrac{I}{K_I}\right)} - a$$

where a is a constant equal to the negative of the intercept on the ordinate and equal to $C[AR]_0$. Thus, a plot of $1/(v+a)$ against $1/[A]$ should yield straight lines, with intercept on the ordinate unaltered by concentration of inhibitor (Fig. 5.3B), in this case dehydro-β-erythroidine. It will be noted that this relationship only suggests, rather than proves, that the inhibitor acts by competition with ACh for the same receptor.

Similar treatment of the response to ACh in the presence of different concentrations of atropine are shown in Fig. 5.4. These

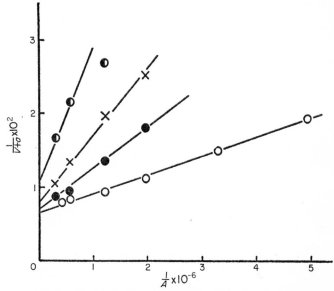

FIG. 5.4. Double reciprocal plot illustrating non-competitive inhibition of ACh by atropine (Kirschner & Stone, 1951). Ordinate shows reciprocal of contraction rate of frog rectus muscle calculated as for Fig. 6. Abscissa shows reciprocal of ACh concentration. The symbols indicate values obtained in the absence of atropine (open circles) and in the presence of atropine $1 \cdot 5 \times 10^{-4}$ M (full circles); $3 \cdot 0 \times 10^{-4}$ M (crosses), and $4 \cdot 0 \times 10^{-4}$ M (half-filled circles).

lines have no common intercept with the ordinate, showing that this is not an example of competitive inhibition (or an allosteric effect). The picture is rather similar to that expected in the case of non-competitive inhibition. The magnitude of the intercept increases with increasing atropine concentrations, but more slowly than the slope. This could be taken to mean that $K_I > K_{ARI}$. However, a purely antagonistic action, in which atropine does not interact with the ACh receptor, is not ruled out.

It should be noted that a linear plot of 1/response versus 1/agonist, with a positive intercept on the ordinate, is not necessarily an indication that response is proportional to occupied receptor. For example, the voltage change resulting from a conductance change can be predicted from the models of a postsynaptic cell discussed in Chapter 2 (p. 64). If g is the conductance change and V the difference between the resting potential and the transmitter equilibrium potential; then the voltage change ΔE is given by the following formula:

$$\Delta E = gV/(g+G)$$

since gV is the current that flows and $1/(g+G)$ the resistance between the inside and outside of the membranes, i.e.

$$\frac{1}{\Delta E} = \frac{1}{V} + \frac{G}{gV}$$

V is the maximum voltage change that could occur. If an agonist combined with receptor, and conductance change was proportional to the amount of complex, i.e.,

$$g = C[AR] = C\,R_t/(1 + K_A/[A])$$

if g was relatively large when [A] was still small compared to K_A.

$$g \simeq C\,R_t \cdot [A]/K_A$$

A plot of $1/\Delta E$ versus $1/[A]$ would yield a straight line, with an intercept on the ordinate equal to $1/E$, that is, an intercept related to *saturation of response* and not saturation of receptor. Both competitive and non-competitive inhibitors would change the slope of $1/\Delta E$ verses $1/[A]$ plots, without changing the intercept on the ordinate. Both would appear to be acting competitively.

Similar results may arise if the agonist–receptor combination (AR) causes a response indirectly, by combining with a second receptor (R') for example. Then if a response were proportional to [AR . R'], inhibition at the level of the first receptor would look like competition, whether it was or not, and competitive inhibition at the level of the second receptor (i.e., with AR) could look like competition with A at the first receptor.

Use of equal responses

It was pointed out by Gaddum (1943) that whether an agent acts by competition or not can in principle be determined without making any assumptions regarding the relation between agonist–receptor combination and response. The formula relating agonist and inhibitor concentrations in the case of competition is (eqn. (17))

$$[A] = \frac{K_a}{C-1}\left(1 + \frac{[I]}{K_I}\right).$$

If [A]' is the concentration in the absence of inhibitor which gives response equal to that produced by [A] in the presence of inhibitor, then

$$[A]/[A]' = 1 + [I]/K_I. \tag{18}$$

This relation was applied (Jenkinson, 1960) to determine the affinity constant for the combination of tubocurarine and the ACh receptor at the frog endplate (Fig. 5.5). As the figure shows, it was only necessary to measure the depolarization produced by various concentrations of the stable ACh analogue carbachol, in the presence (open circles) and absence (filled circles) of a fixed concentration of d-tubocurarine. From these measurements the amounts of carbachol producing the same depolarization in the presence and absence of d-tubocurarine were found and compared according to eqn. (18). The effect of d-tubocurarine was thus characterized by an affinity constant which had the value $1.2 (\times 10^{-6} M^{-1})$ for the experiment of Fig. 5.5A, 1.1 for 5.5B, and 1.7 for 5.5C.

However, there is need for caution in using this method. In the simplest case of non-competitive inhibition (c.f. eqns. (13) and (14B))

$$(1 + K_a/[A])(1 + [I]K_I) = C$$

$$K_a/[A] + [I]/K_I + (K_a/K_I)([I]/[A] = C - 1$$

rearranging, $\quad [A] = K_a\left(1 + \frac{[I]}{K_I}\right) \Big/ \left(C - 1 - \frac{[I]}{K_I}\right),$

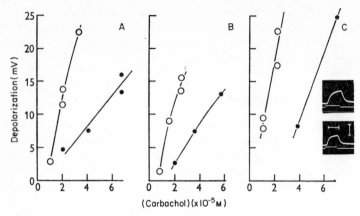

FIG. 5.5. Use of equal response method for determining affinity of tubocurarine for ACh receptors at the frog motor endplate (Jenkinson, 1960). A, B, C, determination of affinity for tubocurarine at three separate endplates. Microelectrodes were used to measure the depolarizations produced by different concentrations of carbachol applied with (filled circles) and without (open circles) 1.27×10^{-6} M tubocurarine in the bathing fluid. The resting potential of the fibre of experiment A was 82 mV at the beginning, and 76 mV at the end. The corresponding figures for experiments B and C were 82 and 78, and 94 and 90 mV respectively. To raise the threshold, three times the normal concentration of Ca was included in the Ringer's fluid of experiment A, and 8·6 mM-Mg in that of experiments B and C.

Inset to Fig. 4C; records of depolarizations produced by 2.2×10^{-5} M carbachol at the beginning and at end of experiment C; this endplate responded particularly slowly to the depolarizing agent. Voltage and time calibrations 20 mV and 1 min respectively.

i.e., a plot of [A] versus [I] yields a curve whose slope increases with [I]. Also,

$$\frac{[A]}{[A']} = \left(1 + \frac{[I]}{K_I}\right)\left(\frac{C-1}{C-1-\dfrac{[I]}{K_I}}\right).$$

It will be noted that if $[I]/K_I$ is small compared to $C-1$, i.e., if [I] is small, or [A] is small, the differences in curves from the case of competitive inhibition may not be large. *Essentially, competitive inhibition may be distinguished from non-competitive inhibition only if the receptor approaches saturation with agonist. If saturation of responses tends to occur before saturation of the receptor, it becomes very difficult or impossible to distinguish between them.*

Log-dose response curves

When the effect of a drug is plotted against the logarithm of the dose, an S-shaped curve of the type shown in Fig. 5.6 usually results. The top part of the S reflects the rectangular hyperbola illustrated in Figs. 5.2 and 5.3 transformed by the logarithmic

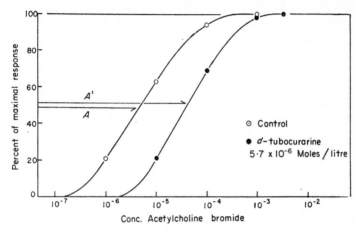

FIG. 5.6. Logarithmic concentration–action curves illustrating the effect of ACh alone (open circles) and on the presence of the competitive inhibitor *d*-tubocurarine 5.7×10^{-6} M (filled circles). Ordinate: isotonic contractions of frog rectus muscle in response to ACh plotted as percentage of the maximum contracture. Abscissa: logarithmic scale of ACh concentrations. *A* and *A'* indicate the concentrations of ACh which produce 50 per cent of the maximal contracture (Van Maanen, 1950).

plot while the initial portion with increasing slope may also arise from the hyperbola but may also reflect some kind of threshold for the response. In this form a change in affinity manifests itself as a change in the effective dose response curve along the log-dose axis. Competitive inhibition such as that demonstrated between ACh and curare (Fig. 5.6) has the action of diminishing the effective drug dose or affinity and therefore also manifests itself as a shift of the dose–response curve to the right along the log-dose axis. It is important to note that the maximal effect of ACh is still obtainable but needs a bigger ACh dose in the presence of curare. This presumably reflects the reversible nature of the competition between the two drugs but could reflect a saturation of tissue responses instead.

The usual method of quantitative comparison for this type of curve is shown in Fig. 5.6 (A', A). A' and A are the concentrations of ACh which produce 50% of the maximal contraction of the frog rectus muscle in the presence (A') and absence (A) of a fixed concentration of d-tubocurarine. This 50% response or AR_{50} is reminiscent of the LD_{50} or dose of a drug which kills 50% of a group of animals. The LD_{50} is found by plotting percentage mortality against logarithm of drug dose. Use of S-shaped curves in molecular pharmacology is derived from their use in this whole-animal type of pharmacology (Gaddum, 1937).

A change in intrinsic activity on the other hand results in an increase or decrease of the maximum effect obtainable and therefore of the slope of the dose–response curves. Non-competitive inhibition is equivalent to a decrease of intrinsic activity and therefore in this form of plot is indicated by dose–response curves which have lesser slopes and lower maxima than have control curves in the absence of inhibition.

Applying drugs to receptors

Application of drugs to cells is useful in two ways. First, the area of chemosensitivity of the cells may be determined, that is the area where receptors exist and the drug receptor conbination exerts an effect. Secondly, it may be used to determine the classes of agent which interact with the receptors. Methods of application are:

(1) In the case of transmitter only, release from the nerve terminal either spontaneously to be detected as miniature potentials or upon stimulation, by nerve impulses triggered higher up on the nerve or by local application of currents.

(2) Administration to the whole or part of an animal; we will consider application locally by ionophoresis and grossly in a tissue bath.

For method (1), it may be assumed that an approximately constant concentration of transmitter is released by nerve impulses delivered at suitably infrequent intervals and the population of receptors may also be assumed constant (Chapter 4). Similarly, miniature potentials are generated by approximately equal amounts of transmitter (Chapter 4). An interesting use of these properties was the use of miniature potentials by Frank & Inoue (1966) to suggest that there was an increase in ACh sensitivity in endplate areas of partially denervated frog muscle. The miniature potential amplitude increased after partial denervation. It had previously been thought (Miledi, 1962) that the endplate area showed little change in sensitivity after denervation while non-endplate areas increased to comparable levels of sensitivity. Transmitter release can of course be combined with bath or electrophoretic application of other drugs. For instance, Fig. 5.5 shows the method of equal responses applied to demonstrate competitive inhibition of the transmitter at the nerve–muscle junction by bath-applied tubo-curarine.

Administration of drugs to the whole animal is of screening value only. The concentration of the applied drug at the active site is unknown as is the fraction of the receptor population involved. Bath application to an *in vitro* preparation offers the advantage of a known concentration of the agonist but the drug is not localized to the active receptors. In many investigations (e.g., those illustrated by Figs. 5.2, 5.3, 5.4, and 5.5) this factor is not important so long as all the receptors are available to the agonist. Although partitioning between inactive and active receptors is in an unknown proportion, the proportion can be presumed to be fixed for any given preparation, and therefore the method is of value even if an excess of drug is not made available. A major disadvantage of bath application, however, is the phenomenon of specific desensitization (p. 195) which may be defined as a loss of responsiveness of the receptors to the agonist after prolonged exposure to the agonist.

To determine the distribution of receptors on a cell, what is required is the localized application of the active agent and the quantitative measurement of the ensuing response. Delicate work has been done by applying drops of substances on to muscle fibres with a fine brush (Langley, 1907) or glass rod (Kuffler, 1943) to localized areas and measuring the subsequent contraction or depolarization, but there is no doubt that the method of choice is now the electrophoretic method combined with intracellular recording. Figure 5.7 illustrates this method as used at the nerve–muscle junction by its originator (Nastuk, 1951, 1953; Nastuk *et al.*, 1966). The substance to be tested, ACh in this case, is ejected from the tip of a fine glass micropipette by a voltage pulse, and the depolarizing response is recorded by a second microelectrode inserted in the muscle fibre at the endplate. The method depends on the compound being an ion in solution. This is true of most substances of physiological and pharmacological interest and in most cases a suitable salt can be chosen which dissociates readily in aqueous solution and in which the complementary ion is pharmacologically inert. This allows the efflux of the active ion to be controlled by the direction of the current passed through the pipette. Normally a small voltage (Fig. 5.7, bias voltage) is applied which hinders

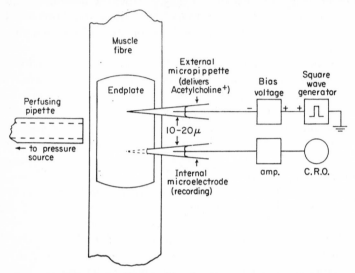

FIG. 5.7. Schematic diagram showing the experimental arrangement used when recording changes in postjunctional membrane potential produced during iontophoretic application of acetylcholine ions to its surface. The pipette to the left is used when the composition of the extracellular fluid in this zone is to be changed (Nastuk, Manthey, & Gissen, 1966).

the passage of the active ion. This ion will be actively ejected when the direction of current flow is reversed. Further information about the procedure can be found in Curtis (1963).

For assessment of relative receptor density and distribution the intracellular recording electrode and the micropipette are usually mounted on separate micromanipulators, the nature of the preparation allowing the distance between the electrodes to be measured optically.

Quantitative measurements

With the electrophoretic method it is not possible to know accurately the active drug concentration. In general the concentration will go down rapidly with increasing distance from the pipette orifice. Unfortunately, the distribution of the drug within the volume of tissue round the pipette orifice is unlikely to be uniform, due to the complex anatomy of the structures close to the synapse. The difficulty is particularly serious when electrophoretic methods are applied in the central nervous system.

In practice it is usual to measure the magnitude of the current used to eject the dissolved substance as an index of the amount of drug ejected. For instance Fig. 5.8 shows that the amplitude of the depolarization produced by electrophoretic ACh is increased as the current pulse applying the drug is increased. Figure 5.9 illustrates the use of the electrophoretic method to measure receptor distribution at nerve–muscle junctions. Relative density of receptors was estimated as the ratios of the depolarization (mV) produced by the ACh to the applying current strength (nano-coulombs,

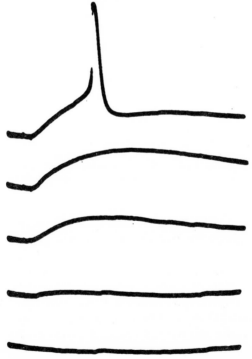

FIG. 5.8. Intracellular recording showing depolarization of the postjunctional membrane produced by iontophoretic application of successively increased amounts of acetylcholine (Nastuk *et al.*, 1966).

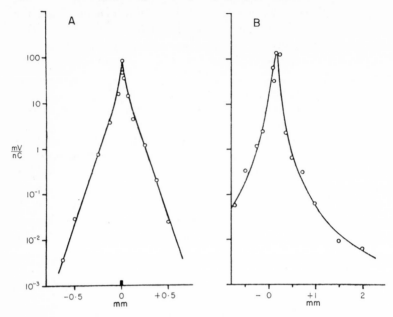

FIG. 5.9. ACh receptor distribution along a rat diaphragm muscle fibre (A) and a frog sartorius muscle fibre (B), tested by micro-electrophoresis of ACh. The abscissae show distance in mm from a recording electrode inserted near the synapse. The ordinates indicate sensitivity to ACh expressed in arbitrary units (ratio of depolarization in mV to number of coulombs of electric charge (nC) passing through the micropipette to release ACh). The approximate diameter of a synapse in diaphragm muscle fibres is indicated by the square on the horizontal axis in A (Miledi, 1962).

nC) at different points. In nerve–muscle preparations, as Fig. 5.9 shows, ACh receptors are found in greatest density in the subsynaptic region but also occur outside the synapse on the surrounding muscle membrane. The electrophoretic technique has also been used to measure the changes in receptor distribution upon denervation and reinnervation (Miledi, 1960*a*, *c*) and to exclude the possibility of changes in receptor density in myasthenia gravis (Dahlback, Elmqvist, Johns, & Radner, 1961). It will be noted that this method reveals the areas in which there are receptors (distribution) and their apparent sensitivity. The studies of Miledi and his collaborators indicate that apparent sensitivity may be equated with number of receptors, so that receptor density is a more appropriate term than apparent sensitivity.

It appears that the chemosensitive area depends on the state of innervation. Taking the specific case of the nerve–muscle junction it is found that foetal muscle and muscles deprived of their nerve supply or poisoned with botulinum toxin have ACh receptors uniformly distributed over the membrane. After birth, and upon reinnervation of denervated or botulinum toxin poisoned muscle, the 'receptor area' shrinks to a focus (Fig. 5.9) with the maximum density inside an area of 0·5 mm (rat, Fig. 5.9A) to 2 mm (frog, Fig. 5.9B) diameter around the subsynaptic region (Ginetzinsky & Shamarina, 1942; Axelsson & Thesleff, 1959; Miledi, 1960a, b, c; Thesleff, 1960; Diamond & Miledi, 1962).

It has become customary to demonstrate that receptors are on the outside of the membrane by showing that an electro- phoretically applied agent is ineffective if applied intracellularly in a dose which was effective when applied from the extracellular position (del Castillo & Katz, 1955a). Some caution should be used in applying this criterion for it has been argued that the lack of effect may be due not to the extracellular position of the recep- tors, but to the inactivation of substances injected inside cells due to their combination with cell constituents (Clark, 1937; Shapo- valov, 1963).

Application of kinetic equations

In order to use the kinetic equations previously discussed, it is necessary to have some measure of drug concentration, at all points where it is active, as well as the biological response. Moreover, it is implicit in the equations that the receptor drug complex is always in an equilibrium state. Responses must therefore be measured at equilibrium, i.e., when the substance has diffused to its site of action and the equilibrium concentrations have been achieved.

The electrophoretic method of application, while it can be used to obtain kinetic data, is unsatisfactory if the receptor area is large compared with the receptor area in the vicinity of the micro- pipette. Such a situation obtains at the vertebrate nerve–muscle junction (Fig. 5.10) where as the amount of drug applied is increased (perhaps above that amount saturating the local recep- tors) distant receptors are progressively activated. Because of their distance, their response is delayed, producing changes in the ampli- tude and form of the response which do not directly add to the

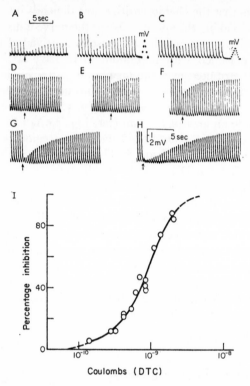

FIG. 5.10. Determination of receptor properties by electrophoretic application of ACh and *d*-tubocurarine (DTC). A–C, effect of constant DTC pulses on different amplitudes of depolarization. DTC pulses (20 msec duration, approx. 4×10^{-10} C) were applied at moments marked by arrows. The records in A, B, and C show carbachol potentials obtained with pulses of three different intensities, largest in C (note the smaller mV scale). The degree of inhibition diminishes as the strength of the depolarizing pulse increases. D–H, inhibition of ACh potentials by DTC pulses. Two separate pipettes were used. ACh pulses: approx. 5×10^{-11} C, 3 msec duration. DTC: single pulses of 0·14 sec were applied at moments marked by arrows; the following pulse strengths were used ($\times 10^{-10}$ C): D, 3·3; E, 4·2; F, 6·1; G, 21·0; H. 2×21. I, relation between strength and effect of DTC pulses. From the experiment illustrated in D–H, using separate ACh and DTC pipettes. Abscissae: coulomb quantity of DTC pulses, on $\log_{10}$ scale. Ordinates: percentage inhibition of ACh potential (ACh pulse approx. 5×10^{-11} C, producing 5 mV depolarization) (Del Castillo & Katz, 1957*a*).

initial local effect. Dose–response curves are thus unreliable. For the same reason an inhibitor applied in a constant concentration will have a lesser effect as the agonist concentration is raised, simply because the agonist is now affecting receptors remote from the site of inhibitory action (Fig. 5.10A–C). Increasing concentrations of a competitive inhibitor applied against a background of the agonist (Fig. 5.10D–H) will be increasingly effective; however, the agonist is displaced from a fixed number of active receptors and in this case the use of the kinetic method seems justified. Indeed as Fig. 5.10I shows, a typical S-shaped curve results when the curare concentration, expressed as the logarithm of the applied current, is plotted against the depression of the effect of ACh pulses, expressed as a percentage of the maximum depression.

In the central nervous system the same difficulties may not always be operative. For example, kinetic equations could be applied to the relationship between the amount of drug applied and extracellularly recorded spike frequency. The difficulty in these studies is of course the location of the receptors. Spikes could be generated by pre-junctional or extra-junctional actions, but provided receptors were involved, kinetic constants could be derived. Other techniques such as intracellular records of responses must be used to distinguish between these possibilities (see e.g., Curtis, 1963).

It has already been noted that there are basic difficulties if in applying kinetic equations the relationship of the measured response to the primary event is not known. Ideally, it would be best to deal with the primary response, e.g., in the case of ACh liberated by nerve impulses, this would be the conductance change or the endplate potential, rather than action potentials or muscle contraction. This procedure avoids ambiguity in the nature of the response. For example, the local anaesthetic drug procaine affects both sub- and postsynaptic receptors (Furukawa, 1957; Maeno, 1966; Shanes *et al.*, 1959; Taylor, 1959) probably effecting threshold as well as drug–receptor interaction and therefore by measuring procaine effects on muscle contraction, one measures the resultant of both types of action.

DESENSITIZATION

Desensitization may be operationally defined as a decrease in the response elicited by an agonist following prior administration of the same agent (specific desensitization) or another agent (non-specific desensitization). The phenomenon is a special variety of tachyphylaxis, the term used to describe the experience of finding that a dose of a drug given shortly after a preceding equal dose of the same drug has an effect which is smaller than the effect elicited by the first dose. This may happen even if the effect induced by the preceding dose has already disappeared.

Desensitization is best known at the nerve–muscle junction. For instance, early investigators of ACh action found that when ACh was first applied to the synaptic region of muscle, it caused contraction, and later applications were ineffective (e.g., Buchthal & Lindhart, 1937). An explanation for this effect was found by Fatt (1950) who reported that at the frog synapse the depolarization produced by high doses of ACh was not well maintained and could not be restored by addition of further ACh. Investigations by Thesleff and his colleagues using electrophoretic application of ACh or its analogues indicate that desensitization might be explained by the formation of intermediate complexes after the initial interaction of ACh and its receptor (Thesleff, 1955*a*, *b*; Katz & Thesleff, 1957*b*; Axelsson & Thesleff, 1958). Alternatively Paton (1961) suggests an explanation based on the kinetics of receptor interaction.

The phenomenon of desensitization is of experimental importance in that drug doses have to be separated by an experimentally determined time interval at which the doses will give equivalent effect.

It should be noted that desensitization, like many other membrane phenomena, is apparently influenced by the cations in the vicinity of the synapse. At the frog nerve–muscle junction *in vitro*, increasing the calcium concentration increases the speed of onset of desensitization and this action is antagonized by increasing the sodium concentration (Manthey, 1966). Furthermore, while desensitization has been described in the course of *in vitro* experiments at the nerve–muscle junction, similar experiments at the mammalian nerve–muscle junction *in vivo* revealed no desensitization (Maclagan, 1962) raising the possibility that the phenomenon appears as the result of the poorly understood but apparently inevitable deterioration of *in vitro* preparations.

Another question which may be of practical importance at a particular synapse is whether the release of transmitter by nerve impulses causes desensitization of the transmitter receptors. For instance, at the vertebrate neuromuscular junction ACh applied electrophoretically for 1–2 msec did not have a desensitizing effect although amounts of ACh producing a depolarization as little as that of a miniature potential did desensitize if maintained for longer periods (3–6 msec). It was, therefore, suggested that de-sensitization might develop during normal synaptic activity (Axelsson & Thesleff, 1958). In conformity with this idea, Thesleff (1959) reported evidence of desensitization at the mamma-lian synapse after a short train of e.p.p.s. The preparation he used, however, paralysed as it was by immersion in a solution with a high NaCl, is prone to spontaneous movement and the response to ionophoretically applied ACh is very sensitive to the positioning of the electrode with respect to the endplate area. When Thesleff's experiments were repeated at frog and rat nerve–muscle junctions by Otsuka, Endo, & Nonomura (1962), they found this movement was the most probable cause of the reported effect. In their hands the response to ionophoretic ACh in the rat nerve muscle *in vitro* (Fig. 5.11) after repetitive nerve stimulation was the same whether the e.p.p. was depressed (Fig. 5.11A, E) or facilitated (Fig.

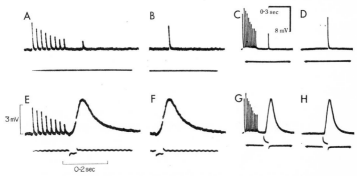

FIG. 5.11. A demonstration that desensitization is not the cause of depression of synaptic potential amplitudes. A, B, E, F. Endplate potentials and potentials in response to electrophoretic application of ACh, recorded from a rat motor endplate treated with *d*-tubo-curarine 5×10^{-7}. In each record the upper trace is the intracellular record and the lower trace the current through the ACh pipette. A, Endplate potential, and E, ACh potential, 0·08 sec after repetitive stimulation. B and F, the endplate and ACh potentials 1·9 sec after repetitive stimulation. Eight conditioning nerve volleys at 50/sec were given every 3·6 sec. Resting potential was 59 mV, and monitor calibration 3 mV = $9·6 \times 10^{-8}$ A. C, D, G, H, a similar experiment at a frog motor endplate. C, G, 0·18 sec and D, H, 10 sec after repetitive stimulation. Conditioning stimuli were given every 20 sec. Resting potential was 80 mV. Monitor calibration was 8 mV = $1·9 \times 10^{-7}$ A (Otsuka, Endo, & Nonomura, 1962).

5.11B, F). In the frog, similarly, there was no relation between changes in e.p.p. amplitude (Fig. 5.11C, D) and the ACh potentials generated electrophoretically at the same intervals after conditioning stimuli (Fig. 5.11G, H). Moreover, Otsuka *et al.* (1962) also observed that the depression of e.p.p. amplitude after a brief train of stimuli was increased by raising the $CaCl_2$ concentration of the bathing medium, but unaltered by the presence of an anticholinesterase. This implies that the depression depended on the amount of ACh released, not the amount reaching the receptors. It has in any case been directly demonstrated that the depression of e.p.p.s produced by prolonged stimulation as well as the depression found after a single conditioning stimulus is due to a presynaptic cause—a reduction in quantal content (del Castillo & Katz, 1954*c*; Thies, 1965; Elmqvist & Quastel, 1965*b*). It may be concluded that in the curarized or Mg-treated nerve–muscle preparations desensitization is not a normal synaptic effect, but it remains an open question whether it might occur under conditions when neither transmitter release nor postsynaptic response to ACh is depressed.

At other synapses, desensitization has been demonstrated in response to synaptic activation. Curtis & Ryall (1966), for instance, observed that if Renshaw interneurones were activated by maximal ventral root stimulation via the motoneurone axon collaterals, which are evidently cholinergic, there is a reduction in sensitivity to electrophoretically applied ACh. Although the synchronous activation of all, or nearly all, cholinergic inputs would not occur physiologically, this observation indicates that desensitization should not be discarded as a possible mechanism by which a synaptic potential is terminated.

TERMINATION OF TRANSMITTER ACTION

It has been calculated that at many synapses diffusion alone would remove the transmitter from the vicinity of the receptors in a time sufficient to account for the observed decay of transmitter action (Ogston, 1955; Eccles & Jaeger, 1957). Presumably to prevent undesirable side-effects at other sites, diffusion is supplemented by mechanisms for permanent transmitter removal. Two different mechanisms are known in some detail—enzymatic destruction and active uptake of the transmitter into the terminals. The questions of interest to investigators are likely to be (1) At a given synapse, what is the mechanism of transmitter removal? and (2) If the mechanism is known, what signs indicate interference with that mechanism? These questions will be considered in connection with the two known mechanisms, but it must be emphasized that electrophysiological analysis may require supplementation by, or be secondary to, biochemical and histological investigations.

Enzymatic destruction

This mechanism is well documented only at synapses where ACh is the transmitter (Werner & Kuperman, 1963). At vertebrate neuromuscular and ganglionic synapses, diffusion of transmitter from the synaptic region is supplemented by a hydrolytic enzyme, acetylcholinesterase (AChE), which splits ACh to choline and acetic acid. The enzyme is present in very high concentration in the subsynaptic membrane in very close proximity to the ACh receptor (Waser, 1960, 1967) and probably binds ACh in a very similar manner to the receptor. The choline moiety of the split ACh is then taken up by the nerve terminals (Perry, 1953) so that active uptake is associated with enzymatic destruction.

At these synapses, due to the cholinesterase action, the time course of the synaptic current is short compared with the time course of the synaptic potential and the time constant of the falling phase of the synaptic potential is similar to that of the post-synaptic membrane. It is natural to conclude then that a rapidly terminated action of the transmitter is indicative of enzymatic destruction, but this concept awaits further support.

Interference with enzymatic destruction (produced usually by drugs inhibiting cholinesterase) should be suspected if the amplitude and time course of synaptic potentials is increased by the experimental procedure (Eccles *et al.*, 1941, 1942; Eccles & MacFarlane, 1949; Fatt & Katz, 1951). This prolongation of ACh action in the absence of AChE can be directly demonstrated in voltage clamp experiments (Fig. 5.12) in which the synaptic current will be found to increase in a similar manner to the e.p.p. Similarly the potential produced by an electrophoretic ejection of ACh (Fig. 5.13A, upper record) will be increased in amplitude and time course if the injection is preceded by exhibition of an anti-cholinesterase (Fig. 5.13, upper record E+A).

Other causes of an increase in amplitude and prolongation of

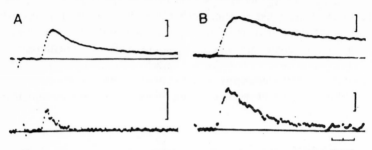

Fig. 5.12. Assessment of AChE inhibition by the voltage clamp technique. A shows endplate potential (above) and endplate current (below) recorded from a curarized frog sartorius preparation. B shows the endplate potential and endplate current from the same synapse in the presence of curare and 1×10^{-5} g/ml physostigmine. Note the increased amplitude and prolonged time course of the e.p.p. in the presence of the anticholinesterase and the associated great increase in endplate current caused by the prolongation of ACh action. Voltage scale: 2 mV. Current scale: 1×10^{-7} A. Time scale: 2 msec. Temperature 18°C (Takeuchi & Takeuchi, 1959).

time course must be excluded to establish the diagnosis of anticholinesterase action. These alternatives include an increase in the membrane resistance and prolongation of the conductance change produced by the transmitter by a direct action on the subsynaptic conductance mechanism rather than an action exerted through the transmitter receptor. This latter mechanism appears to be the means by which ether prolongs the time course of e.p.p.s at the frog nerve–muscle junction (Karis, Gissen, & Nastuk, 1966). An increased release of transmitter, such as is produced by the application of a hyperpolarizing current to nerve terminals, increases the amplitude and prolongs the rise time, but does not prolong the falling phase of synaptic potentials (Hubbard & Willis, 1962). Indeed it has recently been shown that many anticholinesterases increase quantal release as well as having an anticholinesterase action at higher concentrations (Blaber & Christ, 1967).

Proof of an anticholinesterase action can be obtained in two ways:

(1) By pretreating the preparation with a known anticholinesterase in a concentration adequate for complete anticholinesterase inhibition. Any anticholinesterase effect upon e.p.p.s or electrophoretically injected ACh should now be occluded, whereas a postsynaptic or direct subsynaptic effect would still be evident. In practice an anticholinesterase drug may now exhibit other

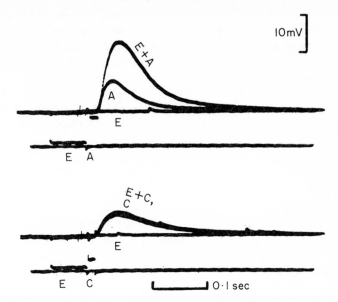

FIG. 5.13. Proof of anticholinesterase action. The upper record shows the depolarization of the subsynaptic region of a frog motor endplate produced by electrophoretic application of ACh alone (A) and preceded by a pulse of edrophonium (E + A). In the lower record the depolarization produced by carbachol alone (C) and preceded by edrophonium (E + C) are compared. In each record three traces were superimposed. 10 mV calibration = 6·7 × 10^{-8} A (Katz & Thesleff, 1957c).

actions. For instance, Katz & Thesleff (1957c) found that when the anticholinesterase effect of edrophonium was occluded by pretreatment of their frog sartorius preparation *in vitro* with neostigmine, the edrophonium now exhibited a weak depolarizing action which was competitive with that of ACh.

Other actions of anticholinesterases may include beside subsynaptic depolarization, fascicular muscle twitching and the generation of antidromic nerve impulses when these drugs are exhibited in the vicinity of mammalian nerve terminals by intra-arterial injection (Masland & Wigton, 1940), or by local application in the whole animal (Feng & Li, 1941) or in the *in vitro* preparation (Van der Meer & Meeter, 1956; Barstad, 1962). The experiments of Hubbard, Schmidt, & Yokota (1965) indicate that there are presynaptic ACh receptors which initiate presynaptic depolarization and that anticholinesterases such as prostigmine can also cause a presynaptic depolarization.

(2) By measuring the depolarization produced by stable ACh analogues such as carbachol, which are not destroyed by AChE, in the presence and absence of the presumed anticholinesterase. Katz & Thesleff (1957c), for instance, found that depolarization produced by electrophoretically applied carbachol (Fig. 5.13, lower trace C) was not affected by pretreatment with edrophonium in concentrations having an anticholinesterase action (Fig. 5.13, lower trace E + C), whereas the depolarization produced by an ACh pulse was increased by similar pretreatment (Fig. 5.13, upper trace, compare A + E and A).

Active uptake of transmitter

It has recently been found that at synapses which release noradrenaline (norepinephrine), transmitter action is terminated by active takeup of the transmitter (Brown, 1965). The uptake mechanism appears to have two portions—a presynaptic membrane mechanism which transports the transmitter into the terminal and another mechanism by which the transmitter is taken up from the terminal cytoplasm on or into the presynaptic vesicles. Each portion has its pharmacology. For instance, reserpine blocks the vesicular uptake mechanism strongly while the imipramine group of drugs block the membrane uptake mechanism (Carlsson, 1966; Kopin, 1966). The importance of uptake mechanisms has been further reinforced by the finding that active uptake is the mechanism by which gamma-aminobutyric acid (GABA) action is terminated at the crustacean inhibitory nerve–muscle synapse (Iversen & Kravitz, 1966).

At adrenergic synapses the time course of synaptic potentials is characteristically longer than can be accounted for by the membrane time constant (Hashimoto, Holman, & Tille, 1966). Unfortunately the actual time course of transmitter action is unknown and it is very probable that the time course of the recorded potential is prolonged because of the electrotonic spread of potentials through the electrical coupling between cells in smooth and cardiac muscle, with consequent exaggeration of low-frequency voltage components. If a test agent produces a block of nervous transmission while spontaneous potentials can still be recorded, the spontaneous potentials being reduced in frequency and/or amplitude, a presynaptic action should be suspected. A further pointer to presynaptic action, if block of transmission is not complete, is a more rapid than normal decrease in synaptic potential amplitude upon repetitive stimulation (Burnstock & Holman, 1962*b*, 1964, 1966). Electrophysiological investigation may thus suggest a presynaptic locus of drug action, but proof that this action is actually interference with transmitter uptake must rest on other forms of investigation. Evidently interference with transmitter uptake should produce effects similar to interference with transmitter synthesis. The fluorescence method of staining noradrenaline in nerve terminals (Falck, 1962) shows that in both cases depletion of noradrenaline in terminals occurs, the effect being more marked for synthesis blockade than for inhibition of uptake (Malmfors, 1964).

THE CONDUCTANCE CHANGE

Combination of transmitter and receptor initiates a change in conductance of the subsynaptic membrane. If the conductance change is for ions with equilibrium potentials removed from the membrane potential, the resultant ion movement moves the membrane potential towards a new level characteristic of the combined ion species. There is evidence (Takeuchi, 1963*a*; Maeno, 1966) that different ion species may move through different membrane channels. Investigation of conductance changes may thus involve:

(1) Measurement of the time course and magnitude of synaptic current.

(2) Investigation of the ion species involved in the conductance change and of their relative contributions to the total change.

(3) Measurement of the equilibrium potential for the synaptic current under various conditions.

The time course and magnitude of synaptic current

Several methods are available for measuring the time course of synaptic current. The earliest to be developed was graphical analysis of the synaptic potential, for which it is only necessary to be able to measure the potential and know the postsynaptic membrane properties. Much more accurate, elegant, and complicated is the voltage clamp. This method depends on holding the membrane potential at a preset value during synaptic activity by applying an opposite current equal to that generating the synaptic potential. This current is injected back into the cell by means of an electronic feedback system. This current can be monitored directly and is equal and opposite to that which would otherwise generate the synaptic potential, and thus a record of the magnitude and time course of the synaptic current can be obtained. A fair approximation of the synaptic current may also be derived from extracellular recordings of the synaptic potential.

The graphic method, used by Eccles and his collaborators in their analysis of the endplate potential of frog muscle (Eccles *et al.*, 1941) and by Eccles (1943) in his analysis of synaptic potentials from ganglia, depends on drastic simplifying assumptions. It is assumed that amplitude of a synaptic potential (V) at any time t increases at a rate dV/dt which is proportional to the intensity of transmitter action (x) and simultaneously decays exponentially with the time constant (τm) of the membrane. Then at any time t

$$dV/dt = x - V/\tau m$$

of which V, τm, and dV/dt are known and therefore x can be calculated. By this method a fair approximation was obtained of the time course of the synaptic current directly measured later by the voltage-clamp technique. The method neglects the conductance change in the subsynaptic region which would alter the time constant of the cell and also is appropriate only for non-cable-like structures in which exponential charging and discharging is to be expected. Nevertheless it appears capable of detecting gross variations in synaptic current such as, for instance, occur when the temperature of the synaptic region is lowered (Eccles *et al.*, 1941;

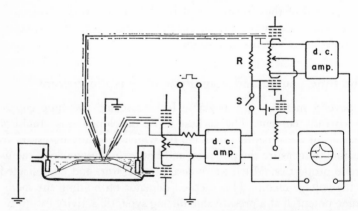

FIG. 5.14. Schematic diagram of voltage clamp as applied to frog muscle fibres by Takeuchi & Takeuchi (1959). R indicates resistor for current recording (0·5–5 MΩ). S indicates a switch.

Takeuchi & Takeuchi, 1959). There are two technical difficulties. One is that synaptic potentials vary considerably in amplitude (Chapter 4). Some sort of average potential must therefore be used for the calculation. In the original applications only extra-cellular records were available and the averaging thus took place at the recording site. With intracellular recording it would clearly be an advantage to have available a computer of average transients. The second difficulty lies in the measurement of dV/dt at any time t. This difficulty can be avoided by putting the potential

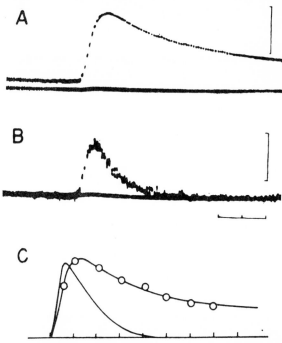

FIG. 5.15. The voltage-clamp method of recording synaptic current. A, e.p.p. recorded intracellularly from a frog sartorius muscle fibre paralysed by addition of 3×10^{-6} g/ml d-tubocurarine Cl' to the bathing medium. B, endplate current I syn) recorded from the same synapse using a feedback circuit. The lower beam shows the membrane potential recorded simultaneously with the current. Voltage scale: 5 mV. Current scale: 1×10^{-7} A. Temperature 17°C. C, superimposed tracings of e.p.p. and endplate current recorded from same synapse. Circles indicate potential change calculated from endplate current, assuming membrane time constant to be 25 msec and effective resistance 320 kΩ, peak amplitude of e.p.p. being 8·9 mV and that of endplate current $1·4 \times 10^{-7}$ A. Time msec (Takeuchi & Takeuchi, 1959).

through a differentiating circuit and using this differentiated record to measure dV/dt.

The voltage-clamp method, as Fig. 5.14 shows, requires that two electrodes be inserted into the cell in the vicinity of the synapse, one to record the membrane potential, the other to pass current. As the figure indicates, fairly elaborate electronic equipment is needed. The power and elegance of the method, however, is convincingly shown in Fig. 5.15 which shows the endplate potential (Fig. 5.15A) in the absence of the clamping action and in Fig. 5.15B the synaptic current recorded simultaneously with the membrane potential. In Fig. 5.15C the endplate potential has been reconstructed from the observed current using Hodgkin & Rushton's (1946) cable equation and the known values for time constant and membrane effective resistance of the frog postsynaptic membrane, which is a very convincing demonstration of the power of this technique. This technique has also been applied with some difficulty to spinal motoneurones (see Chapter 6) (Terzuolo & Araki, 1961).

An alternative method, advocated by Maeno (1966), is simply to record the extracellular potential change during synaptic activity. This is generated by the current passing across the extracellular resistance provided by the close contact of microelectrode and cell membrane. Maeno (1966) showed that at the frog nerve–muscle junction the extracellular e.p.p. indeed has a similar time course to the endplate current recorded during voltage-clamp experiments (Fig. 5.15).

MEASUREMENT OF THE INDIVIDUAL IONIC CONDUCTANCES AND THEIR RELATIVE PROPORTIONS

Exact measurement of individual conductances is at present only possible at peripheral synapses where the ions involved and their equilibrium potential are known with some precision. At the frog nerve–muscle junction, for instance, at normal levels of the membrane potential much the larger fraction of the ionic current is carried by sodium ions. The magnitude of the synaptic current determined from voltage-clamp or extracellular e.p.p. measurement will therefore be an approximate measure of ΔG_{Na}. Other causes of variation of the extracellular e.p.p. amplitude such as changes in quantal content would have to be excluded before the measurements could be taken as reliable indicators of the conductance change.

At the same junction ΔG_K can be estimated from the short-circuit effect of synaptic activity upon action potentials generated near the subsynaptic area (Fig. 5.16B). A convenient definition of the magnitude of the short-circuit action (Maeno, 1966) is the reduction of the overshoot of the action potential of a muscle fibre when synaptic activity is superimposed on the action potential. It is well established that the overshoot is due to entry of Na ions into muscle fibres and that the sodium equilibrium potential

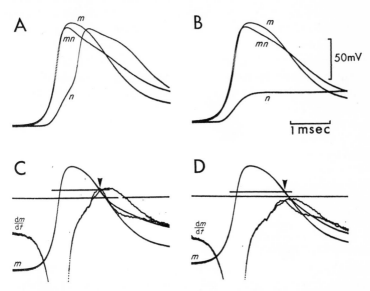

FIG. 5.16. A, B. The determination of the potassium conductance change during synaptic activity. C, D, The poor man's voltage clamp. All at the frog motor endplate in presence (B, D) and absence (A, B) of 10^{-4} procaine. In A and B, the direct muscle action potential (m) and direct muscle action potential with endplate potential alone (n) are shown on the same time base. Procaine depressed the endplate potential amplitude (B) without affecting the reduction in amplitude of the m spike when the endplate potential was superimposed on it (mn).

In C and D direct muscle action potentials (m) with and without endplate potentials are photographed simultaneously with their derivatives (dm/dt). The time at which the effect of the endplate potential on the action potential was reversed (arrows in C and D) was measured from the record of dm/dt. The equilibrium potential (short horizontal bar in C and D) was obtained from the record of the action potential (m) at this moment. The equilibrium is decreased in procaine. The long horizontal line in C and D marks the zero level of voltage. The voltage (50 mV) and time calibration (1 msec) apply to all records (Maeno, 1966).

is slightly more positive than the membrane potential at the peak of the action potential. An increase in ΔG_{Na} thus tends to increase the overshoot. On the other hand an increase in ΔG_K decreases the overshoot since the active membrane potential and the equilibrium potential for potassium are far apart. Consequently, the overshoot of action potentials is reduced in vertebrate muscle when they are superimposed on synaptic activity (Fatt & Katz, 1951; Muscholl, 1957) and this reduction affords a measure of ΔG_K.

In the central nervous system conductance changes attributed to specific ions can be examined by injecting the ion intracellularly by the electrophoretic method and investigating the effect upon synaptic potentials. In motoneurones and many other CNS cells, for instance, Cl^- injection regularly converts inhibitory post-synaptic potentials from a hyperpolarizing to a depolarizing response (Eccles, 1964, p. 174) from which it is inferred that the inhibitory transmitter makes the subsynaptic area highly permeable to Cl^-. Raising the intracellular Cl^- concentration presumably converts the normal net inward flux to a net outward and therefore depolarizing flux.

MEASUREMENT OF EQUILIBRIUM POTENTIAL

Direct method

The voltage-clamp method of recording synaptic current can be used to determine equilibrium potentials by clamping the membrane potential at various values and measuring the membrane current. Figure 5.17 shows the membrane current as a function of clamped membrane potential at a frog nerve–muscle junction. In this experiment the determinations were carried out in the presence of 3×10^{-6} g tubocurarine/ml (Fig. 5.17, open circles) and then repeated in the presence of 4×10^{-6} g tubocurarine/ml (Fig. 5.17, filled circles). The slopes of the two lines are different but when extrapolated each line crosses the abscissa at the same point—the equilibrium potential. The results thus indicate that tubocurarine decreased the magnitude of the conductance change produced by ACh but did not influence the equilibrium potential.

An important result of the voltage-clamp technique is that it validates technically easier means of obtaining values for the equilibrium potential. This result is illustrated in Fig. 5.18, which shows the synaptic current and endplate potential as a function of membrane potential (abscissa). Both current and potential are

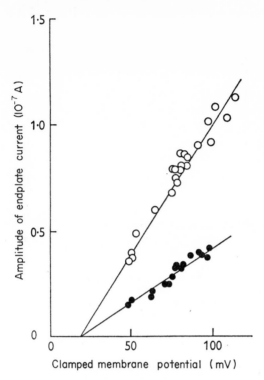

FIG. 5.17. Measurement of the equilibrium potential at a curarized frog endplate by the voltage-clamp method. Open circles show results obtained in the presence of 3×10^{-6} g/ml tubocurarine and filled circles results from the same endplate in the presence of 4×10^{-6} g/ml tubocurarine (Takeuchi & Takeuchi, (1960*a*).

approximately linearly related to the membrane potential and by extrapolation they become zero at a common point, the equilibrium potential. The voltage at which the potential change is reversed is thus a valid measure of the equilibrium potential. This fact has been taken advantage of in two ways. Firstly, methods of estimating equilibrium potentials have been developed (Fig. 6.13) in which two electrodes are used, one to pass current and the other to record. There is no clamping of the membrane potential, however, the potential being merely held at various steady levels by continuous passage of current from the current-passing electrode. The synaptic potential is then evoked and its magnitude at various membrane potentials assessed. In the experiment illustrated, the membrane potential of a cat motoneurone was

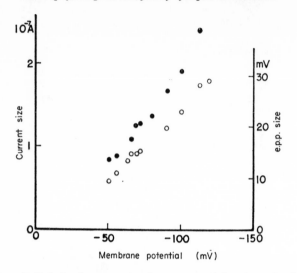

FIG. 5.18. Relation between membrane potential and amplitude of endplate potential and endplate current obtained from same endplate. Abscissa: membrane potential in mV. Ordinates: amplitude of endplate potential (mV) and endplate current (10^{-7} A). Open circles: e.p.p.s. Full circles: endplate currents (Takeuchi & Takeuchi, 1959).

varied by the steady passage of current from one barrel of a double-barrel microelectrode. The inhibitory postsynaptic potential elicited at various membrane potentials (Fig. 6.13A–G) and recorded by the other barrel of the electrode reversed in sign at about -82 mV (Fig. 6.13E) indicating that the equilibrium potential for the synaptic potential had this value.

A second method which depends on the relationship between synaptic potential amplitude and membrane potential to determine the equilibrium potential may be termed the poor man's voltage clamp. This method uses an action potential to shift the membrane potential. As del Castillo & Katz (1954e) showed, e.p.p.s can be evoked at the same time as the depolarizing phase of an action potential evoked by direct stimulation. The superposition of e.p.p. and spike shown in Fig. 5.16 can be adjusted by altering the interval until the e.p.p. is reversed (arrows in Fig. 5.16C, D). The equilibrium potential is then determined as the membrane potential at which the effect of endplate activity on the action potential is reversed. Maeno (1966) made this procedure more precise by recording action potentials through a differentiating circuit so that the membrane potential at which endplate activity was reversed could be accurately measured.

IONIC EFFECTS UPON RECEPTOR ACTIVITY

Many drugs with potent actions at synapses, including ACh, are cations at physiological pH. It seems very likely that their receptors are anionic; for instance, the active centre of AChE contains an anionic group (Wilson & Bergman, 1950*a*, *b*; Wilson, 1952). Such anionic receptor sites would be expected to have some affinity for the inorganic cations in the bathing fluids and indeed effects of this sort have been detected in receptor kinetics and in conductance measurements. For instance, Jenkinson (1960) reported that magnesium and calcium reduced the affinity of the ACh receptor at the frog nerve–muscle junction for tubocurarine. Takeuchi (1963*b*) found that increased extracellular concentrations of calcium and magnesium ions affected the e.p.p. equilibrium potential, probably by decreasing ΔG_{Na}. It may be noted, however, that unless there is a concomitant lowering of the extracellular sodium concentration, the effects upon V_{tr} are not large in the range of calcium and magnesium concentrations normally used to block neuromuscular transmission.

6

THE ELECTROPHYSIOLOGY OF SYNAPTIC
TRANSMISSION IN THE CENTRAL
NERVOUS SYSTEM

THE previous chapters have dealt with the general features of the investigation of synaptic transmission across peripheral junctions. In the remainder of this monograph an overall strategy for the study of synaptic transmission and its organization in the central nervous system (CNS) will be discussed. Although a large body of knowledge is now available regarding the electrophysiology of invertebrate CNS, most of the data to be presented here will deal with vertebrate nervous system.

The study of the electrophysiology of the CNS has been approached in two general ways, (1) by recording the electrical activity generated by single neurones within the CNS, or (2) by recording the compound electrical potential differences generated by the synchronous activation of large assemblies of neurones or their processes. The latter are referred to as field potentials and are the conjunctive product of synaptic and action currents.

Recordings of the activity of single cells are carried out by means of fine microelectrodes which, by virtue of their proximity to a given neural element, can 'isolate' its activity from that generated by neighbouring neurones. This approach can be sub-divided into two broad classes: intracellular recordings (where the cell to be studied is impaled by a fine pipette) and extracellular recordings (where the pipette is outside but very near the nerve cell). In the former case the electrical potential generated across the membrane of the neurone is measured between the interior of a cell (Fig. 6.1 NC) and the extracellular media. The measurements are, in fact, carried out between the electrically conductive electrolyte solution which fills the micropipette lodged in the interior of the cell, and an indifferent electrode in the extracellular fluid (Fig. 6.1A). The voltage measured by the voltmeter of Fig. 6.1 is generated across the resistance of the membrane

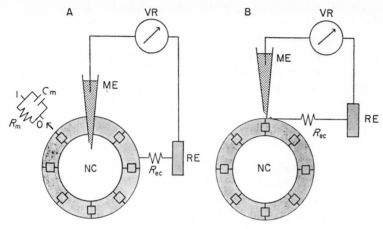

FIG. 6.1. Schematic drawing of general arrangement for recording single cell potentials. A. Recording arrangement for intracellular potential measurement. The tip of the microelectrode (ME) is depicted in the interior of the nerve cell (NC). The potential generated by ionic current flow across the RC components of the membrane (see enlarged area of A) and the resistance of the extracellular fluid (R_{ec}) is measured as the potential difference between the tip of the microelectrode and the indifferent electrode RE by means of the voltmeter, VR. B. Extracellular single cell potentials; in this case the potentials are recorded between the microelectrode tip in the extracellular media and the indifferent electrode and are produced by the transmembrane current flowing across the resistance of the extracellular fluid.

R_m of the impaled cell in series with the resistance of the extracellular medium R_{ec} between the cell and the reference electrode, RE. The extracellular potentials (Fig. 6.1B) are recorded in the immediate vicinity of a cell and are generated solely across the resistance of the extracellular media between the microelectrode and the reference electrode, RE, as current flows across the cell's membranes.

The general description of the properties of field potentials will be treated in the next chapter.

INTRACELLULAR RECORDINGS FROM CENTRAL NERVOUS NEURONES

The study of the ultrastructure of the CNS has demonstrated, as originally postulated by His (1890), that the central nervous system is a highly organized assembly of cells and not a continuous syncytium as originally suggested by the reticularists (Golgi,

1907). Two general types of elements are found in this system, the neurones (Waldeyer, 1891) or nerve cells, and the neuroglia or 'supporting cells'. Although both types of cells are directly concerned with the functioning of the nervous system, the transmission and integration of the information relayed by nerve impulses is, as far as is known at present, the concern of the neurones.

The neurone

Morphologically, the neurone is a complete anatomical unit composed of a nucleus, cytoplasm, and a surrounding membrane which envelops the cell constituents and delimits its boundaries with respect to the other elements in the nervous tissue. The many varieties of neurones differ from each other in relation to their shape and size, their distribution, number, and the spread of their processes. The *'typical'* neurone can be described as having a soma or enlarged portion containing the nucleus, and a series of processes called dendrites and axons. The dendrites stem from the body of the cell and extend radially in all directions, while the axons (usually only one per cell) stem from the soma or from a large dendrite and terminate at varying distances in contact with other nerve cells, with muscle fibres, or with gland cells.

In actual fact the spatial organization of neurones shows considerable variation; they can be monopolar, bipolar, or multipolar depending upon the number of processes arising from them. As regards the shape of the soma, there is a continuous range of variation ranging from spherical to a completely irregular polyhedral shape. The diameter of a neuronal soma varies from a few microns, as in the case of the granule cells in the cerebellar cortex, to close to a tenth of a millimetre for the large vestibular cells of the medulla oblongata and the motoneurones in the anterior horn of the spinal cord of some mammals (Ramón y Cajal, 1911). These dimensions are of practical interest to the neurophysiologist since intracellular recordings are, for purely technical reasons, very difficult in cells having somas of less than 10 μ in diameter, for which reason most intracellular studies are biased towards the investigation of the large cell population of a given neuronal cluster.

Before developing the subject of intracellular recording, it must be kept in mind that the term 'extracellular record' remains valid, although it now appears that the only extracellular space normally present in the CNS is the 200 Å gap which separates the different cells in the nervous tissue (de Robertis, Gerschenfeld, & Wald, 1960; de Robertis & Gerschenfeld, 1961; Luse, 1960; Palay, 1958, 1967; van Harreveld, Crowell, & Malhotra, 1965). The recording probe (which for intracellular recording is generally a micro-pipette with a tip of 0·5 μ or less in diameter and a d.c. resistance of 10 to 100 MΩ) in effect creates the extracellular space from which it records by separating and rupturing the fine structure of the CNS tissue.

A number of criteria have been developed for distinguishing intracellular recordings from those obtained from the immediate vicinity of a given neurone in the extracellular medium. These are the presence of: (1) membrane resting potential, (2) the action potentials which are rapid positive voltage transients which in general overshoot the zero membrane potential level, becoming positive to the indifferent electrode, and (3) synaptic potentials, which are slower depolarizing or hyperpolarizing deflections related in an approximately linear manner to the level of the resting potential. In the extracellular media the latter two generate potentials of the opposite polarity which can be recorded when the electrode is withdrawn from the cell (this last statement is not necessarily true for all situations as will be explained in the next chapter). In addition, in a successful intracellular penetration, the microelectrode behaves as if an RC circuit had been added to its tip (the RC values of the cell's membrane, Fig. 6.1A) such that if a square pulse of current is passed across the cell's membrane, the microelectrode will record a potential change having a time constant related to the RC value of the membrane. These different signs of intracellular recording will be considered in the above sequence.

Resting potential*

A resting potential has so far been described for all types of nerve cells studied, but it is by no means a unique characteristic of neurones. For example, Granit & Phillips (1956) have found membrane resting potentials up to -80 mV in cerebellar cortical cells believed to be neuroglia. More directly, Hild & Tasaki (1962) have demonstrated the existence of resting potentials in neuroglia grown in tissue culture. Such potentials have also been found in

* We shall limit our remarks to CNS neurones; for general comments see Chapter 2, p. 31.

glial cells of leech (Kuffler & Potter, 1964) and of the optic nerve in amphibia (Kuffler, Nicholls, & Orkand, 1966). It is therefore impossible to ascertain whether an electrode is inside a neurone simply by reference to the recording of a membrane resting potential. Furthermore, microelectrodes act as pressure transducers, with the result that a potential similar to the membrane resting potential may be recorded when the microelectrode is slightly deformed as it penetrates the tissue or as a result of movement in the preparation.

Since even in deeply anaesthetized animals a certain amount of excitatory and inhibitory background bombardment remains on most neurones and causes a continuous deviation of their potential from their resting level, no absolute membrane potential can be estimated in most CNS neurones. The background synaptic activity is of particular interest and must be considered when studying phenomena related to the resting potential of neurones in unanaesthetized animals in decerebrate or deafferented conditions.

In addition to the background bombardment, the metabolic state of the cell may influence the membrane potential, although it has been shown that during anoxia no drastic change in the membrane potential is observed (Nelson & Frank, 1963; Eccles, Løyning, & Oshima, 1966). On the other hand, since in certain cells the terminal dendrites do not seem to generate all-or-none action potentials (Eccles, 1957), it is possible for the dendrites to be continuously depolarized by synaptic impingement and thus reduce in a very gradual fashion the membrane potential at the soma. This dendritic depolarization would be especially marked during asphyxia (van Harreveld & Biersteker, 1964).

Action potential

Most of our present knowledge concerning the physiology of single cells in the central nervous system is derived from research utilizing the intracellular recording technique in the spinal motoneurones of small mammals. Intracellular action potentials from these neurones were first obtained from the lumbar region of the cat's spinal cord and were identified by their antidromic invasion following electrical stimulation of the proximal end of a severed ventral root (Brock, Coombs, & Eccles, 1952). It was immediately apparent from the records that the shapes of the intraneuronal action potentials were in several ways different from the intraneuronal action potentials obtained in a simple cylindrical axon (Hodgkin & Katz, 1949a).

The rising phase of the potential consisted of three distinctive components and the falling phase was followed by a short after-depolarization and a large after-hyperpolarization. The three-stage rising phase of the potential was attributed to the successive invasion of the different regions of the neurone. The very sound postulate that the most probable place of microelectrode penetration was the soma of the motoneurone, and that the largest trans-membrane potential was generated nearest to the recording site, led to the conclusion that the third and largest spike is generated by the soma and near-by dendritic stems of the cell (Brock, Coombs, & Eccles, 1952). The other two components which precede the large soma dendritic ('SD') spike have been postulated to arise from two other locations—the earlier and smaller (the 'M spike') representing the antidromic invasion of the axon close to the cell body, and the second (the 'IS spike') from invasion of the initial segment of the cell (Coombs, Eccles, & Fatt, 1955a). These three components are illustrated in Fig. 6.2A. The recording was obtained from a motoneurone impaled with a double-barrelled microelectrode so that current could be applied through one electrode while the potential was recorded from another. In the series of records illustrated in Fig. 6.2A the cell was at first depolarized to – 60 mV and later hyperpolarized to – 87 mV inside (Coombs, Eccles, & Fatt, 1955a). At the level of maximum hyperpolarization, the antidromic volley invaded only the axon, and thus only the small (5 mV amplitude) all-or-nothing M potential was recorded. At – 82 mV membrane potential, the second and larger (40 mV amplitude) IS action potential was observed. At a resting potential of 77–78 mV the third and largest potential, the SD spike, was evoked. The identification of these potentials with the activation of the different regions of central neurones was strongly supported by studies of the field potentials generated by a single motoneurone (Fatt, 1957)[*] but was questioned by Freygang (1958) in the case of the antidromic invasion of the lateral geniculate cells of the thalamus following stimulation of the optic nerve, and later by Freygang & Frank (1959) for the antidromic invasion of the motoneurone. Since then, however, other studies

---

[*] Although Fatt agreed with the idea that these potentials were generated by different portions of central neurones, his interpretation of the actual sites involved was different from that of Coombs *et al.* (1955a).

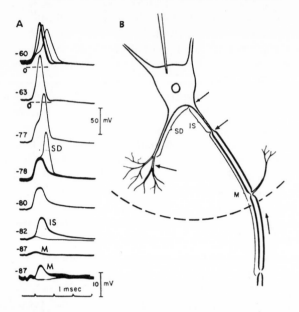

FIG. 6.2. Different types of intracellular potentials recorded in a motoneurone following antidromic activation, and their blockage by extrinsic changes of the membrane potential level. (A) The resting potential of the neurone was initially – 80 mV, and was displaced artificially to the values shown at the left of each record. The lowest record is taken at higher amplification (note voltage calibration) and the stimulus was lowered to the threshold value in order to demonstrate the all-or-none character of the M response. In (B), a schematic drawing of a neurone illustrates the site of origin of the different components shown in A. M, medulated axon and axon collateral; IS, initial segment; SD, soma dendritic region. The brackets denote the approximate portions of the cell which generate the three different spike components and the arrows their theoretical place of blockage. Voltage time calibrations are indicated. The second and third records in A demonstrate the level of overshoot of the action potential over the zero membrane potential level (dashed lines) Eccles, 1955).

by Terzuolo & Araki (1961) and Nelson & Frank (1964*a*) have confirmed the earlier views. The generation of the antidromic action potentials is best understood when the extracellular field potentials are simultaneously recorded. This particular topic will be treated in the next chapter (see p. 279).

Under normal conditions action potentials are generated orthodromically, that is, as a result of excitatory postsynaptic potentials (EPSPs) secondary to activation of their excitatory afferents (Fig.

6.3B). Action potentials can also be induced artificially by passing a current across the neurone membrane to generate a 'direct' action potential (Fig. 6.3C). The characteristic differences resulting from the mode of excitation are shown in Fig. 6.3.

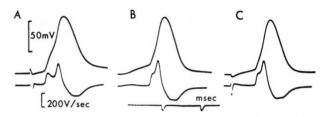

FIG. 6.3. Intracellular potentials from motoneurones generated antidromically (A), orthodromically (B), and by the direct application of current across the membrane (C). The lower traces show the electrically differentiated records to illustrate the rates of rise of the different components. Note that the IS-SD inflection is largest in the antidromically activated spike, but the firing level for the SD action potential is the same for all three forms of activation. Time and voltage and rate of rise calibrations are the same for all records (Coombs, Curtis, & Eccles, 1957).

Orthodromic action potentials were at first believed to be generated in a different manner from antidromic action potentials, since no IS–SD separation was observed on the rising phase of the orthodromic action potentials (Brock, Coombs, & Eccles, 1952). However, it was pointed out by Araki, Otani, & Furukawa (1953) that the rising phase of the orthodromic action potential in amphibian motoneurones did indeed have an IS component as in the case of the antidromic spike. These investigators therefore suggested that, as in the case of the antidromic action potential, the orthodromic activation of the motoneurone was initiated at the initial segment by synaptic depolarization conducted electronically from the soma-dendritic region of the cell.

Similar results were later obtained for the feline motoneurone (Fuortes, Frank, & Becker, 1957; Fatt, 1957; Coombs, Curtis, & Eccles, 1957; Terzuolo & Araki, 1961; and Araki & Terzuolo, 1962). Intracellular recordings from other central neurones have since confirmed that the initial segment is the site of impulse initiation for most cells (Granit & Phillips, 1956; Phillips, 1959; Kandel, Spencer, & Brinley, 1961; Purpura & Schofer, 1963). However, dendritic trigger zones have been found in the case of motoneurones undergoing chromatolytic degeneration (Eccles,

Libet, & Young, 1958), as well as in hippocampal neurones (Cragg & Hamlyn, 1955; Andersen, 1960; Spencer & Kandel 1961*b*), motor cortex neurones (Purpura & McMurtry, 1965; Purpura & Schofer, 1964) and immature cortical cells (Purpura, 1961; Purpura, Shofer, & Scarff, 1965), Purkinje cells (Eccles, Llinás, & Sasaki, 1966*b*; Llinás, Nicholson, Freeman, & Hillman, 1968; Fujita, 1968), thalamic neurones (Maekawa & Purpura, 1967) and red nucleus neurones (Maekawa & Purpura, personal communication). Two important points must be remembered in attempting analysis of this type of data. As pointed out by Bennett (1964), potentials simulating IS–SD fragmentation can be recorded from injured axons. In these cases the injury decreases the excitability of fibres at the recording site in such a manner that an SD-like component is artificially brought about by the activation of this high threshold region (Bennett & Fox, 1962; Hern, Phillips, & Porter, 1962). Secondly, it is dangerous to ascribe the first low threshold action potential evoked, by direct or orthodromic means, to generation at the axon hillock unless axonic propagation is actually demonstrable. In fact, such a component could be generated in a dendrite and then conducted electrotonically to the soma.

Direct activation of central neurones occurs whenever a current imposed between the intracellular electrode and the medium produces a reduction of the membrane potential to a certain level, known as the firing level of the cell (Araki & Otani, 1955; Coombs, Eccles, & Fatt, 1955*a*; Frank & Fuortes, 1956; Spencer & Kandel, 1961*a*; Creutzfeldt, Lux, & Nacimiento, 1964). This level, under certain circumstances, is constant regardless of the manner in which the action potential is initiated (Coombs, Eccles, & Fatt, 1955*a*; Frank & Fuortes, 1956). The method of 'direct' neuronal stimulation then allows the excitatory process of neurones to be studied in a more precise manner than by means of the antidromic or orthodromic activation, since it permits complete control over polarity, magnitude, time course, and total duration of the transmembrane potential change. An added advantage is that since only the cell under consideration is activated, errors due to field potentials or possible ephatic interactions (Washizu, 1960; Nelson, 1966; Grinnell, 1966), which can be brought about by synchronous activation of a large number of neighbouring cells in a small volume of nervous tissue, are obviated. In a similar fashion the possible interaction between afferent volleys at a presynaptic level as well as the postsynaptic nonlinear summation makes the study of excitability changes on the basis of the synaptic activation of a given cell prone to error. Finally, the method allows the electrical characteristics of the membrane, i.e., resistance and capacitance (see Chapter 3, pp. 91–103), to be measured as well as the dynamic behaviour of the excitatory process itself, i.e., accommodation and adaptation. The study of these phenomena is very relevant to an understanding of the firing characteristics of synaptically activated cells and must be measured whenever the integrative activity of the neurones is to be analysed (Granit, 1964).

Accommodation and adaptation

The term 'accommodation' was introduced by Nernst in 1908 to describe 'the reduced efficacy of a prolonged constant current or a gradually increasing current in generating action potentials from nervous tissue' (quoted from Katz, 1939). Today it seems likely that variations of accommodation may be directly correlated with the variation of the sodium inactivation rate in different cells (Hodgkin & Huxley, 1952*b*; Frankenhaeuser & Vallbo, 1965).

The early investigations of threshold depolarization in central neurones employing slowly rising currents (Araki & Otani, 1959; Frank & Fuortes, 1960) showed accommodation to be much less prominent in spinal motoneurones than in peripheral nerve. This point is of considerable theoretical interest since the accommodation process seems to be a universal characteristic of all nervous elements (Katz, 1939). It appears that a 'de-accommodating' mechanism must be present in these neurones in order to keep their firing level constant. Further studies on the accommodation of spinal motoneurones (Sasaki & Otani, 1961; Bradley & Somjen, 1961) demonstrated two types of cell responses. One type showed some accommodation to slowly rising currents and had a short-lasting after-hyperpolarization, while the other type showed almost no accommodation and had a long after-hyperpolarization. These two groups were related to the 'tonic' and 'phasic' type cell originally described in relation to their maximum firing frequency and the duration of their after-hyperpolarization (Granit, Henatsch, & Steg, 1956; Eccles, Eccles, & Lundberg, 1958). However, this differentiation of cells into two groups may not be as sharp as was first supposed, since the differences now seem to be only quantitative and not qualitative. Sasaki & Otani (1962) actually demonstrated transition from one type of response to the other, the behaviour depending on background synaptic impingement. They concluded, therefore, that this level of background activity can modulate the ability of the cell to fire repetitively. These results indeed indicate that synaptic barrage and after-hyperpolarization may have a 'de-accommodative' effect on the cells, which would explain the paucity of their accommodative process.

In support of this hypothesis is the finding of an increased accommodative tendency of motoneurones following strychnine administration (Kawai & Sasaki, 1964). Strychnine is believed to act by removing the inhibitory synaptic barrage normally present in central neurones. This conclusion is debatable, however, since strychnine is known to act also in the nonsynaptic regions of neurones and thus may have a direct action upon the electrogenic component of the cell membrane (Washizu, Bonewell, & Terzuolo, 1961).

The term 'adaptation' has been used to describe a transient state at the initiation of an abrupt depolarization in which the impulse frequency first increases and then diminishes before the cell reaches a steady firing frequency (Granit, Kernell, & Shortess, 1963). This kind of adaptation can be explained to a large extent on the basis of the current–voltage non-linearities which generate the under- and overshoot of the transmembrane potential of motoneurones shown to occur when a long-lasting current step is applied across the membrane (Araki, Ito, & Oshima, 1961).

Delayed and anomalous rectification

The term 'rectification' as used in electrophysiology denotes a nonlinearity in the current–voltage relation of cell membranes. It is simple to understand that if the membrane resistivity of a cell is fixed, action potentials could not be explained on the basis of ionic permeability changes (Hodgkin, Huxley, & Katz, 1952). The first demonstration that a conductance change accompanied the generation of action potentials was produced by Cole & Curtis (1938, 1939) in *Nitella* and in the squid giant axon. The term rectification was used by Cole (1941) to denote the departure of the electrical characteristics of a nerve membrane from that of a dynamic resistor when a voltage step is applied across this type of membrane.

Further investigation by means of the voltage-clamp technique demonstrated in the squid axon a relation between the level of membrane potential and the permeability of the membrane to certain ions (Hodgkin, Huxley, & Katz, 1952). A slow-rising, long-lasting potassium activation was described during the imposed membrane depolarization and the term 'delayed rectification' was used to designate this phenomenon in order to emphasize the delayed nature of its onset as compared to the faster sodium activation processes (Hodgkin & Huxley, 1952a). On the other hand, early studies on the electrical characteristics of motoneurone membrane showed that motoneurones exhibit on the whole an almost linear current voltage relation up to their firing levels (Coombs, Eccles, & Fatt, 1955a). Since that time, however, several cases of nonlinearity have been demonstrated in mammalian and invertebrate neurones (Ito & Oshima, 1965; Kandel & Tauc, 1966; Nelson & Frank, 1967).

Ito & Oshima (1965) found that delayed rectification occurs in motoneurones during a prolonged passage of depolarizing current. Its time course is much slower than that observed for the squid axon. More recently another form of nonlinearity has been found by Kandel & Tauc (1966) in *Aplysia* and by Nelson & Frank (1967) in some feline motoneurones. In this type of rectification a decrease of the input resistance of the cell is observed during hyperpolarization (Fig. 6.4) evoked by an inward current that is in many ways similar to the 'anomalous' rectification which is found in striated muscle fibres. In addition to the increased membrane conductance during hyperpolarization, Nelson and Frank found that a subthreshold depolarization tends to increase the resting membrane resistance. The presence of anomalous rectification was shown to explain some of the non-linearities between the amplitude of synaptic potentials and the transmembrane potential as the latter is changed artificially by means of current injection.

The ionic mechanism for delayed rectification in central neurones is still obscure. Grundfest (1966) has pointed out that rectification can occur as a result of activation of either Cl^- or K^+ ionic conductance. The increased resistance during depolarization in anomalous rectification implies, however, an inactivation of one of the ionic conductances following reduction of the cell's membrane potential (Grundfest, 1961).

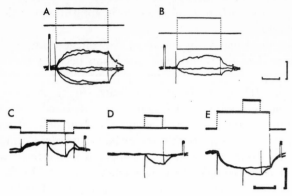

Fig. 6.4. Intracellular potentials evoked by square current pulses in motoneurones. A. Voltage displacement (lower traces) produced in a motoneurone by the application of depolarizing and hyperpolarizing currents of identical magnitude. The time constant and amplitude of the potential is similar in both directions. In B, another cell showing anomalous rectification. The potential generated by a hyperpolarizing current is smaller than the potential evoked by a similar current in the opposite direction. Membrane resistance as measured by short current pulse is larger during a depolarization (C) and smaller during hyperpolarization (E) than at resting potential level (D). Voltage calibration at the beginning of records A and B and at the end of C, D, and E, 10 mV. Time and current calibration at lower right of the two rows, 10 msec and 1×10^{-1} A (Nelson & Frank, 1967).

SYNAPTIC POTENTIALS IN VERTEBRATE CENTRAL NEURONES

In the vertebrate central nervous system, synapses can be grouped into two general categories: (1) the excitatory synapses, which generate a depolarizing potential across the postsynaptic cell; and (2) inhibitory synapses, which hyperpolarize the postsynaptic elements. These transmembrane potentials are referred to when depolarizing as 'excitatory postsynaptic potentials' or EPSPs, and when hyperpolarizing as 'inhibitory postsynaptic potentials' or IPSPs.

A number of characteristics are shared by the excitatory and the inhibitory synaptic potentials in the central neurones: (1) They are graded phenomena. Their amplitude is related to the number of presynaptic fibres activated at a given time and the amount of transmitter released at each nerve terminal. (2) They have a time course with a rise much faster than the decay, the latter being close to the time constant of the postsynaptic cell. (3) Except in the case of electrotonic junctions, the synaptic potentials are generated by ionic mechanisms which differ from those which generate action potentials and are secondary to interaction between a transmitter substance and a specialized region of the postsynaptic cell, the subsynaptic membrane. As a result the PSPs have equilibrium potentials which are related to the algebraic sum of the electromotive forces of the ion species involved in their generation. (4) Although the potentials are not actively propagated, they are electrotonically conducted along the dendrites, soma, and axon of the post synaptic neurone—their effective spread being determined by the cable properties of the postsynaptic cells, their site of origin and their initial amplitude. This implies that synaptic potentials are the result of the summation of the potential gradients produced by many small synaptic currents occurring at different sites over the postsynaptic membrane.

The intracellular potential changes evoked in motoneurones following the electrical activation of a particular set of presynaptic fibres were first recorded in cat spinal cord in a series of epoch-making studies by Brock, Coombs, & Eccles (1952). These investigators demonstrated for the first time that the synaptic activation of neurones was produced by a short-lasting depolarization (about 15 msec) which could be recorded intracellularly by means of microelectrodes and which, when large enough to reach the firing level of the cell, would evoke a full-sized action potential in the impaled cell. Also reported in the same paper was the unexpected finding that synaptic inhibition was produced, or at least accompanied by, a hyperpolarization of the postsynaptic neurone. These early recordings were taken from lumbar motoneurones, the EPSP being generated by the activation of the group 1A sensory fibres from synergistic muscles, which were known to terminate in direct synaptic contact with the motoneurones (Renshaw, 1940; Lloyd, 1943). The inhibition corresponds to the so-called 'direct inhibition' produced by the activation of 1A nerve fibres from antagonistic muscles (Lloyd, 1941). Given that most of our knowledge concerning the physiological properties of central synapses has been derived from motoneurone research, it will be used as a model central neurone.

Excitatory postsynaptic potentials (EPSPs)

Since the time of the first intracellular recordings, a large series of investigations has confirmed and enlarged the basic findings and extended them to other types of CNS elements. The early studies showed that a single electrical activation of the 1A efferent system is able to evoke a graded excitatory synaptic potential in the penetrated cell, its time course being virtually unrelated to the volley size. The experimental results suggested that the EPSP represents the algebraic summation of the synaptic potentials generated by each of the activated endings and thus that the final amplitude of the EPSP is a function of the number of presynaptic fibres activated at a given time.

Amplitude and time course of unitary synaptic potentials

Subsequent studies on the nature of the synaptic depolarization in motoneurones confirmed the hypothesis that EPSPs were built up by the summation of smaller synaptic depolarizations (Katz & Miledi, 1963; Kuno, 1964*a*; Burke & Nelson, 1966; Burke, 1967) and, in fact, characterize the EPSP as a compound potential generated by the summation of responses at many individual excitatory synapses, each of which contributes a certain number of units of quantal synaptic potentials. These 'quanta', which correspond to those described at the neuromuscular junction by del Castillo & Katz (1954*b*), were measured by Kuno (1964*a*) following the stimulation of single 1A afferent fibres in the cat lumbar cord. He concluded that each quantum of excitatory transmitter (see Chapter 4) produces in motoneurones a potential change of 120 to 240 μV. The calculations were based on the statistical analysis of the fluctuations in amplitude of the EPSP when the mean number of unitary components, '*m*' (del Castillo & Katz, 1954*b*), was less than three. Furthermore, a single activation of a 1A fibre will, according to Kuno, release on the average only one quantum of synaptic transmitter as opposed to the large number of quanta released at other synapses (see p. 138). Other calculations of the voltage displacement by synaptic quanta (Burke, 1967) indicate it to be in the vicinity of 700 μV, which is close to the quantal size of 750 μV estimated for the red nucleus cells from interpositus nucleus afferent fibres (Toyama, Tsukahara, Kosaka, Udo, & Matsunami, personal communication). In a recent paper, however, Kuno (Blankenship & Kuno, 1968) has confirmed his previous findings and suggests that the larger miniature potentials recorded in motoneurones have a quantal content larger than unity. It must be remembered that the size of miniature PSPs is related to the size of the neurones studied (the smaller the neurone the larger its input resistance, and thus the larger the voltage produced by a given synaptic current) and to the site of synaptic impingement with respect to the place of recording. The relation between time course and amplitude of the unitary EPSPs* and amplitude and time course of EPSPs evoked by a 1A synchronous volley has been studied in detail (Burke & Nelson, 1966; Burke, 1967). Unitary EPSPs were evoked by a moderate stretch of agonistic muscles which, according to the authors, activated mainly the intrafusal fibres of the muscle spindle and thus relayed information to motoneurones by way of 1A afferent fibres. This experimental technique demonstrated that the time course of the unitary EPSP can be very different from that of the total EPSP evoked in the same neurone by a synchronous 1A volley (Fig. 6.5A, B, C). The time course of the unitary EPSP was shown to be such that the rise and decay time were proportional to each other, this relation being unaltered by repetitive activation. The latter point demonstrates that the time course is not produced by a fortuitous blend of synaptic quanta released by different afferent fibres, but represents the synaptic depolarization produced by a single action potential in a single fibre. Moreover, the calculation of 'shape indices' (Rall *et al.*, 1967), that is, the relation between the duration at half amplitude of the unitary potentials and their time to peak, gave a characteristic distribution (Fig. 6.8). The significance of shape indices will be discussed below (p. 261).

A series of representative examples of unitary EPSPs from nine different cells (Fig. 6.5D) demonstrates the wide range in the time course of the potentials evoked by 1A activation.

This range of time courses is, of course, explained by assuming that the faster rising short-lasting unitary EPSPs are generated by boutons located in the vicinity of the recording site, while the unitary EPSPs with a longer time course appear prolonged because of the distortion suffered as only the slow frequency components of the potentials are electrotonically conducted from the place of origin to the recording site (Rall, 1967) (see Chapter 2). Since, for the most part, the commonest place for intracellular impalement of motoneurones is the soma (Eccles, 1957), the results suggest that the short duration unitary potentials are

* Potentials evoked by the activation of a single afferent fibre and which are composed of several synaptic 'quanta'.

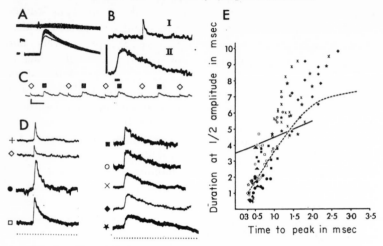

FIG. 6.5. Intracellular synaptic potentials recorded from feline motoneurones. A. EPSP evoked by electrical stimulation of the plantaris muscle nerve. Upper trace afferent volley recorded at dorsal root entrance. B. Unitary synaptic potentials enlarged from C to show the difference in their time course. C. Moving film record of the two unitary synaptic potentials evoked by a 25 g stretch of the plantaris muscle. Unit I (as in B above) is marked with an open diamond, unit II (as in B below) with a square. Time voltage calibration 5 mV for A and 1 mV for B and C. Time 1 msec for A and B; 25 msec. In D, examples of unitary EPSP from nine different sets of synaptic potential records. All potentials shown are 0·75 to 1·5 mV in amplitude. Same time scale for all potentials (Burke, 1967). E. Shape index plot for the unitary EPSP evoked by eleven different groups of 1A fibres. Some of these are shown in D, and are marked with corresponding symbols. For explanation of shape index see p. 26 (Rall *et al.*, 1967).

generated near the soma while the long-lasting potentials are generated in the dendrites far from the soma. This finding is in total agreement with other features of the distribution of 1A synapses in motoneurones and emphasizes the importance of the dendritic input to neurones. Two similar types of results have been reported recently for unitary synaptic potentials generated by single afferent fibres. Mendell & Henneman (1968) recorded the synaptic potentials associated in time with the activation of a single afferent fibre by means of a post-activation average computation technique. Willis *et al.* (1968) were able to perform simultaneous penetrations of spinal ganglion cells and motoneurones and evoked, by current injection of the ganglion cells, unitary EPSPs in the motoneurones. With this latter technique the

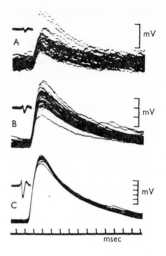

FIG. 6.6. Excitatory postsynaptic potentials (EPSPs) recorded intra-cellularly from a spinal motoneurone and generated by electrical activation of muscle nerves. A to C. EPSP recorded from a biceps-semitendi-nosus motoneurone. There is a con-tinuous increase in the amplitude of the EPSP as the afferent volley size gets larger (left upper inset of A to C). Note the different amplitude cali-bration at the right of each trace. The time calibration is the same for the three records (Coombs, Eccles, & Fatt, 1955c).

results for the amplitude of the quantal potentials agreed with those of Kuno (Willis, personal communication).

Amplitude and time course of EPSPs evoked by a synchronous afferent volley

When a large number of 1A afferent fibres are synchronously activated by means of an electrical stimulus at a peripheral site, the incoming volley generates a large EPSP on the target cells (Fig. 6.6). If the number of fibres activated is increased or de-creased by modifying the amplitude of the stimulating current, a family of EPSPs can be obtained, the minimum depolarization being a miniature EPSP (see above). The summation of these small synaptic depolarizations was found to be linear in the ranges studied (Eccles, Eccles, & Lundberg, 1957) and thus suggested that changes due to reduced membrane potential during the course of the synaptic depolarization and the shunting effect produced by the conductance change generating the synaptic current were small enough to be neglected. However, in the more detailed studies by Burke (1967) this situation was found only in about 60% of the motoneurones considered, the remainder showing summation of a non-linear fashion. In Fig. 6.7 the EPSP evoked in a gastrocnemius motoneurone by a 1A activation from lateral gastrocnemius soleus (LG–Sol) and medial gastrocnemius (MG) muscle nerves showed a clear linear summation of the monosynaptic EPSPs. On the other hand, summation of monosynaptic EPSPs from flexor digitorum longus (FDL) and medial gastrocnemius in another neurone are seen to reach only 83% of the expected sum. The demonstration of nonlinear summation is important since it implies that linear summation of EPSPs occurs only when their sites of maximal conductance change are located far enough from each other not to shunt their respective synaptic currents. The EPSP has been shown to have a time course of about 16 msec duration (Fig. 6.7) with a time to peak of 2 msec and a falling phase of 14 msec (Eccles, 1957). On the other hand, if different 1A afferent fibres to a particular motoneurone are activated separately (Fig. 6.7), a different time course can sometimes be observed

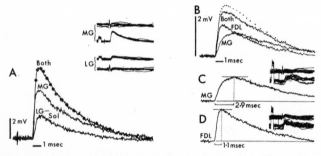

FIG. 6.7. Averaged EPSPs evoked by electrical stimuli to muscle nerves to demonstrate linearity of EPSP summation and time course of monosynaptic EPSP when evoked from two different afferent fibre systems. A. Averaged EPSP evoked in a gastrocnemius motoneurone by afferent volleys from the medial gastrocnemius (MG) and the lateral gastrocnemius–soleus (LG–Sol) muscle nerves. When the two branches are activated simultaneously (Both), the EPSP is the algebraic sum of the two EPSPs (solid dots). In B, C, and D, average EPSP (25 responses) from a presumed FDL neurone. C, EPSP evoked by electrical stimulation of medial gastrocnemius (MG). D, EPSP evoked by flexor digitorum longus (FDL). Note the different times to peak for these two records (broken line) as well as the difference in the duration of the falling phase. In B, superimposition of records C, to show differences in peak time and time course and EPSP produced by the summation of these two EPSPs (Both). The amplitude is 83% of the expected algebraic sum (dots). Photographic records of these potentials and the dorsal root volleys are shown at the right of the records A, C, and D. Time and voltage calibration of photographic records in A, 2 mV and 1 msec; in C and D, 5 mV and 1 msec. Calibrations for averaged records as stated in the figure (Burke, 1967).

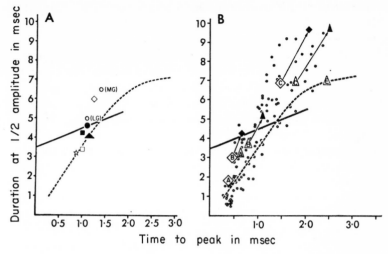

FIG. 6.8. Shape index plot for electrically evoked EPSP. The broken lines in A and B represent the shape indices for computed EPSP occurring in single compartments at different electrotonic distances from the soma, and the solid lines the shape indices for computed EPSP occurring by uniform impingement over the whole of the soma dendritic area (see Fig. 6.25 for further explanation). In A, the distribution of shape indices of 7 of the cells from which Fig. 6.5 was taken (the symbols used are the same as used in that figure). Note that the area covered by the electrically evoked EPSPs overlap with the area covered by the unitary EPSPs. In B, several combinations of inputs to different compartments (open and closed triangles and diamonds) to match experimental data (small circles). Diamonds are short duration inputs and triangles medium duration inputs. Diamond A, combination of compartments 1–2–9–10; Diamond B, 1–2–3–4–9–10; Diamond C, 3–4–9–10. Triangle A, combination of compartments 1–2–9–10; Triangle B, 1–2–3–4–9–10; Triangle C, 3–4–9–10. Arrows to solid symbols denote shift in calculated EPSP indices when time constant is changed from 5 to 7 msec. Triangle E, input into all compartments (Rall *et al.*, 1967).

for the two sets of fibres impinging on the same cell (Burke, (1967). In the example illustrated, the time course of the FDL EPSP has a faster rise and decay time than the monosynaptic MG EPSP. Burke suggests, on the basis of the theoretical studies of Rall (1967), that the different time course is produced by the different location of the synapses of these two nerves on the motoneurone. The faster EPSP would be nearer the recording site (possibly the source) while the slower EPSP would be further away from the recording site and thus would be distorted by the electrotonic conduction up to the recording site (Rall, 1967). The fact that these two EPSPs do not sum linearly implies that part of the site of generation of the EPSP is shared by these two inputs and, thus, that the 'fast' EPSP must have a dendritic component. It is indeed essential, in order to postulate any dendritic component for the fast EPSP, that such an interaction be demonstrated. Calculations based on this mathematical model of a neurone have led Rall to formulate a series of quantitative relations between different parameters of EPSPs which can be directly applied to experimental data (1967). One such formulation relates the half-time to the time to peak of the EPSP, as we have seen to be the case for the time course of the unitary potentials.

As seen in Fig. 6.8 the shape index plot for a series of electrically evoked EPSPs covers very much the same area as the shape index of unitary potentials. In order to match the distribution of experimental points in the shape index (Fig. 6.8B) to shape indices calculated in Rall's mathematical model, the potentials must have been generated by a mixed soma–dendritic distribution of the 1A input (Rall *et al.*, 1967). Together with the evidence already described, this result strongly suggests that in motoneurones at least, the 1A EPSP arises as a compound potential produced by synaptic depolarization arising at both somatic and dendritic sites.

EPSP ionic mechanisms

The original postulate by Coombs, Eccles, & Fatt (1955*c*), that the EPSP results from an inward ionic current at the postsynaptic subsynaptic membrane which discharges the neurone membrane capacity, is for all practical purposes universally accepted. The ions involved in the motoneurone EPSP were thought to be K^+, Na^+, and Cl^- (Coombs, Eccles, & Fatt, 1955*c*). These ions are known to be distributed in such a manner that if Na^+, K^+, and Cl^- ionic currents were involved in the production of the EPSP, it would have an equilibrium potential of approximately zero volts. Since then, however, it has been considered that by analogy with the endplate potential (Takeuchi & Takeuchi, 1960*b*), only K^+ and Na^+ are in fact involved in the generation of the EPSP.

During the EPSP, ions are envisaged as flowing down their electrochemical gradient across the subsynaptic membrane (Coombs, Eccles, & Fatt, 1955*c*), Na^+ being the main ionic species moving since at testing level the driving potential for Na^+ is about

130 mV while for that K+ is only about 20 mV (Eccles, 1957). Thus the conductance change produces a net inward ionic current at the subsynaptic site. There is, of course, an equal outward current which is at first capacitative as the membrane capacity is discharged. Later some ionic currents pass through the postsynaptic membrane carried mainly by K+ and perhaps Cl− (moving in the opposite direction) since these are ions towards which the membrane has a reasonable resting conductance. Given that the outward current flow takes place all along the cell membrane, remote from as well as close to the subsynaptic site of transmitter action, it follows that, if an electrode is located in the extracellular medium in the vicinity of the cell, a negativity will be recorded close to the site of activated synapses where net membrane current is inward and a positivity elsewhere, where current exists from the cell (see p. 288).

Intracellular current injections

As discussed on p. 94, it is possible to change artificially the resting potential of cells by passing a current between the inside of the cell and the extracellular media. In this manner the study of the relation between the resting potential of the cell and the amplitude and time course of EPSPs is greatly simplified. Coombs, Eccles, & Fatt (1955c) showed that the amplitude of the EPSP decreases as the resting potential is lowered and reaches a null level at a resting potential near zero. Furthermore, if the current application was continued such that the intracellular potential became negative with respect to the reference electrode (Fig. 6.9), the EPSP was reversed showing that the main ionic movement across the subsynaptic membrane had changed its direction and that instead of an inward current, an outward current was generated. Given the intracellular and extracellular ionic concentration (Eccles, 1957), it was calculated that in order for the EPSP to have an equilibrium potential* near zero, it had to be generated by Na+, K+, and perhaps Cl− conductance changes (Coombs, Eccles, & Fatt, 1955a). The conductivity for these ions had to

---

* The membrane potential at which there is no net ionic movement during the period of increased membrane conductance produced by the synaptic transmitter action on the postsynaptic membrane. Since there is no net ionic movement, there is no current flow across the membrane and no synaptic potential is observed.

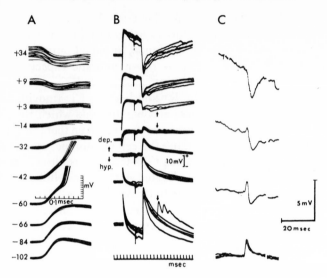

FIG. 6.9. Changes in the amplitude and polarity of EPSPs as a function of resting potential. A. EPSP recorded intracellularly in a biceps-semitendinosus motoneurone at different levels of membrane potential. The potential was altered through one microelectrode while a second intracellular microelectrode recorded the potential changes. The resting potential was – 66 mV. Note the change in the EPSP time course as the cell is hyperpolarized to – 102 mV and the reversal of the potential at membrane level of o to +9 mV (Coombs, Eccles, & Fatt, 1955c). B. EPSP evoked in a Purkinje cell by a climbing fibre activation; the equilibrium potential was near zero membrane potential. Arrows mark EPSP evoked by the 'climbing fibre reflex'. The intracellular current was applied by means of a Wheatstone bridge (Eccles, Llinás, & Sasaki, 1966a). C. Biphasic reversal of motoneurone EPSP by means of a double-barrelled microelectrode (Smith, Wuerker, & Frank, 1967). Time and voltage calibrations as indicated.

be turned on simultaneously and at the same rate (unlike the conductance changes which generate action potentials, see p. 52).

The demonstration of an equilibrium potential and the fact that the amplitude of the EPSP is related linearly to the resting potential imply that the EPSP must be produced by ionic movements down their electrochemical gradients. One conclusion from these findings is that the synaptic potentials are generated by a process independent of the electro-responsive mechanisms of the membrane (Grundfest, 1961; also see Chapter 2). The EPSP reflects ionic movements which depend upon the ionic composition of the postsynaptic cell and its extracellular environment, and is not related in a direct manner to the ionic movements across the membrane of the presynaptic element as would be the case for electrotonic interaction. Similar observations have been described for the EPSP generated by the climbing fibres on to the Purkinje cells (Fig. 6.9B) (Eccles, Llinás, & Sasaki, 1966a). As in the case of the motoneurone, the equilibrium potential in this case is near zero membrane potential and the voltage–current relation is fairly linear.

For the most part it is possible to reverse EPSPs (Coombs, Eccles, & Fatt, 1955c; Eccles, Llinás, & Sasaki, 1966a; Smith, Wuerker & Frank, 1967) only under very particular circumstances. The impalement must be very sturdy and the microelectrode must have excellent properties. Several investigators have found the reversal of EPSPs in motoneurones hard to attain (Smith, Wuerker, & Frank, 1967) and have, in fact, demonstrated that in the majority of cases a true reversal does not occur. Since the current applied in the soma of a cell does not depolarize uniformly (see Rall, 1967) but much more locally than at the distant dendritic branches, those synapses located far from the place of the current injection are less affected than those located in the vicinity of the current source and can continue to supply depolarizing current although the potential at the soma may be at near zero resting potential. In large cells such as Purkinje neurones dendritic penetration may tend to facilitate the reversal of the EPSP since the current is more effectively distributed along a segment of the dendrite. Furthermore, given that the core resistance of the dendrites is large, only slight interference from potential changes generated in other dendrites of the same cell may be expected.

Voltage clamp

Several attempts have been made to measure directly (by means of voltage-clamp techniques) the current generating the EPSP. The accurate application of this technique to spinal motoneurones or to any other elements with complex geometrical structure is, however, impossible. Prerequisites for a true clamp are the fixing of the membrane potential at a given level and the attainment of isopotentiality in the interior of the impaled cell. In order to achieve this goal, the current density across the membrane must be uniform for all parts of the cell. This condition is attainable in structures such as the squid giant axon which is large enough to permit an axial wire to be introduced along its length, throughout the centre of the fibre. A current pulse applied between this conductor and a similar external electrode produces a constant current per unit length of fibre and thus a 'space clamp' can be attained (Hodgkin, Huxley, & Katz, 1952). Other structures where a space clamp can be obtained are those which can be approximated to spheres (Hagiwara, 1960). In this situation a single point source (an intracellular microelectrode), if located in the centre of the sphere-shaped cell, will produce an isopotential state if the interior of the cell is isotropic. A motoneurone, on the other hand, cannot be approximated accurately to any of the two examples given above since its geometry is such that only very complex models can begin to approximate its actual shape (Rall, 1962–7). This difficulty is due to the presence of the dendritic tree and the axons. Despite this limitation a reasonable clamp has been obtained (Araki & Terzuolo, 1962; Nelson & Frank, 1964*b*). Even under

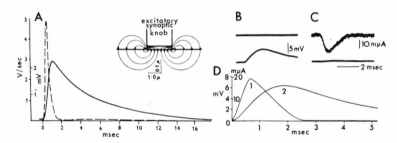

FIG. 6.10. Time course of EPSP current. A. Calculation of EPSP current from the experimentally estimated value of the time constant of the motoneurone (see text). The broken line curve represents the current, the full line the EPSP. Ordinate: current in the V/sec scale, voltage of the EPSP in the mV scale. Abscissa: time in msec. The inset to the right gives the directions of current flow across the postsynaptic membrane. Note the dimensions of the current spread (Curtis & Eccles, 1959). B and C. Voltage clamp of motoneurone EPSP; the upper trace is current, the lower trace potential. In B, the time course of the EPSP before the clamp. C, time course of the synaptic current when the membrane potential is clamped at the resting level (C lower trace). D, traces of the time course of the synaptic current and synaptic potential from B and C. Note the lack of residual current (Araki & Terzuolo, 1962). Current, voltage, and time calibrations as indicated.

these conditions of partial clamp, given that isopotentiality could not be fulfilled for the length of the dendrites (Araki & Terzuolo, 1962), EPSPs were successfully clamped on several occasions (Fig. 6.10). The current which generated the EPSP (Fig. 6.10) and which would include current from dendritic subsynaptic areas, was found to have a time course of 2 msec with a peak at 0·7 msec, very much as had been estimated given the potential change and the input resistance and capacitance of the nerve cells (Curtis & Eccles, 1959). However, a clear deviation from this estimate was the absence of residual current which had been assumed in order to account for the deviation from a single exponential of the time course of the decay phase of the EPSP (Coombs, Eccles, & Fatt, 1955c; Curtis & Eccles, 1959). This departure from a simple exponential has been explained on the basis of the dendritic component of the EPSP (Rall *et al.*, 1967).

Impedance changes accompanying the generation of EPSPs

Measurement of impedance of cells during the generation of EPSPs (Smith, Wuerker, & Frank, 1967) shows that only in certain cells can a definite impedance change be found associated with the synaptic depolarization. Figure 6.11 illustrates two EPSPs, one of which was associated with a definite impedance change while the other was not. The implication of these findings is that the second EPSP must be generated far from the recording site or else that some EPSPs might not be produced by conductance changes across the membrane, but by electrotonic conduction from the presynaptic fibre. Katz (1966) has recently summarized the reasons why the latter type of transmission is most unlikely in the case under discussion. The theoretical possibility of electrical transmission produced by a low resistance pathway between the presynaptic fibre and the motoneurone has been considered (Rall *et al.*, 1967).

The situation regarding our understanding of the EPSP can thus be summarized as follows. The EPSP is a depolarizing potential generated by the sum of smaller depolarizations, the so-called unitary synaptic potentials, which are generated more or less uniformly over the soma dendritic surface. This depolarization is secondary to the release of a chemical mediator, from presynaptic terminals, which generates a selective conductance change for Na^+ and K^+ across the postsynaptic subsynaptic

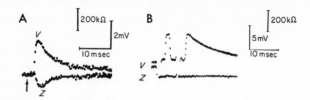

FIG. 6.11. Conductance changes concomitant with the generation of
EPSP in motoneurones. A. Averaged motoneurone EPSP and
concomitant in-phase impedance change. V, synaptic potentials;
Z, impedance change. Downward deflection in lower beam indicates decreased impedance. Arrow, stimulus to gastrocnemius
nerve. B. As in A, EPSP evoked by gastrocnemius stimulation.
Note the lack of impedance change (Z) during the generation of
the synaptic potential. Voltage, impedance and time calibrations
as indicated   (Smith, Wuerker, & Frank, 1967).

membrane and which allows these ions to move down their
electrochemical gradients. This inward current is matched by
outward capacity and ionic currents, across the rest of the membrane, associated with the depolarization. Voltage clamp studies
of the currents generating the EPSP demonstrate a time course
much as expected from theoretical considerations, that is, shorter
than the time course of the synaptic potential and having an earlier
rise and a faster decay. The impedance changes which accompany
the generation of the EPSP confirm the postsynaptic site of
generation of this potential and together with the demonstrated
non-linear summation of EPSP indicate that the EPSP is
generated across both somatic and dendritic membranes, as had
been previously postulated on indirect evidence (Fatt, 1957;
Fadiga, & Brookhart, 1962; Terzuolo & Llinás, 1966).

INHIBITORY POSTSYNAPTIC POTENTIALS (IPSPS)

As in the case of EPSPs, the inhibitory postsynaptic potentials
(IPSPs) were first observed by means of intracellular recordings
from feline motoneurones (Brock, Coombs, & Eccles, 1952).
These transient hyperpolarizations were immediately identified
as the mechanisms underlying the 'direct inhibition' described
by Lloyd (1941) following the activation of 1A afferents from antagonistic muscle groups.

Although most of our knowledge about IPSPs in the CNS was

originally gained through the study of motoneurones (Brock, Coombs, & Eccles, 1952; Eccles, Fatt, & Koketsu, 1954; Coombs, Eccles, & Fatt, 1955b and d), the generation of IPSPs and the relation between the IPSP and the general problem of inhibition have been examined in many other neurone types.

In all vertebrate CNS sites investigated so far, many characteristics appear common to all IPSPs. For instance, the inhibitory potentials are generated by 'downhill' ionic movements across the subsynaptic membrane. Again, the ionic currents are brought about by conductance changes to specific ions when an inhibitory transmitter substance, released by the presynaptic terminal, reaches the postsynaptic subsynaptic surface. It has been suggested that the ions involved are Cl^- and K^+, the net current being outward at the subsynaptic membrane and inward through the rest of the membrane. This flow of current will produce a hyperpolarization of the cell, i.e., the membrane potential will become more negative than it is at rest (Coombs, Eccles, & Fatt, 1955b).

The ability to evoke IPSPs, i.e., to produce and release an inhibitory transmitter substance, has been postulated as a characteristic exclusive to small short-axoned neurones, the so-called 'inhibitory interneurones' (Eccles, 1957).

The implications of this suggestion are very important. For example, long fibres (especially those belonging to sensory pathways) should be excitatory to all their target cells. That is, synaptic transmitter acting between these fibres and any type of cell they innervate should cause the ionic conductance changes associated with excitatory action (most probably Na^+ and K^+ permeabilities as for the motoneurone EPSP). In accord with 'Dale's Principle', it can be assumed that all axon terminals of a neurone liberate the same neurotransmitter. It is natural to extend this to the hypothesis that at all its terminals a neurone should exert the same effects, either excitatory or inhibitory as the case may be, but not both (Eccles, 1957, p. 163). Since sensory fibres are excitatory (e.g., 1A), by this argument any inhibitory action evoked by sensory stimulation must act through an interneurone which transforms or translates excitation into inhibition.

A very clear case of this translation is the inhibition which appears subsequent to 1A stimulation. The time between the electrical stimulation of the afferents and the onset of inhibition at the motoneurones (1·2 to 1·5 msec) is so short (Eccles, Fatt, &

Landgren, 1954) that only one neurone can be interposed between the afferent volley and the motoneurone. It was originally postulated that the inhibitory cell belongs to the intermediate nucleus of Cajal in the dorsomedial part of the spinal cord (Eccles, Fatt, & Landgren, 1954), and direct evidence for this view was found when microelectrode stimulation of the nucleus of Cajal was seen to produce an IPSP on flexor motoneurones, with 0·5 msec latency, after degeneration of 1A afferent fibres following dorsal root sectioning (Eide, Lundberg, & Voorhoeve, 1961).

Amplitude and time course of IPSPs

The time course of the intracellular IPSPs in motoneurones (Fig. 6.12) is close to that of the monosynaptic EPSP. An important difference, however, is the time course of return to the resting potential (Fig. 6.12A, B, C) which is very close to a single exponential (Coombs, Eccles, & Fatt, 1955*b* and *d*; Curtis & Eccles, 1959) and corresponds closely to the time constant of motoneurones as measured with intracellular application of current pulses (Fig. 6.12) rather than being prolonged as in the case of the EPSP. The

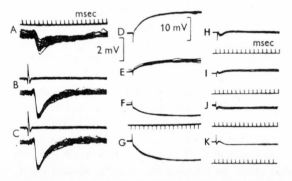

Fig. 6.12. Time course of the intracellularly recorded IPSP from motoneurones and their relation to the time constant of the cell's membrane. A. to C. IPSP evoked in a posterior biceps-semitendinosus motoneurone by increasing electrical stimulation of group 1A fibres in the quadriceps nerve. Incoming dorsal root volley is illustrated in upper trace of B and C. D to G, time constant of the cell as measured by applying a square current pulse of 6×10^{-9} A through one barrel of a double micropipette. D and E, depolarizing currents; F and G, hyperpolarizing currents. Records H to K taken in the extracellular media following square pulses of current identical to those used in D to G. Time and amplitude as illustrated (Curtis & Eccles, 1959).

amplitude of the IPSP is graded, being directly related to the number of afferents activated (Fig. 6.12A to C), as well as to the driving force for the ions involved in its production. The driving force is, of course, governed by the electrochemical gradient of these ions across the membrane and thus changes when either the intracellular or extracellular ion activity of any of the ions is altered, or when the membrane potential level is modified. Since, as will be seen later, the equilibrium potential for the IPSP in motoneurones is -80 mV (Coombs, Eccles, & Fatt, 1955b) and the resting potential of motoneurones is normally -70 mV, the maximum amplitude for an IPSP recorded under normal circumstances is 10 mV. Although the IPSP is composed of quantal units (Blankenship & Kuno, 1968), research such as that done to estimate quantal sizes of EPSPs (Kuno, 1964a; Burke, 1967) is complicated by the fact that the pathway is disynaptic and thus no simple relation exists between the action potentials in the 1A afferent fibres and the generation of unitary synaptic potentials. In some instances it has been possible to obtain defined conditions under which reversed unitary IPSPs could be observed (Fig. 6.15C, D, F and G).

IPSP ionic mechanism

The equilibrium potential for the IPSP was first studied by artificially changing the membrane potential level with a double microelectrode (Coombs, Eccles, & Fatt, 1955b). One electrode was utilized for passing current, the second for measuring the potential across the membrane. Under these circumstances the relation between the amplitude of the membrane potential and the amplitude and polarity of the IPSP was studied (Fig. 6.13). It was found that the equilibrium potential was approximately -80 mV.

Furthermore, following ionic injections by means of these double-barrelled microelectrodes, it was found that only small ions having a radius comparable to that of Cl^- or K^+ (such as NO_3^-, Br^-, SCN^-) could traverse the subsynaptic membrane. On the basis of these findings, it was concluded that during the IPSP the inhibitory transmitter triggered a conformational change in the subsynaptic membrane such that a sieve-like behaviour of this membrane was observed. This sieve, it was suggested, had pores which would allow movement of ions, the limiting factor being

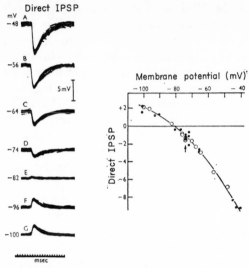

FIG. 6.13. Relation between IPSP amplitude and polarity to the membrane potential. A to G, intracellular IPSP recorded from a biceps-semitendinosus motoneurone by means of a double microelectrode filled with Na₂SO₄. The membrane potential was altered as indicated at the left of each trace. Record D is at normal resting potential. The equilibrium potential was in the vicinity of – 80 mV (record E). The plot to the right relates membrane potential in mV (abscissa) to amplitude and polarity of the IPSP in mV (ordinate). The equilibrium potential is at the crossing point between the plotted line and the null point for the amplitude of the IPSP. Filled circles before, open circles after a depolarizing current (10^{-8} A) was passed through the cell for 90 sec, demonstrating no alteration of the resting potential (arrow). Time and voltage calibrations as indicated (Coombs, Eccles, & Fatt, 1955*b*).

only their diameter, with the permeability change being independent of their charge (Coombs, Eccles, & Fatt, 1955*b*). In a later series of experiments (Ito, Kostyuk, & Oshima, 1962) a large series of ions was tested for penetration through the subsynaptic membrane. The results (Fig. 6.14) gave further support to the idea that the only selective aspect of this permeability change was ion size.

The ionic species normally carrying the IPSP current were postulated to be Cl⁻ and K⁺ (Coombs, Eccles, & Fatt, 1955*b*). The evidence for the role of K⁺ in the generation of the IPSP was based on the calculation of the intracellular concentration of the Cl⁻ ion ($[Cl^-]_i$). Given that $[K^+]_o$ is 5·5 mM and $[Cl^-]_o$ is 125 mM and that the $[K^+]_i$ could be calculated by assuming that the

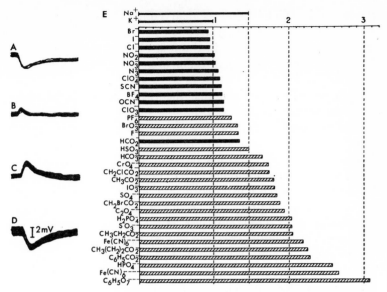

FIG. 6.14. Ionic permeability of the subsynaptic IPSP membrane. A to D, intracellular records from a biceps-semitendinosus motoneurone showing reversal of IPSP by diffusion of Cl^- ions into the cell. In A to C, the IPSP is reversed to its original hyperpolarizing nature by artificially lowering the membrane potential from -59 mV to -27 mV (Coombs, Eccles, & Fatt, 1955b). E. Relation between hydrated diameter of injected ions in ordinate (1 is hydrated diameter of K^+) and the classification of ions as penetrating (black lines) and non-penetrating (broken lines) (Ito, Kostyuk, & Oshima, 1962).

equilibrium potential for the hyperpolarization is that of the K^+ ion (the computation gives $[K^+]_i$ of 151 mM (Coombs, Eccles, & Fatt, 1955b), $[Cl^-]_i$ could then be calculated by means of the constant field equation (see Chapter 2), the value for the equilibrium potential of the IPSP being known. The results indicated $[Cl^-]_i$ as being $8\cdot9$ mM (Coombs, Eccles, & Fatt, 1955b). The equilibrium potential for Cl^- (E_{Cl}) could then be calculated by means of the Nernst equation and was found to be -71 mV. However, this analysis assumed that $[Cl^-]_i$ is distributed passively across the membrane. In a more recent series of experiments, Eccles, Eccles, & Ito (1964a, b) have shown that following the injection of ion pairs by means of double-barrelled electrodes the permeability to K^+ is at least one-half that for Cl^- and thus that the calculation for E_{Cl-} may have been erroneous. An alternative explanation for the hyperpolarizing sign of the IPSP at resting potential is to postulate that $[Cl^-]_i$ is maintained lower than 8·9 mM by active transport, in which case K^+ activation need not be considered. Indeed, the only reason to involve K^+ in the first place is the fact that the IPSP has a hyperpolarizing direction even at the resting membrane potential level.

With regard to the view that the IPSP membrane of motoneurones behaves as a sieve with pores which allow movement of ions of particular hydrated sizes (Coombs, Eccles, & Fatt, 1955*b*; Araki, Ito, & Oscarsson, 1961; Ito, Kostyuk, & Oshima, 1962), a similar series of investigation on snail ganglion cell (Kerkut & Thomas, 1964) and Mauthner cells of fish (Asada, 1963) have confirmed the sequence illustrated in Fig. 6.15E. This implies that the ionic mechanism for IPSPs could be similar for all inhibitory synapses (Eccles, 1964). However, at the crayfish neuromuscular junction, Takeuchi & Takeuchi (1967) have demonstrated that the grouping of anions into penetrating and non-penetrating may be an oversimplification for the ionic movement across the IPSP membrane at this synapse, since in this case the ionic mobility is not directly related to hydration size. In a series of measurements of membrane conductance in the presence of gamma-aminobutyric acid (GABA) ,which is thought to be the inhibitory transmitter substance in that preparation (Otsuka, Iversen, Hall, & Kravitz, 1966), it was shown that the relative membrane conductance is not the same for all penetrating anions. The relation is such that the relative permeabilities have the following sequence: $Br^- > Cl^- > SCN^- > I^- > NO_3^- > HCOO^- > ClO_3^- > ClO_4^- > BrO_3^-$. The most permeable ion, Br^-, has approximately 120% of Cl^- conductance and the least, BrO_3^-, approximately 28%. These results indicate that the IPSP membrane conductance change is graded with respect to the ion species tested in a manner which is inconsistent with the sieve hypothesis. Moreover, Takeuchi & Takeuchi (1967) have suggested, in the light of the conductance changes produced by altering the pH of the media, that there are interactions between the anions and positive fixed charges in the membrane. It is also of interest that the permeability of IPSP subsynaptic membrane for K^+ was only 0·43% of that of Cl^- ions.

The IPSPs which have been recorded in many other regions of vertebrate CNS are similar to those in motoneurones, with regard to their hyperpolarizing nature and their reaction to Cl^- injections. To enumerate only a few examples, in cortical pyramidal cells long-lasting IPSPs were first recorded intracellularly by Albe-

Fessard & Buser (1953, 1955). Similar IPSPs were evoked by antidromic activation of the pyramidal cells (Phillips, 1959, 1961; Stefanis & Jasper, 1964; Kubota, Sakata, Takahashi, & Uno, 1965) as well as by orthodromic stimulation of these cells (Li, 1963; Klee & Lux, 1962; Purpura & Shofer, 1964; Klee & Offenloch, 1964; Nacimiento, Lux, & Creutzfeldt, 1964; Purpura, Shofer, & Musgrave, 1964) and also by direct activation of the surface of the cortex (Phillips, 1961; Krnjević, Randić, & Straughan, 1966). Long-lasting IPSPs have also been found in the ventral nucleus of the thalamus (Purpura & Cohen, 1962; Purpura & Shofer, 1963; Andersen, Eccles, & Sears, 1964), hippocampus (Kandel & Spencer, 1961*b*; and Andersen, Eccles, & Løyning, 1964), and the cerebellar Purkinje cells (Andersen, Eccles, & Voorhoeve, 1964; Eccles, Llinás, & Sasaki, 1966*f*; Llinás, Hillman, & Precht, 1968). The outstanding characteristic of these IPSPs is their long duration (Fig. 6.15). However, when the unitary IPSPs are recorded (Fig. 6.15), it is found that the long duration of these potentials is related to a repetitive discharge of the inhibition pathway, the duration of the unitary potential being fairly short. This repetitive activation, which is very characteristic of inhibitory interneurones such as Renshaw cells (Eccles, Fatt, & Koketsu, 1954), produces a temporal summation of the otherwise short duration IPSP to evoke the long-lasting hyperpolarization (Fig. 6.15).

The IPSPs recorded in higher centres can be reversed by Cl⁻ injections in the same manner as shown for the motoneurone IPSPs. A good example of this is illustrated in Fig. 6.15A and B. The IPSP which was evoked by fimbrial stimulation of a hippocampal pyramidal cell (lower record A) was reversed to a depolarizing direction (A, upper record) by Cl⁻ diffusion from the recording microelectrode. The records in B show a series of IPSPs taken at short intervals as the Cl⁻ ions diffused into the pyramidal cell (Kandel & Spencer, 1961*b*). It is interesting to note that the depolarizing IPSP does not have the same time course as the original hyperpolarizing potential. A similar situation is shown in records C and D from a Purkinje cell. The Purkinje cell was inhibited through the activation of basket and stellate cells by a parallel fibre volley, the amplitude of the IPSP being related to the stimulus intensity. As in records A and B, Cl⁻ diffusion into this cell produced a reversal of the IPSP (D), the time course being again shorter than originally. In a similar

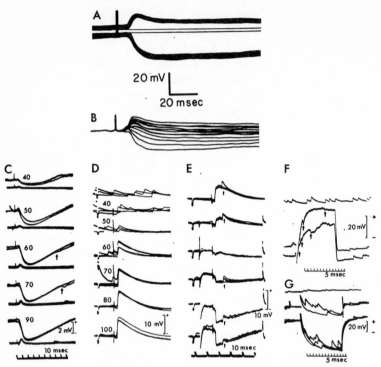

FIG. 6.15. IPSP recorded intracellularly from pyramidal cells in the hippocampus and from cerebellar Purkinje cells. A. Lower trace, IPSP generated in a hippocampal pyramidal cell by stimulus to the fimbria. The upper trace illustrating the reversal of the IPSP following Cl⁻ diffusion from the recording microelectrode. In B, the series of transitional states of the IPSP as Cl⁻ gradually leaks out of the microelectrode. Note the change in time course of the depolarizing IPSP (Kandel & Spencer, 1961*b*). C to G, IPSP from Purkinje cells following local (C) and juxtafastigial (D, E) stimulation of the cerebellum. In records C, the amplitude of the IPSP is shown to be related to the magnitude of the stimulating currents (40 to 90 in relative scale). Note in the third and fourth records spontaneous unitary IPSP (arrows). In D, the spontaneous unitary IPSPs are reversed after diffusional Cl⁻ injection (first record). A similar series of stimuli, as in C, evokes a large depolarizing potential which is graded and can be reversed back to the hyperpolarizing direction by depolarizing the cell artificially through a Wheatstone bridge (E). The arrows denote climbing fibre EPSP not reversed. In F and G, the unitary depolarizing IPSPs are shown reversed (arrows) by depolarizing current (F, lower record) and increased by hyperpolarizing current (G, lower two records) (Eccles, Llinás, & Sasaki, 1966*f*). Time and voltage calibration as illustrated. The time calibration for records D are the same as those of records E.

manner to the motoneurone IPSP, these potentials can also be reversed back to a hyperpolarizing direction by an extrinsic depolarization of the membrane (E). Besides the reversal of the evoked IPSP, the unitary IPSP (arrows in sequence C) can also be reversed by Cl⁻ injection (Fig. 6.16C and F). The amplitude and polarity of these unitary IPSPs can also be modified by extrinsic regulation of the membrane potential (F and G) (Eccles, Llinás, & Sasaki, 1966*f*). As will be seen below, the change in the time course of the IPSP following Cl⁻ injection can be explained by postulating that the increased intracellular concentration of Cl⁻ injection is not uniform throughout the cell (Llinás & Terzuolo, 1964). This is reasonable since, as demonstrated by Coombs, Eccles, & Fatt (1955*c*) in motoneurones, the membranes of these cells are quite permeable to Cl⁻. Under these conditions, where [Cl⁻] is injected, there will be a Cl⁻ gradient inside the cell and synapses located near the injection site will be affected more than those at a distance from the place of impalement. This finding permits the differentiation of IPSP as somatic (near the place of Cl⁻ injection) or dendritic since the reversal of the two to synaptic hyperpolarization does not occur at the same time with small (Cl⁻) injections (Llinás & Terzuolo, 1965; Burke, Fedina, & Lundberg, 1968). As pointed out by Bennett, Freeman, & Thaddeus (1966) following a localized current injection able to reverse the IPSP, the non-uniformity of the e.m.f. change for the E_{IPSP} should produce a change of the time course of those inhibitory synaptic potentials which are generated in a distributed fashion along the soma-dendritic surface of a cell. The nature of the change would be such as to render the IPSPs shorter than in the normal state. This explanation seems especially attractive in accounting for the records obtained from Purkinje cells in the cerebellum, where it has been shown that inhibition is both somatic, by means of the basket cell synapses, as well as dendritic through the action of the inhibitory axodendritic synapses from the superficial stellate cells (Eccles, Llinás, & Sasaki, 1966*b*; Llinás, Hillman, & Precht, 1968). With respect to the Cl⁻ injection itself, it is important to point out that since the inward current is advanced not only by Cl⁻ outward movement but also by the inward movement of permeable cations, the internal potential distribution is not an index for the distribution of the Cl⁻ concentration change, at a given time. Another complicating factor is the rather free diffusability of Cl⁻ in the intracellular media (Coombs, Eccles, & Fatt, 1955*b*).

I

Voltage clamp and impedance change measurements during IPSP

In a series of experiments similar to those described above (p. 235) for the EPSP, Araki & Terzuolo (1962) applied the voltage-clamp technique in order to measure directly the current which generates the IPSP. Since the 1A IPSP seems to be generated, for the most part, across the somatic membrane (Eccles, 1957), the voltage-clamp approach was particularly successful in this case. As illustrated in Fig. 6.16B, a double impalement of a biceps–semitendinosus motoneurone shows the IPSP simultaneously recorded by the two electrodes. In C the membrane potential is clamped at resting level (upper trace); the lower trace indicates the current applied to maintain the potential constant. A reconstruction of the time course of the potential based on the measured IPSP current and the membrane resistance of the cell, assuming that the cell behaves as an RC circuit with a single exponential time constant of 1·6 msec, is seen in Fig. 6.16. The calculated values (dotted line in E) and the recorded IPSP (solid line) matched very closely. The current measured had a peak value of about 10 mμA, reached its peak in about 0·7 msec and was over at 2·5 msec. This agrees well with the results calculated by Curtis & Eccles (1959) (Fig. 6.16A) based on the resistivity and time constant of the neurones. Measurement of the impedance changes accompanying the generation of the IPSP in motoneurones (Smith, Wuerker, & Frank, 1967) has confirmed the voltage clamp experiments illustrated in Fig. 6.16B–E. These results are completely in keeping with a somatic localization for the 1A inhibition (Eccles, 1957 and 1964).

DISFACILITATION AND DISINHIBITION

In addition to the membrane potential changes produced by the activation of excitatory and inhibitory synapses described above, definite membrane potential changes can be produced whenever a sustained synaptic bombardment is removed from a given neurone. The two theoretical possibilities, removal of a background depolarization or a background hyperpolarization of synaptic origin, have both been demonstrated experimentally and are now known to play an appreciable role in the functioning of the central nervous system.

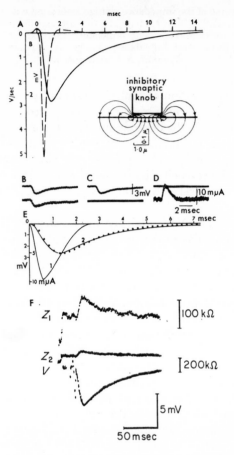

FIG. 6.16. Currents and impedance changes accompanying the IPSP in motoneurones. A. Plot of IPSP current (broken line curve) calculated from the time course of the IPSP (solid curve) in motoneurones. Abscissa, time in msec. Ordinate, IPSP voltage in mV and IPSP current in V/sec. The inset at the right of the figure illustrates the path of the inhibitory synaptic currents at the inhibitory site. Note the spatial dimensions (Curtis & Eccles, 1959). B to E. Voltage clamp of biceps–semitendinosus IPSP. In B, simultaneously recorded IPSP by double microelectrode penetration. Lower record of C, current before clamp, and in D, IPSP current after clamp has been fully applied (see upper trace in D). E. Plot of the time course of the IPSP current (1) and comparison of the actual IPSP (2) with the calculated IPSP (dots) utilizing the experimentally obtained current. Abscissa, time in msec. Ordinate, IPSP current and voltage as indicated (Araki & Terzuolo, 1962). F. Impedance measurement of anti-dromic IPSP in a motoneurone. Z_1 and Z_2 (two different gains)

are time course of the impedance change associated with the generation of an IPSP. The records are the average of 350 samples. Upward deflections represent impedance increase (Z_1 and Z_2). Time amplitude and impedance change as illustrated (Smith, Wuerker, & Frank, 1967).

The hyperpolarization of central neurones by the removal of a tonic depolarizing barrage was first demonstrated in spinal extensor motoneurones in the decerebrate cat as the mechanism underlying the cerebellar inhibition of extensor reflexes (Terzuolo, 1959; Llinás, 1964a). This process has since been found to mediate also the cerebellar inhibition of red nucleus cells (Tsukahara, Toyama, Kosaka, & Udo, 1964; Toyama, Tsukahara, & Udo, 1967).

The hyperpolarization produced in this manner (Fig. 6.17) is in some ways similar to that produced by a sustained inhibitory synaptic barrage and has, as in the latter case, a direct action on the excitability of the neurones. The outstanding differences between these two forms of hyperpolarization relate, of course, to their mechanisms of generation. In the case of disfacilitation, the hyperpolarization exists only because a tonic depolarization is removed. The maximum value it can attain, therefore, is the resting membrane potential of the cell, while in the case of a tonic inhibitory barrage the hyperpolarization has an equilibrium potential (E_{IPSP}) which is, as in the case of the direct IPSP (Eccles, Fatt, & Koketsu, 1954), more negative than the resting potential of the cell (Llinás & Terzuolo, 1964). The fact that the increased membrane potential due to disfacilitation is not produced by the ionic mechanism generating the inhibitory synaptic hyperpolarization means that it will not respond in the same manner as the IPSP to changes in the E_{IPSP}. That is to say, it will not be reversed by intracellular Cl^- injections, or by artificial displacement of the membrane potential able to reverse IPSPs (Terzuolo, 1959; Llinás, 1964a). On the contrary, it will be greatly reduced if the membrane is artificially depolarized to a level near the E_{EPSP} (Tsukahara *et al.*, 1964) as shown in Fig. 6.18, and it is increased by hyperpolarizing current. Other differences between the two forms of hyperpolarization can be demonstrated by the changes in the membrane resistance associated with their generation. In the case of the synaptic inhibition, a marked decrease of the membrane resistance is generated by the increased ionic conductance of the postsynaptic membrane (Coombs, Eccles,

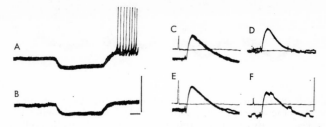

FIG. 6.17. Motoneural hyperpolarization by disfacilitation. Records A and B, sustained hyperpolarization produced by repetitive stimulation of the cerebellar vermis (A) and of the bulbar reticular formation (B) on the same quadriceps motoneurone. Although the amplitude of the hyperpolarization is similar for A and B, a rebound repetitive activation of the cell is seen only after the cerebellar stimulation. C to F, reversal of reticular hyperpolarization by Cl⁻ leakage from micropipettes does not alter the cerebellar hyperpolarization. The upper trace in C to F monosynaptic quadriceps reflex. Lower traces superimposed EPSP recorded intracellularly with a d.c. amplifier and generated simultaneously with the reflex by the afferent volley. The lower records are displayed at a faster sweep speed. C, control record showing quadriceps EPSP and the monosynaptic reflex. In D, reticular stimulation is able to inhibit completely the monosynaptic reflex producing a large depolarization of the motoneurone membrane due to Cl⁻ leakage (see displacement of the lower trace in D as compared with C). Note also that the falling time of the EPSP in D is much faster than in C, demonstrating a large increase in membrane conductance, E, as in C. In F, cerebellar inhibition of the monosynaptic reflex is accompanied by a hyperpolarization of the membrane potential and a slight increase of the falling time of the EPSP. Cl⁻ leakage, therefore, does not affect hyperpolarization by disfacilitation. Time and voltage calibration in A and B, 50 msec and 10 mV, respectively. In records C to F, 10 mV and 1 msec, respectively. Note in D and F stimulus artefacts produced by repetitive stimulation of the reticular formation and of the cerebellum (Llinás, 1964d).

& Fatt, 1955c). On the other hand no such reduction, but even an actual increase of the membrane resistance, has been observed for disfacilitation (Llinás, 1964a) as expected on the basis of a reduced background bombardment.

Finally, since the presence of disfacilitation is related to the amount of excitatory synaptic barrage, any technical procedure which reduces the tonic excitatory input to a cell (i.e., interruption of afferent excitatory fibres or deep anaesthesia) will interfere with its generation (Llinás, 1964b).

The concept of disinhibition was developed by Hartline & Ratliff (1957) to explain the facilitation produced by the removal

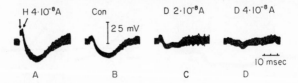

FIG. 6.18. Disfacilitation produced in red nucleus by stimulation of the cerebellar cortex. A. Intracellular records showing EPSP evoked by activation of interpositus nerve cells. Activation followed by a large hyperpolarization produced by the removal of background synaptic bombardment from the same interpositus neurones. In records B to D, the membrane potential is altered by the application of extrinsic current, and as seen in record D, both the initial EPSP, as well as the long-lasting hyperpolarization which followed, have the same equilibrium potential. Time and voltage calibration as illustrated (Tsukahara, Toyama, Kosaka, & Udo, 1964).

of an inhibitory action in the eye of the Limulus crab. However, it did not become widely understood and accepted until Wilson & Burgess (1962) demonstrated that the mechanism responsible for the recurrent facilitation of motoneurones (Fig. 6.19) (Renshaw, 1941) was a removal of a tonic inhibitory background. These investigators showed that during a period of recurrent facilitation a small potential change can be recorded intracellularly from motoneurones. The potential—a depolarization of 0·4 to 3 mV in amplitude, 4 to 7 msec latency, and a duration ranging from 50 to 70 msec—is known today as the recurrent facilitatory potential (R.F.P.). During the R.F.P. there is an *increase* in the amplitude of the EPSPs as well as in the excitability of the cell as tested by direct and orthodromic stimulation. The displacement of the membrane potential by currents applied through the microelectrode showed that the R.F.P. is reversed by hyperpolarizing currents and increased by depolarization, and has approximately the same equilibrium potential as the recurrent IPSP. These findings could all be explained on the basis of a removal of an inhibitory background bombardment from local interneurones, mediated by the axon collateral activation of Renshaw cells. According to Wilson and Burgess, the facilitatory action of the R.F.P. is due more to the increased membrane resistance than to the actual potential change. This increased resistance would explain the increase in the amplitude of the EPSPs evoked during the R.F.P. The same facilitatory mechanisms can also be proposed for the facilitatory action evoked by low-frequency stimulation of the

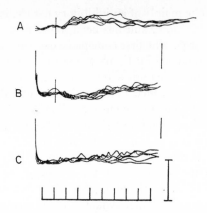

FIG. 6.19. Depolarization by recurrent disinhibition. In A, intra-cellular record showing a depolarization in a deep-peroneal motoneurone. In B, the reversal of this potential produced by a hyperpolarization of the membrane potential. In C, lack of mem-brane potential and change produced by the hyperpolarizing current alone. Time and voltage calibration 10 msec and 10 mV respectively (Wilson & Burgess, 1962).

cerebellar cortex on the extensor rigidity and extensor reflexes (Moruzzi, 1948). It has been shown that local stimulation of the cerebellar cortex at low frequency produces inhibition of the Purkinje cells by the activation of the interneurones of the mole-cular layer (Andersen, Eccles, & Voorhoeve, 1964; Eccles, Llinás, & Sasaki, 1966c, d, f). Since the Purkinje cells are themselves inhibitory neurones (Ito & Yoshida, 1964, 1966; Eccles, Llinás, & Sasaki, 1966c) their inhibition would produce a disinhibitory action on the cerebellar and vestibular nuclei (Ito, Kawai, Udo, & Mano, quoted in Eccles, Ito, & Szentágothai, 1967), and these in turn would produce a facilitatory action upon the spinal moto-neurones.

It is thus important in studying intracellular potentials in the CNS to keep in mind that both disfacilitation and disinhibition can produce protentials simulating the potentials evoked by the activation of excitatory and inhibitory synapses.

PRESYNAPTIC INHIBITION

In recent years an increasing amount of experimental evidence has demonstrated that interactions of nervous messages take place at the presynaptic level of afferent fibre systems. This interaction, which seems to be mainly of an inhibitory nature, is now known as 'presynaptic inhibition', and has been found at many sites in the CNS (Eccles, 1964). The first conclusive evidence for this form of inhibition was reported by Frank & Fuortes (1957) and by Frank (1959). These investigators showed that a conditioning muscle afferent volley can produce a large reduction of EPSPs evoked by adjacent afferents on motoneurones. The depression occurred when the conditioning and test stimuli were separated by intervals of 10 msec or longer, and did not involve any direct action on the motoneurones themselves. The conclusion at this time (Frank, 1959) was that the reductions in the amplitude of the intracellularly recorded EPSP could be explained as due either to a presynaptic depression of the synaptic transmission or to direct inhibitory action on the dendrites at a site remote from the soma. Further research on the subject has shown quite definitely that this inhibition must be presynaptic in nature (Eccles, Schmidt, & Willis, 1962) and that the same mechanisms of action are operative wherever such inhibition is present (Eccles, 1964).

The general character of presynaptic inhibition can best be explained by reference to that produced in the lumbar spinal cord by a conditioning volley from a flexor afferent system (the posterior biceps–semitendinosus) or an extensor monosynaptic reflex (plantaris) (Eccles, Eccles, & Magni, 1961). We shall be concerned first with the reduction of the intracellularly recorded EPSP and the resulting inhibition of the monosynaptic reflex, and will then provide the relevant data concerning the changes produced at the presynaptic afferent system.

As illustrated in Fig. 6.20 (Eccles, Eccles, & Magni, 1961), the amplitude of a plantaris motoneurone EPSP can be obviously reduced without any sign of direct synaptic impingement on to the motoneurone by the conditioning volley. The graph in B shows the time course of this depression. A more dramatic example of the reduction of the amplitude of the EPSP is illustrated in A, where the plantaris EPSP is preceded by 22 volleys to the posterior biceps–semitendinosus muscle nerve. These latter records show very clearly that there is no change in the time course of the EPSP during the presynaptic inhibition.

Simultaneous with the reduction of the amplitude of the EPSP, there is a reduction of the amplitude of the monosynaptic reflex observed (Fig. 6.21) by recording the reflex from the corresponding ventral root.

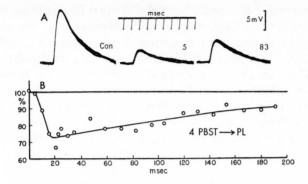

FIG. 6.20. Reduction of the amplitude of EPSP in motoneurones by presynaptic inhibition. In A, control EPSP evoked by a 1a afferent volley, and its reduction by a conditioning tetanus of 22 group 1 volleys taken at 5 msec and at 83 msec after the end of the tetanus. B. Plotting of the time course of the EPSP depression as percentage of the control. Abscissa, time in msec. Ordinate, percentage of control. The records were taken from a plantaris motoneurone, the inhibition being evoked by four group 1 conditioning volleys from the posterior biceps–semitendinosus muscle nerve (Eccles, Eccles, & Magni, 1961).

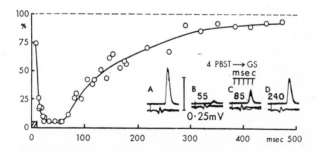

FIG. 6.21. Time course of the depression of the monosynaptic reflex by presynaptic inhibition. The monosynaptic reflex discharge was recorded at the ventral root level. Inset on the right shows control amplitude of a gastrocnemius–soleus monosynaptic reflex (A). The 1A volley is recorded at the dorsal root level (lower trace). In B, C, and D, amplitude of the monosynaptic reflex, 55, 85, and 240 msec following 4 conditioning pulses to the posterior biceps–semitendinosus muscle nerve. The plot shows reduction of the amplitude of the monosynaptic reflex in percentage of the control (ordinate) and time between end of the conditioning volley and the stimulus to the gastrocnemius nerve in msec (abscissa). Time and voltage calibrations indicated (Eccles, Schmidt, & Willis, 1962).

Occurring concurrently with the changes in amplitude of the monosynaptic reflexes, there is a depolarization of the afferent fibres which evoke this reflex. Such depolarization of the afferent fibres, which is known today as primary afferent depolarization (P.A.D.), can also be ascertained by measuring the increase in fibre excitability produced because of their decreased membrane potential (Fig. 6.22). The method of testing the excitability of nervous elements, which is quite elegant, was developed by Wall (1958) and consists of measuring the amplitude of the response

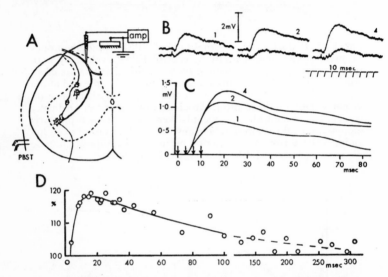

FIG. 6.22. Intracellular reading from primary afferent fibres demonstrating time course and amplitude of the depolarization generated during presynaptic inhibition. A. Experimental arrangement, the microelectrode penetrates a group 1A afferent fibre from the gastrocnemius soleus muscle nerve. In B, intrafibril recording showing the depolarization generated by 1, 2, and 4 conditioning volleys to the combined posterior biceps–semitendinosus and gastrocnemius soleus muscle nerves. Lower traces, potentials recorded at the same gain in the extracellular media in the immediate vicinity of the recorded fibre. C, actual depolarization and its time course as measured by subtracting the extracellular from the intracellularly recorded potentials in B. (Abscissa in msec, ordinate in mV.) In D, time course of the excitability changes which a single PBST volley produces in a group 1A gastrocnemius afferent fibre, as tested at the region of the synaptic terminal in the ventral horn of the spinal cord. Ordinate excitability changes in percentage of control. The time course of the excitability change (ordinate, in msec) was tested by changing the interval between the conditioning and the testing stimuli (Eccles, 1963).

produced 'directly' at a given site in the nervous system when a brief current pulse is passed through a microelectrode in the vicinity of the elements in question. The use of this technique has allowed the study of presynaptic inhibition to be carried into the higher regions of the nervous system. It appears, however, that presynaptic inhibitory actions are less common in these higher centres than in the spinal cord. Pharmacologically, this inhibition has been shown to be strychnine resistant (Eccles, Schmidt, & Willis, 1963; Llinás, 1964*b*) which is to be expected since this drug does not affect other excitatory synapses (Coombs, Eccles, & Fatt, 1955*e*). It has, however, been partially blocked by picrotoxin (Eccles, Schmidt, & Willis, 1963; Llinás, 1964*b*; Rudomin, 1966) and by mephenesin (Llinás, 1964*b*; Rudomin, 1966). This latter drug possibly blocks the discharge of the interneurones which are, in general, arranged in polysynaptic pathways (Wright, 1954). At present the most widely accepted view concerning the genesis of presynaptic inhibition is that the afferent fibres affect each other by means of collaterals which innervate interneurones. These in turn establish synaptic contacts with the presynaptic terminals of other afferent fibres. In this manner a volley in the afferent fibre (A in Fig. 6.23), for instance, will produce a depolarization of the presynaptic terminal of a neighbouring fibre (B) through the action of the interneurone (C). Such depolarization of the presynaptic terminal reduces the amount of transmitter released from the (B) presynaptic terminal by reducing the amplitude of its action potential (Eccles, 1964). Alternatively, by analogy with findings in the squid giant synapse, the magnitude of the resting potential of the presynaptic fibre can, *per se*, alter the amount of transmitter liberated by any rapid potential transient such as, for instance, an action potential (Bloedel, Gage, Llinás, & Quastel, 1966). If this finding can be extended to the vertebrate CNS, it implies that any mechanism able to modify the resting potential of central fibres would, in fact, regulate synaptic transmission and, in this manner, both presynaptic inhibition and facilitation can in theory be expected at any synapse.

FUNCTIONAL SIGNIFICANCE OF THE SYNAPTIC DISTRIBUTION ON THE SOMA-DENDRITIC REGION OF NEURONES

Finally, some of the general questions which arise regarding the significance of the synaptic distribution on the neurones and its

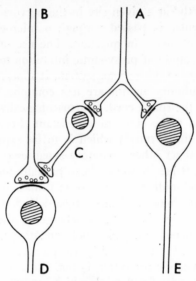

FIG. 6.23. A. Presynaptic terminal depolarizing, by means of collaterals and through an interneurone (C), another presynaptic terminal (B). D and E are other target cells.

relation to the process of integration will be briefly considered. It has become obvious that the location of synapses in the different regions in the soma-dendritic complex of a neurone determines to a large extent their influence on the activity of a cell. We have previously seen that at least in some of the central neurones the soma-dendritic region is less excitable than the initial segment (Araki & Otani, 1955; Coombs, Curtis, & Eccles, 1957). This means that in such cells the closer a given synaptic depolarization is to the initial segment, the more apt it is to initiate an action potential in that cell, since the synaptic depolarization has to be electrotonically propagated to the spike triggering zone in the axon hillock (see p. 217). A similar case can also be argued for the hyperpolarization associated with dendritic IPSPs. In this case there is another definite advantage to a somatic location of inhibitory synapses since the shunting effect accompanying the generation of the IPSP will be added to the inhibitory action produced by the hyperpolarization (Eccles, Fatt, & Koketsu, 1954; Frank & Fuortes, 1961). Also, since the driving potential of the IPSP is much smaller than that of the EPSP, its amplitude is smaller and will be greatly decreased by electrotonic conduction. Dendritic inhibition (Llinás & Terzuolo, 1965; Diamond, 1968; Burke,

Fedina, & Lundberg, 1968) would, however, be very effective in regulating the potential level at dendritic branches and in this manner controlling dendritic input to the neurone (Rall, 1967) as well as inhibiting action potentials at dendritic level (Llinás, Nicholson, Freeman, & Hillman, 1968). A remarkable example of axosomatic inhibitory endings are the terminal boutons of basket cells on to the soma and initial segments of the pyramidal cells of the hippocampus (Andersen, Eccles, & Løyning, 1964) and on the Purkinje cells of the cerebellar cortex (Andersen, Eccles, & Voorhoeve, 1964; Eccles, Llinás, & Sasaki, 1966*b, d, f*). The localization of the inhibitory synapses around the axon hillock is the more impressive when, as in the case illustrated by Estable (1923) (Fig. 6.24), the axon of a Purkinje cell is shown to arise from a

FIG. 6.24. Schematic drawing of a Purkinje cell modified from Estable (1923). Note that the typical 'basket' termination of the basket cell axons is formed around the axon hillock, which in this case arises from a dendrite.

dendrite. In this particular case, the 'basket' arrangement of the axons of the basket cell interneurone does *not* surround the soma as in normal Purkinje cells, *but surrounds the initial segment of the dendritic axon*. It can be envisaged that the axosomatic forms of excitatory and inhibitory synaptic inputs would be more suitable for phasic type responses which may be more related to fast reflex action. This type of proximal input might, however, lack the ability to exert the fine control of the neurone's excitability which a distant synaptic input can offer (Fadiga & Brookhart, 1960; Rall, 1964; Llinás & Terzuolo, 1964; Llinás & Terzuolo, 1965; Terzuolo,

Llinás, & Green, 1965; Rall, 1967; Rall *et al.*, 1967). Due to their particular location, synapses in the vicinity of the axon hillock have —with respect to the initial segment—a fast rising time and a decay with a time course close to the fastest component of the membrane time constant, and thus exert a strong but brief action on to the axon hillock.

The synapses situated in the dendrites, on the other hand, have longer lasting excitatory (Fadiga & Brookhart, 1960; Fadiga & Brookhart, 1962; Tsukahara & Kosaka, 1966) and inhibitory actions (Llinás & Terzuolo, 1965) and thus may be more involved with sustained actions, as is suggested by terms such as 'central excitatory' or 'central inhibitory' states. The activation of such synapses would allow a very fine 'modulation' of the excitability of the cell and thus a fine control of the synaptic actions exerted by the more cogent axosomatic inputs. In addition to the tonic character of this synaptic input, dendritic synapses produce less shunting effect on the soma region of a cell (Terzuolo & Llinás, 1966; Tsukahara & Kosaka, 1966; Smith, Wuerker, & Frank, 1967). This latter property further insures a fine type of excitability control since the membrane potential can be modulated without having, near the site of spike initiation, the large shunting actions which accompany the excitatory synaptic event.

As already pointed out, the functional role of the dendritic tree has been analysed from a theoretical point of view by Rall. He has developed in recent years a series of mathematical models which have proven very useful in the analysis of electrophysiological data (Rall, 1957, 1959, 1960, 1962*a*, *b*, 1964, 1967). His models are based on reasonably realistic assumptions about the extent, number, diameter, and branching characteristics of dendrites in the mammalian motoneurone (1957, 1959, 1960, 1964, 1967). The solutions for the partial differential equation developed with one of these models (1959, 1960) show the great dominance of passive membrane components of dendrites over that of the soma when a square current pulse is applied by a microelectrode lodged in the neurone's soma. The computation led Rall to the derivation of ρ, which is defined as:

$$\rho = \frac{\sum Gd}{Gs}$$

where $\sum Gd$ is the overall conductance contributed by the dendritic cell (numerically equal to the sum of the reciprocal of all dendritic resistances added in parallel) and *Gs* the conductance contributed by the soma of the cell (numerically equal to the reciprocal of the overall resistance to the current flow across the membrane of the somatic region). A value of ρ larger than one means that more of the current applied between the soma of the cell and the extra-cellular media passes across the dendritic membrane than across the soma. The value of ρ has an important bearing on the calcula-tion of time constant of neurones (Rall, 1957) and thus on the interpretation of the dendritic and somatic components contribut-ing to the time course of a given synaptic depolarization.

Shape index

In a more recent series of papers (1964–7), Rall has presented his analysis of the soma–dendritic surface of a cell, which is repre-sented as mathematically equivalent to five or ten 'compartments' in series. In Fig. 6.25 (B) the division into ten compartments is shown; each compartment has the same membrane surface area.

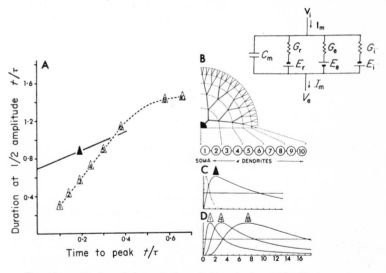

FIG. 6.25. A, plot of shape index of the calculated EPSP shown in C and D. In B, a diagram of the 'compartment model', as des-cribed in the text. The inset at the right is an equivalent circuit of the mathematical transformation of a segement of dendrite into a cell compartment. C_m is the membrane capacitance; G_r are rest-ing membrane conductance and potential; G_e and E_e, synaptic inhibitory conductance and the ISP driving force; I_m is mem-brane current density and V_i and V_e intracellular and extracellular potentials (Rall, 1967; Rall *et al.*, 1967).

The resistance and capacitance of each segment is lumped, i.e., spatial non-uniformity within each compartment is ignored. Compartment 1 is the soma compartment, 10 is the lumping of the most peripheral dendritic segments (Fig. 6.25B). The electrotonic distance Z, between the soma and any point in the dendritic tree (x_1) is defined by the integral

$$Z = \int_0^{x1} \delta\chi/\lambda$$

χ being the distance along the length of the dendrite and λ the space constant. Each segment represents an equal moment in electrotonic distance. It is assumed on the basis of histological evidence that each electrotonic increment ΔZ (one compartment) has a value of 0·2 λ; the maximum value for λ is 1·8 (Rall, 1967). Computation on the basis of this mathematical model has provided solutions giving the relations between sites of synaptic impingement and their contribution to the potential change at different sites in the model neurones. These solutions have been compared to experimental data (Rall *et al.*, 1967). For instance, this model was able to show what duration of the I_{EPSP} will give the most realistic time course for the EPSP when the synapses are located in dendrites (Burke, 1967). Similarly λ could be also altered in order to try to match experimental results.

The model allows the comparison of EPSP shapes when active synapses are located uniformly over the soma-dendritic region (Fig. 6.25C) or restricted to particular compartments (Fig. 6.25D). Of a series of useful shape indices describing the time course of synaptic potentials, the most useful was found to be the relation between time to peak (t/τ), where t is time from the foot of the EPSP, and τ is the passive time constant of the cell, and half-width time, defined as the duration of the synaptic potential in T units (t/τ) between the rising and falling phases at one-half the peak amplitude. A plot for shape indices from the computed EPSP shown in C and D is shown in Fig. 6.25A. The solid triangle represents the shape index for an EPSP generated by synapses uniformly distributed along the soma dendritic surface. The solid line gives the locus of the EPSP generated under these conditions. The open triangles give shape indices of EPSP generated in single compartments (the number inside each triangle indicates the corresponding compartment). The dashed line represents the locus as the solid line. The very good correspondence between experimentally obtained monosynaptic EPSPs in motoneurones and the calculated results based on Rall's model gives persuasive support to the idea that the monosynaptic EPSP is generated at both somatic and dendritic levels (Rall *et al.*, 1967).

A very clear example of the difference between dendritic and somatic EPSPs can be found in the red nucleus neurone where the axosomatic input arises from the nuclear interpositus and the dendritic from the cerebral cortex (Tsukahara & Kosaka, 1966). As illustrated in Fig. 6.26, the axosomatic EPSPs have a shorter

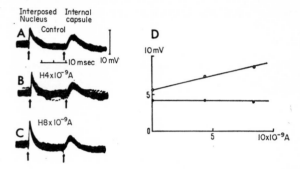

FIG. 6.26. Dendritic and somatic EPSP in red nucleus cells. In A to C, intracellular EPSPs recorded from red nucleus neurones. The first EPSP (left arrow) is evoked by electrical stimulation of the contralateral interpositus nucleus, the second from a stimulus to the internal capsule (right arrow). Note the different time courses of the two synaptic potentials. In B and C, the membrane potential is hyperpolarized artificially and an increase in the amplitude of the interpositus EPSP is observed, while the cortical EPSP is not changed. The plot to the right is a current-voltage relation, showing in open dots, the changes in the amplitude of the somatic and closed dot, the dendritic EPSP in mV (ordinate), while currents of different intensities were applied across the membrane (abscissa current in 10×10^{-9} A). Time and voltage calibration as indicated (Tsukahara & Kosaka, 1966).

time course with a faster rise time than the axodendritic EPSPs. Moreover, if current is passed across the somatic region of the cell, the axosomatic potentials are more affected by the new potential level than the axodendritic, as is to be expected since the density per unit area of the applied current, and therefore the potential change, will be maximal at the soma.

A quite different situation is found in those cells known to generate dendritic spikes, as seems to occur in the Purkinje cells of the cerebellum. In such a case dendritic inhibition is necessary in order to control the spike generation since the somatic inhibition is not, by itself, able to control completely the excitability of this cell (Eccles, Llinás, & Sasaki, 1966*b*). Furthermore, in the alligator where Purkinje cells have been shown to generate dendritic spikes, dendritic inhibition by the activation of stellate cells (no true basket cells are present) is able to block very effectively these dendritic action potentials (Llinás *et al.*, 1968).

It appears, then, that in neurones of complex functional characteristics such as those representing Sherrington's 'final common path', i.e., the motoneurones, integration is the product of both 'sustained' and phasic synaptic inputs.

7

EXTRACELLULAR FIELD POTENTIALS IN THE CENTRAL NERVOUS SYSTEM

THIS chapter is devoted to the interpretation of the extracellular field potentials which are generated by the activity of single cells or groups of cells in the central nervous system, and which can be recorded with extracellular electrodes. The field potentials produced by a group of cells reflect in an indirect way the membrane potential changes, i.e., the synaptic and action potentials, which the cells undergo in unison. A study of such potentials therefore gives invaluable information regarding the average activity of the cells in the group, and is a basic prerequisite for the understanding of the physiological characteristics of any neural assembly. When the anatomical arrangement of a neural assembly or pool is well understood, the activity of the pool as a whole can often be treated as if generated by a small number of single 'ideal' elements, each representing the average behaviour of the particular cells which are activated synchronously from specific sites or modes of stimulation.

GENESIS OF EXTRACELLULAR FIELD POTENTIALS

The way in which extracellular field potentials are generated, though now reasonably well understood both qualitatively and quantitatively by those who have gone deeply into the question, seems unfortunately to be quite obscure both to students and to a large proportion of those who find themselves forced to work with them. This situation has not been aided by most textbook discussions, which concentrate on methods of analysis which have been designed mainly for consideration of the electrocardiogram, the extracellular potential related to the action currents of the heart, which is of course very much a special case. Such formulations as that of the equivalent dipole, or that of the solid angle subtended at the field point by each active area element (for exact derivation and discussion see Plonsey, 1965), though often useful, will not be discussed further in this monograph. Instead, emphasis will be placed on providing a description which will, we hope, lead to a better intuitive understanding of the processes which take place.

As was seen in Chapter 2, a cell whose membrane potential is changed non-uniformly so that one part of the membrane is depolarized more than another will have current flow within it. Together with this intracellular current, there is by necessity a corresponding flow of current in the extracellular medium, where the current path is completed. It is obvious that if the extracellular space is approximately isotropic, no preferential path will exist for the current field (which is a vectorial field) through this medium so that the field will extend throughout the conducting mass. The conductance of the extracellular fluid is finite, i.e., its resistance is not zero, therefore this current field is associated with an extracellular potential field, the current at any point being proportional to the potential gradient. It is of importance to keep in mind that an extracellular field potential is generated only as a result of current flow within a cell or cells. If a cell is at any time uniformly polarized or depolarized, then whatever its geometry there will be no current flow within it (since all points inside are at the same potential) and thus no external current or extracellular potential fields. The second important point is that the extracellular field potentials generated from the action currents within a number of cells will add linearly and algebraically at every point in the space concerned. Thus, cancellation of fields can take place (Lorente de Nó, 1939)—the spatial orientation and geometrical configuration of the cells concerned being for this reason always crucial.

Many of the features of field potentials, including the reason why both positive and negative deflections can be generated in different areas as a result of a monophasic intracellular potential, can be seen in the diagram of Fig. 7.1. It is supposed that the cell can be divided into two discrete regions (e.g., soma and dendrite, or muscle fibre and endplate area). In the region with capacity C_1 there is a membrane conductance change which causes current to flow into the cell at that point ($\bigcirc$). The current must also leave the cell. One outward path is simply back to the extracellular medium (from I_1 to O_1) via the membrane capacity (C_1) or the membrane conductance in parallel with it ($1/R_1$). This purely

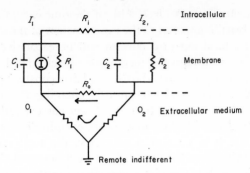

FIG. 7.1. Equivalent electrical circuit for a patch of neurone membrane having at the point O_1 a locus of conductance change which simulates a synaptic event. The patch of membrane consists of two transverse circuits—C_1R_1 and C_2R_2. These are linked internally (intracellularly) by R_i at I_1 and I_2 and externally (extracellularly) by R_o and the resistances in the path—O_2 to Remote Indifferent to O_1. The intracellular potentials are measured between the intracellular compartment and the indifferent electrode; the extracellular potentials between O_2 and the indifferent electrode or O_1 and the indifferent electrode (see text for further explanation).

transverse current does not generate an extracellular field since it does not travel across the extracellular space, given that we define the locus of exit (O_1) as a point, and thus the current path has no longitudinal component. The other current pathway is through the internal conductor of the cell with resistance (R_i) to region I_2. This current must also pass through the membrane, i.e., through C_2 and/or R_2, and return from O_2 to O_1, through the multitude of paths available in the extracellular medium. For convenience only two paths are drawn from O_2 to O_1, one direct (with resistance R_o), the other via the remote reference electrode at zero potential. Obviously, region O_2 must be positive and O_1 negative with respect to the indifferent electrode. Provided the extracellular medium is ohmic in its behaviour, the magnitude of the positivity at O_2 and negativity at O_1 and the potential at any point in the extracellular fluid, will be linearly related to the magnitude of the current that flows, both extracellularly and intracellularly. The region where current goes into the cell is the current 'sink'; where current exists there is a 'source'.

If a sink, or source, is restricted to a very small area of a cell, the amount of current which flows back through that particular spot is very small. Thus, the current which flows across the extracellular path is nearly equal to the total current across the spot where the conductance change took place. Also, if the time course of the sink or source is brief, compared to the time constant of the membrane, almost all the local outward current will be capacitive and thus will pass mainly through the membrane capacity not far from its origin. Thus, as a first approximation, a fairly constant proportion of the total current will go towards charging the membrane capacity close to the locus of transmembrane current and the membrane potential will be close to a constant multiplied by the time integral of the total current. Conversely, the total extracellular current, and therefore the extracellular field potential close to the source or sink, will be roughly proportional to the first derivative with respect to time of the intracellular potential change. It will be seen that this will in general not be true if the time course of the active source or sink is of the same order of magnitude as the membrane time constant; an indefinitely maintained source or sink will generate an indefinitely maintained extracellular potential. Along a cable-like fibre the external potential profile will in this case be proportional to a mirror image of the potential across the intracellular medium, except for a displacement so that the total spatial integral of the outside potential is zero. Evidently most situations will be somewhere between the two extremes.

The case of the field potential generated by an action potential propagated along a nerve fibre is somewhat special. Qualitatively it is easiest to understand if one considers the quasi-stationary field which exists at any one moment. In the region where the internal potential is greatest, there is an active sink. Behind this is an active source where G_k has increased ('active' repolarization) and current flows outward. Ahead of the sink the area behaves as a passive source. To see how things will look with a propagated action potential, one can perform the following thought experiment. Instead of imagining the action potential as moving in one direction, one visualizes an extracellular recording electrode as moving in the opposite direction. It records first a small, slowly rising positivity which turns abruptly into an intense negativity, as it passes over the sink. Then there is another reversal, not quite so large, to a more slowly rising positivity, which then decays. The essentially monophasic intracellular action potential is converted into a triphasic extracellular potential. The net result is similar in shape to the second derivative with respect to time of the intracellularly recorded action potential.

The same result emerges if one applies Kirchoff's laws to a

small section of the axon cylinder (cf. Chapter 2, p. 71). The current flowing into or out of the membrane i_m corresponding to a small length of fibre (δx) is equal to the change in current flow (i_1) in the intracellular medium, i.e.

$$-i_\mathrm{m} = \frac{\delta i_1}{\delta x}.$$

The internal current flow, however, is proportional to the potential gradient ($\delta V/\delta \chi$)

$$-r_1 i_1 = \frac{\delta V}{\delta x}$$

therefore
$$i_\mathrm{m} = \frac{1}{r_1} \frac{\delta^2 V}{\delta x^2}$$

Since the internal potential, V, has the same shape plotted against time as plotted against distance along the fibre—this is true for any wave conducted without decrement at a constant velocity—one has

$$I = \frac{a}{2R_2} \frac{\delta^2 V}{\delta t^2} \frac{1}{\ominus^2}.$$

When I is membrane current density, a is the radius of fibre, $\ominus$ is the conduction velocity, and R_2 is the specific resistance of the axoplasm (Hodgkin & Huxley, 1952c). If the current going through the extracellular medium at this point were only the local current going into or out of the membrane, the extracellular potential recorded would be exactly proportional to the second derivative of the action potential as recorded intracellularly. The conditions for this may be met fairly closely in the case of a recording electrode just outside a node of Ranvier of a myelinated nerve fibre. In the more general case where the extracellular current comes from and goes to spatially distributed sources and sinks, the situation is quite complicated and a fairly sophisticated analysis is necessary (Clark & Plonsey, 1966). Such an analysis shows that even as a first approximation it is not valid to neglect the non-longitudinal, i.e. axial, current flow in the external conducting medium. The external current lines are in fact skewed (Offner, 1954), with the result that total longitudinal current and surface current density are not simply proportional.

A detailed and quantitative theoretical analysis of extracellular potential fields for a variety of situations would be justified if it were not for the fact that considerable theoretical grounds exist against their application in practice. The interpretation of field potentials is straightforward only if two assumptions are made:

(1) That the nervous tissue behaves as a perfect ohmic resistor, that is, a medium containing no capacitative or inductive elements, and whose resistance is independent of the current flowing through it.

(2) That the nervous tissue behaves as an isotropic medium, i.e., a medium whose conducting properties are the same independent of the direction of current flow.

In fact, neither assumption can be exactly true for the central nervous system. In a medium made up largely of cells, with fairly large membrane capacity, the total impedance for high-frequency components of a current wave form must be less than for low-frequency components. Objections have also been raised regarding the second assumption (Rushton, 1937; Tasaki, 1964). In nerve trunks, the transverse resistance appears to be as much as fifty times greater than the longitudinal (Tasaki, 1964). However, it is likely that as a first approximation the anisotropicity in the central nervous system is not a source of grave distortion, since the lack of uniformity of the tissue is small over the distances across which the potential fields are recorded.

Because of these limitations it would seem most useful to consider extracellular field potentials in a semi-quantitative rather than strictly quantitative way. This approach will be illustrated in the following sections.

EXPERIMENTALLY OBSERVED EXTRACELLULAR FIELD POTENTIALS
GENERATED BY A NERVE IMPULSE

The current fields which surround a nerve during the propagation of an action potential in a volume conductor have been estimated by measuring the potential changes which such currents generate between an electrode in the vicinity of the nerve and an indifferent electrode some distance away.

A very elegant experimental analysis was published by Lorente de Nó (1947b). He measured the field potentials which can be recorded in a two-dimensional conductive medium (filter paper soaked with electrolyte) when a nerve segment was placed in contact with this medium and the nerve was activated by a short-lasting electrical pulse. The experimental design is illustrated in Fig. 7.2. The nerve, a frog sciatic, had one end submerged in a paraffin-oil pool, where a bipolar stimulating electrode was used to initiate nerve impulses (Fig. 7.2A). The rest of the nerve was laid flat across the filter paper for a length of 26 mm. The amplitude and time course of the potential field was recorded between an indifferent electrode at a distant point and a microelectrode, each at a different site in the vicinity of the nerve (Fig. 7.2B). The recording sites were distributed in three rows of four loci each. The first four points lay against the nerve at 0, 7, 15, and 26 mm from the point of exit of the nerve from the oil pool. The other two rows of four points were located at the same longitudinal coordinates along the nerve bundle, but 3 and 10 mm away from the first row, respectively (Fig. 7.2C). The field potentials at each one of these points were recorded and their amplitude and polarity was then measured at distinct time intervals (Fig. 7.2D) after the stimulating current pulse. This type of data, as will be shown later, allows the computation of the current field which generates the external potential and thus the description of the sequence of events which produces the propagated disturbance in neural elements.

The fields generated at each one of these recording points are shown in Fig. 7.2D. They are biphasic at the point of exit (0,0) and perpendicular to it (points 0,3 and 0,10), and at the end of the nerve segment (26,0), but are triphasic elsewhere.

The polarities of the fields are negative-positive at 0,0 implying that the membrane at that point is acting as a sink of current as the action potential exits from the pool, and a source of current as it propagates down the length of the nerve trunk. At points 7 and 15 mm along the nerve (points 0,7 and 0,15), the potential is positive-negative-positive, implying that these loci at first behave as current sources as the impulse approaches them. The negativity indicates that the area of the membrane near the recording site then behaves as a current sink, the action potential at that moment being associated with an inward current across that particular membrane area. As the action potential is conducted away, this membrane area behaves as a current source once again. The explanation of these results is now classical. As was first demonstrated by Hodgkin (1937), the action potential is conducted from one point of a nerve to another by the spread of local currents. These currents

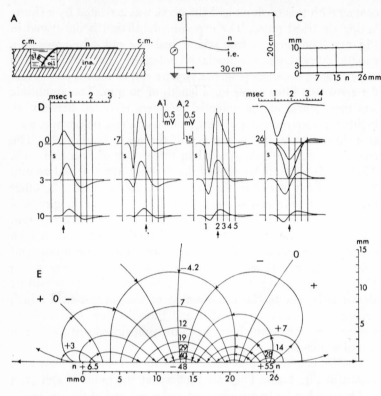

FIG. 7.2. Electrical field potentials and fields of current generated by a nerve segment on a two-dimensional conducting media.
A, B, and C, experimental arrangement. In A, the nerve segment
(n) is laid on top of a block of insulating material (ins) which is
covered by a thin conducting medium (c.m.). The conducting
medium was a sheet of blotting paper soaked with Ringer's solution. One of the ends of the nerve was submerged in an oil pool
(oil), where the bipolar stimulating electrodes were located (st).
The indifferent recording electrode was placed in one corner of
the square 20 × 30 cm blotting paper area (B). The active electrode
had a diameter of 40 μ. Diagram C illustrates the twelve recording
sites from which the records in D were obtained. The abscissa
represents the distance in mm from the exit of the nerve from the
oil pool to the place of recording, along the length of the nerve.
The ordinate represents the transversal distance in millimetres
between the main axis of the nerve and the recording loci. In D,
the field potentials produced by the compound action currents as
the nerve impulses travel from one end to the other of the nerve
segment in contact with the blotting paper. The field potentials
correspond to the twelve recording sites diagrammed in C. The
vertical lines demarcate particular time intervals after the
stimulus artefact, which are the same for all twelve recording

points. In E, the amplitude and polarity of each one of the fields recorded at the twelve points was measured at t_2 (see arrows). A plot of the isopotential surfaces was then drawn (E) by writing down the amplitude and polarity of the field at each recording point and joining together by means of lines, all points having the same potential and polarity (these are marked in E as numbers representing arbitrary units). If now a series of lines perpendicular to the isopotential surfaces are drawn (lines with arrows), the current field generated by the propagation of the action potential at time, t_2, can be visualized (Lorente de Nó, 1947*b*).

are produced by the mechanisms already described (Chapter 2). The essential feature is that in response to a threshold depolarization at a given region of an electroresponsive membrane there has developed an inward current, which spreads longitudinally along the intracellular core and is therefore accompanied by a simultaneous outward current across areas of the cell's membrane at both sides of the sink. The outward flow of current will be detected as a positivity in the outside media, the inward current as a negativity.

If the values of the field potentials are measured at any particular instant at the 12 recording sites (Fig. 7.2D), a graphical representation of isopotential areas can be drawn (Fig. 7.2E) for that instant in time. Given that the medium is isotropic, the current must flow at right angles to the isopotential surfaces. A series of current lines, demarcated by arrows which indicate the direction of flow, is illustrated in Fig. 7.2E. The current density (current per unit area) is expressed by the number of lines which cross that area at a given time. The diagram shows that at time 2 of Fig. 7.2D the centre of the nerve segment is acting as a sink, while the two ends act as sources for that sink. It must be remembered that in order to draw isopotential lines and reconstruct the action currents in any medium, it is necessary to measure the potential field value from different sampling points at exactly the same instant, since the current flow is for all practical purposes instantaneous (close to the speed of light). This point is of special interest when measuring the field potentials generated in the CNS, as will be seen later.

A similar situation to that illustrated in Fig. 7.2D is found when an action potential is initiated in the soma of a (theoretical) neurone which lacks dendrites. In this case a negative-positive field will be recorded near the soma membrane. If, on the other hand, the cell is activated antidromically (that is, an action potential is initiated at a distant point in its axon) and then propagated towards the cell's body, the potential recorded near the soma will be triphasic, the negativity generated by the antidromic invasion of the soma being preceded by positivity where the soma acts as a source for the sink on the axon. The presence of dendrites considerably complicates the analysis of the field potential associated with action potential generation, especially since the exact geometrical distribution of the dendritic tree cannot be known in advance for any given cell in the CNS.

ELECTRICAL SIGNS OF CENTRAL NEURONE ACTIVATION

As pointed out by Lorente de Nó (1939), the propagation of an action potential from the axon to the soma of a neurone should be, and is, different in several respects from the propagation of an action potential between portions of an axon. For instance, the soma of most cells is extremely short in length as compared with the length of their axon. Thus, the mere fact that the antidromic invasion of the soma of a nerve cell can be recorded as a distinct component means that it is different from the extracellular potential generated by the axon in at least one aspect—the speed of propagation. The propagation time is, in fact, much greater. This is to be expected as a result of the relatively enormous somatic membrane area, which acts as a large capacitative load per unit length. It takes a comparatively long time for the action current supplied by the axonal active area to bring the soma to threshold level.

The theoretical considerations regarding the field potential generated by the soma dendritic invasion of a nerve cell were originally stressed by Lorente de Nó as being the following: If a microelectrode records the potential generated by a cell having a rounded soma and dendrites which spread radially in all directions, it will 'see' very different potentials, depending upon its location in relation to the soma dendritic complex. If the electrode is near the cell soma, it will record mainly the potentials generated by the currents flowing across the membrane of the soma, since most of the dendritic tree is radiating outwards from that place and so away from the microelectrode tip. Thus, an action potential generated at the soma will be a biphasic negative-positive wave. If the microelectrode is near a dendrite halfway between its terminal end and the soma, it will be theoretically a triphasic positive-negative-positive field, if the dendrite is able to generate an action potential which propagates out past the electrode. This point holds, however, only if the appearance of a sink in the dendritic tree follows in time the sink at the soma. If the conduction time across the soma is larger than the utilization time for the activation of the dendrites, by the electrotonic spread from the soma, as in the case of the Purkinje cell (Eccles, Llinás, & Sasaki, 1966*b*), the dendritic tree will become a sink while the soma is still active, and thus a negative field similar to the one recorded at the level of the soma will be observed at the dendritic layer. In the particular case of the Purkinje cell, the dendritic field has a similar latency for the negative peak, but a faster rising time, and begins 0·2 msec after the initiation of the sink at the soma. Finally, if the microelectrode is at the end region of a dendrite, a positive-negative or a purely positive potential should be recorded, according to Lorente de Nó. It is important to remember, however, that this author emphasizes that a negative field does not imply active invasion at that particular place, since sinks can also occur in other circumstances such as at the end terminal of a nerve segment (Lorente de Nó, 1947*b*; Frey-gang & Frank, 1959; Rall, 1964). A passive blind end can act as a sink at the time when there is active repolarization (due for instance to increased G_k) in the proximal region of the nerve segment.

IDEAL ELEMENTS

In studying the evoked field potentials in the central nervous system, one of the most common problems encountered is the analysis of fields generated by the synchronous activation of large numbers of cells belonging to a certain pool or nucleus. In most cases this is not the reflection of true physiological activity, but merely one of the sequels of experimental electrical or gross sensory stimulation.

One of the aims in the study of evoked synchronized activity is the reduction of the simultaneous activation of a large group or pool of cells to that of an equivalent single ideal element, allowing an approximate evaluation of the overall average activity in the particular neurone assembly. By means of the method outlined in Fig. 7.2, but mapping in three instead of two dimensions, it is possible to approximate this goal. If the substitution has been correctly developed, the current field produced by the statistical model unit is similar to the field produced by the pool. Lorente de Nó has developed, on intuitive grounds, what he called the elementary types of current fields for neurone pools, for each of which the unit is arrived at in a different way. These are described in the following sections.

The closed field

This concept applies to a pool in which most of the elements are multipolar cells with more or less radially oriented dendritic trees, arranged in such a way that the great majority of the somas are in the centre of the area and the dendrites are arranged in the periphery of this central core. This is the case for the III and IV cranial nerve motoneurone pools (Lorente de Nó, 1947a). Such a pool can be substituted by a single element consisting of a central soma and a series of radially directed dendrites, as illustrated in Fig. 7.3A.

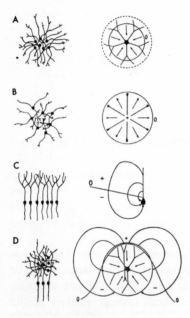

FIG. 7.3. Configuration of the different types of neurone pools in the CNS. A and B, closed field types. In A, left, a series of neurones having their somas in the centre of the pool and the dendrites in its periphery; right, schematic diagram of the simplified pool element. In B, left, closed field where the somatic elements are arranged in the periphery of the pool and the dendrites are located in the centre; to the right, schematic diagram of the field. C, left, an open field where the neural elements are oriented so that the somas are all in one region and the dendrites are oriented towards the opposite side; at the right, the diagram of the field. D, left, open-closed field where the two types of groupings are mixed together. At the right the diagram of the type of field evoked (Lorente de Nó, 1947b).

The reasons for such simplification are readily understandable. Since the dendrites of the cells in the centre of the pool extend radially in all directions, the extracellular potentials generated by these dendrites will tend to cancel each other at the core of the pool, where their more or less simultaneous currents are of similar magnitudes but opposite direction. In the periphery the dendrites radiate in all directions outward from the central core so that the currents which run in the same direction add and are equivalent to those that would be produced by large dendritic branches extending radially from a single large soma.

If a large number of cells in such a pool were to be activated in a synchronous manner, the resulting field at the time the somas were activated would be negative at the core and positive in the periphery of the pool, since the dendrites would serve as sources of current to the centrally located somas. The zero isopotential surface of such a pool would be spherical, its diameter depending on the electrical excitability of the dendrites of these cells. If the dendrites are not able to support an action potential, or if the potential change produced is only a somatic subthreshold EPSP, the dendrites would serve as current sources exclusively and thus only a positive field would be located at some distance between the core and the tips of the dendrites. If, however, the dendrites are able to support action potentials through some of their lengths, the initial negativity would spread outwards and not only the tips of the dendrites would behave as current sources, but also the somas of the cells. An electrode in the centre of the pool would record at this time a positivity, as the action potentials travel outwards to the proximal dendritic segments. To an electrode situated between the central core and the tips of the dendrites the field would be positive-negative, since these dendritic segments would tend to act as sources of current for somatic spikes and then as sinks as the action potentials reached them. The peripheral dendrites would, however, behave as current sources and in this manner, only a positivity would be recorded at the periphery. The zero isopotential line under these circumstances would still be a sphere, but it would have a larger diameter.

Another situation in which a closed field would be generated would be the converse of the above, one where most of the dendrites are located in the centre of the pool while the somas lie in the periphery, as in the case of the superior olive (Lorente de Nó, 1947a) (Fig. 7.3B). Under these conditions the field would be negative at the periphery and positive at the centre as the cell bodies are excited. The field would, however, reverse to a negative centre and a positive periphery as the action potentials invade the dendrites.

The most important point about the closed fields is that, because the currents flow radially between the centre and periphery of the pool in all directions, no sign of the activity of the cellular group would be detected by an electrode until it was in the interior or close to the peripheral surface of the pool. Hence the term 'closed field pool' (Lorente de Nó, 1947*a*).

The open field

A second type of pool arrangement is that typically found in the cerebral cortex, the cerebellum, or the hippocampus, where the dendrites of the large pyramidal or Purkinje cells are located at one end of a large volume conductor and all the somas are accumulated towards the opposite end (Fig. 7.3C). This type of pool, designated an 'open field' pool, can be substituted by a single element having a soma and a single cylindrical core conductor dendrite oriented in the same direction as the main axis of the dendrites which represent the dendritic tree. If such a pool is activated synchronously at the somas, the current field (generated between the somatic sink and the dendritic source) spreads throughout the volume of the conductor, generating a negative field potential at all points at the somatic side of the zero isopotential surface and a positive field potential at all points at the dendritic side of the zero isopotential surface. The zero isopotential surface extends *ad infinitum* horizontally, with the result that a recording microelectrode would be able to 'see' the field potentials on either side from a relatively large distance. Of course, the field potential amplitude decays approximately as the square of the distance. If action potentials invade the dendrites of the neurones in the pool, a microelectrode located midway between the soma and the tip of the dendrites will record a positive-negative-positive field as the action potential approaches, reaches and leaves the recording site. At the tips the field will be (as in the case of the end of the nerve segment) positive-negative, or positive only if the action potential fails to invade a large part of the peripheral dendritic tree (Eccles, Llinás, & Sasaki, 1966*b*).

The open-closed field

The third arrangement which can be encountered is the 'open-closed' field in which both kinds of neural elements, the radial dendrites and the elongated dendrites, are co-existent in the pool. Depending on the number of neural elements of each given kind, the types of fields found would be expected to vary from a completely closed to a completely open field, with the full gamut of variations in between. However, if the number of cells of each kind is roughly equal, a field of the type shown in Fig. 7.3D could be found, that is, all points above the zero isopotential line would be positive and all points below the zero isopotential line negative with respect to ground. The concepts briefly outlined are to be used only as a general working hypothesis as they provide only a very rough approximation of the situation.

EXTRACELLULAR POTENTIAL CHANGES EVOKED BY ACTIVATION OF
DIFFERENT REGIONS OF CENTRAL NEURONES AND THEIR RELATION
TO THE INTRACELLULAR POTENTIAL

Data gathered by extracellular and intracellular recordings from various types of central neurones (Coombs, Eccles, & Fatt, 1955*a*, *c*; Frank & Fuortes, 1956; Fatt, 1957; Freygang, 1958; Freygang & Frank, 1959; Terzuolo & Araki, 1961) have demonstrated that there are definite differences between the extracellular potential field generated by action potentials conducted along axons and the extracellular field generated by the activation of their somas.

The genesis of the fields generated by the antidromic activation of a single cell is best understood when simultaneous intracellular and extracellular recordings are performed from the different regions of the cell, i.e., its axon, soma, and dendrites. A typical record of the intracellular potential generated by the all-or-none activation of a central axon can be seen in record 7.4A, lower trace. In the upper trace a second electrode immediately outside the cell recorded the field potential produced by the action currents accompanying the spike potential. It shows a typical triphasic all-or-none positive-negative-positive field potential very much like those recorded from nerve action potentials in a volume conductor (Lorente de Nó, 1947*b*). This axon was stimulated antidromically from the ventral root in the lumbar spinal cord of a cat. The baseline demonstrates the all-or-none nature of these potentials. Records 7.4B to D illustrate similar recording situations from other cells which suggest that the recordings were made at decreasing distances from the axosomatic junctions. As would be expected, a series of changes in the shape of the records appear which can be related to the site of recording. For instance, record 7.4B is supposedly taken in the axon near

K

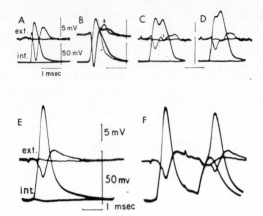

FIG. 7.4. Simultaneous intracellular and extracellular potentials generated by the antidromic activation of motoneurones and recorded at different sites along the axon-soma junction. In all records the lower trace is the intracellular action potential and the upper trace the extracellular action current. In A to D, potentials obtained at the axon or axon hillock at decreasing distances from the motoneurone's soma. E and F, intracellular recording from the motoneurone's soma. In F, a second stimulus, at short interval, activates antidromically the motoneurone and fails in one instance to invade the soma. In this case, an IS (initial segment spike) is conducted electrotonically to the recording site and appears as a low amplitude all-or-none depolarization. The simultaneous extracellular electrode records the current produced by the activation of the soma as well as the current across the membrane when the soma is not able to generate an action spike. Time and voltage calibrations as illustrated (Terzuolo & Araki, 1961).

the soma; the intracellular potential shows the usual positive spike recordable in myelinated fibres plus a late all-or-none positive component (arrow).

Extracellularly (upper trace) the field is triphasic positive–negative–positive, but when the late intracellular depolarization is present (Fig. 7.4B, arrow) there is a further all-or-none negative–positive wave on top of the late positivity. If two antidromic stimuli are applied at short intervals, there is a disappearance of the late negative–positive component, which suggests that this is produced by a process having a longer refractory period than the earlier response generated by the axon. In the experiment illustrated in Fig. 7.4C, D the microelectrode was most probably inside the axon hillock of a motoneurone. In C the intracellular record consists of two positive potentials of about the same magnitude.

Extracellularly the third positivity of the potential field has been cut short by the generation of a negativity (arrow), a positive potential which corresponds in time with the second intracellular positivity. In Fig. 7.4D the second intracellular positivity is longer than the preceding one and is accompanied by a small negativity in the extracellular field which masks the positivity following the first spike and is followed by a large positivity. Finally, in record 7.4E the usual intracellular potential recorded at the soma is illustrated. The rising phase of the action potential consists of two components: the IS or initial segment spike which was fully developed in records B to D, and the SD (soma dendritic spike) generated across the somatic and part of the dendritic membrane which was seen on the second positivity in B to C. The extracellular potential recorded in the proximity of the cell body is tetraphasic, positive-negative-negative-positive. Where two antidromic volleys follow each other at close intervals, the SD component of the second is abolished due to the refractoriness of the soma dendritic membrane. When this happens (Fig. 7.4F), the second extracellular field is biphasic positive–negative, like the potential recorded when the action potential reaches a nerve terminal.

Although it has been pointed out (Terzuolo & Araki, 1961) that the recordings illustrated in Fig. 7.4 are not a 'surface' record at the membrane in the strict sense, a reasonable agreement between the intracellular potential and the action current was found in most cases. Of special importance in the understanding of the antidromic invasion was the finding that the action current generated across the membrane of the soma during the SD spike is close to the second derivative of the intracellular action potential. The fact that the extracellular field potential is tetraphasic implies (Terzuolo & Araki, 1961) that the cell in question is of the closed field type; the currents generated by a sink in the soma are supplied mostly by the dendritic tree since no obvious outward current is seen at the initial segment level. Under these conditions the field generated is a negativity having a zero isopotential spheric surface somewhere at the periphery of the dendritic tree. The positivity produced by the source at the axon hillock (see Fig. 7.4E) will be overridden by this negative field potential. The positivity which follows would be generated by outward current from soma to dendrites as the electrotonically or actively conducted potentials invade the dendrites.

GIANT EXTRACELLULAR SPIKES

It is well known that large extracellular potentials, up to 25 mV in amplitude, can be recorded when a microelectrode is in close proximity to a neurone generating action potentials (Granit & Phillips, 1956; Freygang, 1958; Freygang & Frank, 1959; Terzuolo & Araki, 1961). These spikes, which are generally biphasic (positive–negative), can be recorded for long periods of time (up to half an hour) without signs of injury, and are thus regarded as being generated by uninjured cells when the microelectrode is in actual contact with the cell membrane (Freygang, 1958). Studies in which simultaneous intra- and extracellular recordings from neurones have been achieved (Freygang & Frank, 1959; Terzuolo & Araki, 1961) have shown that this giant extracellular potential follows closely the first derivative of the intracellular action potential. These findings have been taken to indicate that the membrane around the intracellular microelectrode becomes inactive (Freygang & Frank, 1959). Since Terzuolo & Araki (1961) showed that a very slight withdrawal of the microelectrodes (small enough not to dislodge the intracellular electrode) can produce an extracellular potential close to the second derivation of the intra-cellular spike (Fig. 7.5B and C), it has been presumed that the area of inactivation is produced by the contact of the extracellular electrode with the membrane. The large amplitude of the potential is explained on the basis of the large extracellular resistance between the electrode tip (and the membrane close to it) and the surrounding extracellular fluid, associated with the dimp-

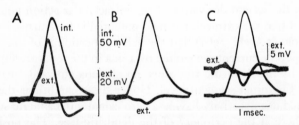

FIG. 7.5. Giant extracellular action potential antidromically evoked from motoneurones. A. Intracellular (int.) and extracellular (ext.) potentials simultaneously recorded. In B, the extracellular electrode was slightly moved so that the usual extracellular field could be seen (ext.). In C, the extracellular field is shown at higher gain. Time and voltage calibration as indicated (Terzuolo & Araki, 1961).

ling of the surface of the neurone, by the microelectrode. This dimpling will produce a high resistance path between the glass walls of the microelectrode tip and the neurone's membrane (Wolbarsht, 1960). Under such conditions the microelectrode should be in effect capacitatively coupled via the neurone's membrane to the cell's interior. There would be then no need to postulate an inactive area under the microelectrode tip (Terzuolo & Araki, 1961). Simultaneous intra- and extracellular recordings from other tissues (Håkansson, 1957; Murakami, Watanabe, & Tomita, 1961) have also shown similar results. The latter authors found a wide range of variations of extracellular field potentials from the first to the second derivative of the intracellular action potentials. These variations were attributed to the state of the specific ionic conductance systems of the cell membrane; the current, in fact, varied between a mainly capacitative current (the ohmic component being very small) and the usual capacitative plus ionic currents. It is believed that the late component is the most labile of the ionic currents. This explains why in semi-deteriorated cells the first part of the extracellular potential follows closely the second derivative of the transmembrane potential, whereas the second positive component approaches the first derivative.

ACTION POTENTIALS IN DENDRITES

The field potentials which can be recorded with a microelectrode in the proximity of the dendrites of a given neurone depend on two distinct parameters. Firstly, the relative position of the microelectrode tip with respect to the dendrite (i.e., initial, middle, or end portion) and secondly, the ability of the dendrite to generate an action potential. If it is supposed that the dendrite can conduct a non-decremental potential to the vicinity of its ending, the field potential generated would be very similar to that produced by a nerve in a conducting medium. It would thus be biphasic negative-positive near the soma, triphasic positive-negative-positive midway through the dendrite, and biphasic positive-negative near the dendrite tips. Records of these different types have been published (Lorente de Nó, 1939, 1953) and have formed the basis of the above interpretation. Dendritic impulse propagation has been strongly suggested in the case of spinal motoneurones by Fatt (1957) and confirmed by Terzuolo & Araki (1961), since simultaneous penetration of the soma and a presumed dendrite (Fig. 7.6A and B) yielded intracellular potentials with a time delay between spike peaks of 0·3 msec. It was concluded that the later spike was recorded at a dendrite. The fact that no decrement of the dendrite spike was observed strongly suggests a non-decremental conduction. A similar conclusion was reached (by the same authors) with simultaneous intra- and extracellular recordings from motoneurones. In Fig. 7.6C the intracellular and

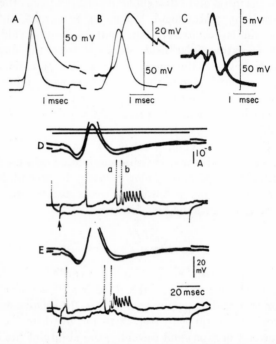

FIG. 7.6. Intrasomatic and intradendritic recordings from moto-neurones. A. Simultaneous double penetration of a motoneurone showing action potentials with slightly different latencies and longer duration for the alleged dendritic spike. In B, another example showing a similar characteristic. In C, the intracellular dendritic electrode is withdrawn and the extracellular field potential is recorded at the vicinity of the cell. In this case, the field is positive-negative-positive-negative, suggesting that the action potential invades the dendrite after it has served as a source of current for the soma (Terzuolo & Araki, 1961). D. Upper traces: current monitor. Middle: cortical surface recruiting response. Lower trace: intracellular record. Two superimposed traces, control and during current injection. Membrane hyperpolarization reveals a small complex EPSP. E. Same as in D. Note underlying EPSP of the first response (Maekawa & Purpura, unpublished). Time and voltage calibration as indicated.

extracellular potentials most probably were recorded from the same cell. The extracellular fields show two positive peaks at the time of the IS and SD spikes and a late negativity. This field potential suggests that the dendrite behaved as a source of current for the IS and SD spikes and then became a sink itself as the action potential propagated into it. Another type of evidence which can be used for the postulation of dendritic spikes is the intracellular recording of action potentials having multiple firing levels. One such type of record is illustrated in Fig. 7.6D and E from a red nucleus neurone (Maekawa & Purpura, personal communication). The changes in the spike's firing level (lower records in D and E) are direct evidence for the existence of multiple impulse initiation sites. The partial spikes which follow the third action potential in D (b) and E appear to be generated by action potentials in dendrites rather than by the activation of the initial segment given its fast rise time. A very intriguing explanation for this type of record is that, as pointed out by Ramón y Cajal (1911), some of the neurones of the mesencephalic neurones have axons which arise from large dendrites and thus synaptic activation of a dendritic site close to the axon could generate 'antidromic'-like responses in the soma. The fact that these action potentials are smaller than usual indicates their failure to invade the impalement site (Purpura, 1967).

As far as extracellular negativities are concerned, as stated above even if completely passive behaviour of the dendrites is assumed, the discharge of the membrane capacitance by electrotonic spread from an active soma can produce a negative field potential at the dendritic region (Freygang & Frank, 1959). This subject has been extensively elaborated by Rall (1964). Recent experiments on the antidromic invasion of Purkinje cells in deafferented cerebella (Eccles, Llinás, & Sasaki, 1966*b*) have shown that a negativity of the same magnitude as that seen in the region of the soma can be recorded in the dendritic region of the Purkinje cells up to 250 μ from the surface (Fig. 7.7A). From that point on to the surface, the negativity is still present but declines rapidly in amplitude as distance from the soma is increased. The peak also becomes very late, so that it corresponds with the late positivity seen at the soma level. These records indicate that while Purkinje cell dendrites conduct an all-or-nothing action potential, the conduction is decremental as it approaches the terminal branches. At the time of peak antidromic invasion, which reaches only as far as 300 μ from the cerebellar surface (Fig. 7.7), a rapid positive field is

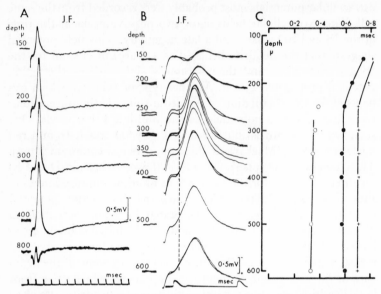

Fig. 7.7. Field potential evoked by antidromic activation of Purkinje cells in chronically deafferented cerebellum. A. Field potential generated at different depths from the surface of the cerebellar
cortex. Note the triphasic field at the white matter level (800 μ)
and how it becomes larger and broader as it reaches the Purkinje
cell level. B, as in A, but at a higher sweep speed. The vertical line
shows the conduction time for initial negativity of the field
potential from depth to surface. In C, closed circles, time to
summit at different depths; open circles, time to reach 0·15 mV
negativity at different depths. Note that there is an increase in the
latency at the more superficial levels; crosses represent summit
latencies in another set of records. Time and voltage calibration as
indicated (Eccles, Llinás, & Sasaki, 1966*b*).

observed near the surface which corresponds to the negativity
recorded deeper. Following Lorente de Nó's ideas, the peripheral
negativity has been explained as follows. The upper parts of the
dendrites are not active, but they serve as sources to the somatic
sink. Consequently they become depolarized, from electrotonic
spread of the antidromic action potential. Since this region does
not become active, there is no recovery current produced by
activation of K^+ conductance. Repolarization comes about through
recovery current which flows from the soma and previously active
dendrites as these repolarize actively. This recovery current produces the late deep positivity in depth and superficial negativity.
Large negativities associated with dendritic spikes have been

observed in alligator Purkinje cells (Llinás, Nicholson, Freeman, & Hillman, 1968). Further study on this preparation has lead to the postulate of centripetal unidirectional conduction for the dendritic spikes (Llinás, Nicholson, & Precht, 1968).

FIELD POTENTIALS PRODUCED BY SYNAPTIC CURRENTS

In addition to action currents, the field potentials recorded in the central nervous system are generated by the currents accompanying the activation of synaptic junctions between nervous elements. These synaptic currents produce nearly all of the field potentials which can be recorded in the central nervous system, except when gross synchronous electrical stimulation is used.

In order to understand the nature of the external current fields generated by the synaptic activity, some comments should be made regarding the mechanism of action of the synaptic junctions. As elaborated in Chapters 2 and 5, the combination of the synaptic transmitter substance with the receptor site in the postsynaptic membrane brings about a change in the permeability of this membrane to certain ion species. In the case of an excitatory synapse, during this time there is a large inward current at the subsynaptic membrane and an equally large outward current at all places some distance from the subsynaptic membrane (Fig. 7.8). An electrode situated near the synapse will record a negative potential since it is near the sink which has been created. At locations distant from the synapse the current leaves the cell, and so a microelectrode placed near the membrane at a distance from the focus will record a positivity with respect to a remote earth point (Fig. 7.8 and 7.9A).

Conversely, an inhibitory synaptic potential is produced by an increase of permeability to small ions, K^+ and Cl^-, which generates an out-going current across the subsynaptic membrane. This site is therefore a source, and thus will produce a positive field potential in the synaptic region and a negative field potential at the membrane sinks a certain distance away (Fig. 7.9B). It must be remembered, however, that the EPSP produces a depolarization at all places across the postsynaptic membrane. The fact that the polarity of the fields is reversed does not mean that the transmembrane potential changes induced by this current have different signs in different parts of the same cell. This mistake is sometimes made as a result of confusion of transmembrane potentials evoked by

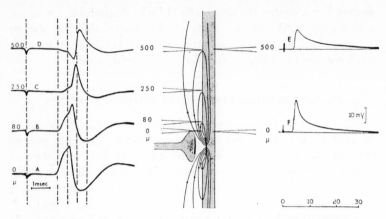

FIG. 7.8. Extracellular fields and intracellular potentials recorded in the vicinity of a frog neuromuscular junction, following activation of the motor nerve. The field potentials were recorded at different distances from the neuromuscular junction along the length of the muscle fibres. A to D, records taken at 0, 80, 230, and 500 μ from the neural junction. In A, the presynaptic volley evokes a synaptic current which is recorded at that site as a large negativity. As the electrode is moved away from the synaptic site, the potential generated by the synaptic current becomes smaller and at 500 μ it is observed as a positivity. Note the increase in the latency of the action potential at the different sites. At 500 μ, the muscle fibre serves as a source of current for the synaptic potential, and then as a source to the on-coming action potential. The second positivity is changed to a negativity as the action potential reaches the recording site (Kuffler, 1942a). In E the intracellular potential recorded at 500 μ from the neuromuscular junction following a presynaptic volley. F, endplate potential at the level of the junction (Fatt & Katz, 1951). The diagram in the centre of the figure represents a muscle fibre and its neuromuscular junction. Synaptic currents are indicated; their direction is indicated by arrows. The microelectrodes to the left are located extracellularly at the distance indicated. The two electrodes to the right correspond to the location of the intracellular penetration. Records A to D negative up; records E and F positive up. Time and amplitude as indicated. The time in msec for E and F is indicated in the scale at the lower right corner.

chemical synapses with those evoked by extracellularly applied extrinsic currents. The essential difference between these two forms of depolarization is that in the case of the chemical synapse the potential is generated by a battery placed across membrane while in the other case both poles of the battery lie outside the cell. In the latter case, current flows across the nerve membrane and through the axoplasm between the anode and cathode, generating

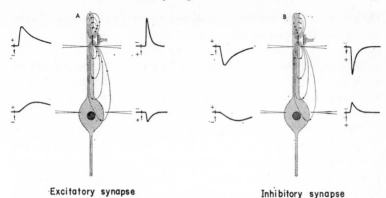

Excitatory synapse   Inhibitory synapse

FIG. 7.9. Diagram of fields generated by excitatory and inhibitory synaptic current in CNS cells. In A, an excitatory synapse in a dendrite generates a negative field in its vicinity and a positive field at a distance along the core conductor. In B, an inhibitory synapse in a dendrite generates a negative field in its vicinity and a positive field along the core conductor.

a depolarization near the cathode, where current is coming out across the membrane, and a hyperpolarization near the anode, where current passes inward across the membrane. Under these conditions a potential change of similar amplitude and time course occurs at both places although they have opposite polarities.

LAMINAR FIELD ANALYSIS

It is now quite clear that in order to understand the meaning of the field potentials generated by the activation of any neural assembly a *thorough knowledge of the microscopic organization of the neural elements in question is essential.* This point cannot be over-emphasized; the field potentials recorded at a specific location in the nervous system are of little use in the analysis of its physiology unless a good correlation with the anatomical organization of the region is possible. Thus it is simple to visualize the problem arising if one had to determine the origin of, for instance, a negative field evoked by peripheral stimulation in a region of unknown anatomical structure. The negativity could, in fact, be generated by the presence of a sink in the vicinity of the recording site. Such sinks occur when all-or-none action potentials, or even decrementally conducted potentials, invade structures in the proximity of the recording microelectrode. Another possibility, of course, is the presence of an excitatory synaptic current from synapses in the vicinity of the microelectrode, or of inhibitory synaptic currents generated in the same neural element a certain distance from the recording site. Other possibilities are local disinhibition and distant disfacilitation. Finally, such a negativity could be due to a field generated at some distance from the electrode, having no relation whatsoever to the site under consideration.

The study of the anatomical structure must take into account, firstly, the spatial arrangement of the neural element, i.e., the orientation of the somas, axons, and especially of the dendritic trees with respect to the path of the microelectrode in the particular neurone pool. Whenever possible the type of pool to be expected (open, closed, or mixed) should be ascertained by applying the statistical model approach of Lorente de Nó. This facilitates the interpretation of field potentials enormously. Knowledge of the distribution of the synaptic inputs to the elements of the pool is of great relevance, especially if a non-random pattern for the distribution of the synaptic contacts is suspected.

Once the anatomical arrangement of the region is understood, field potential recordings can be attempted. Any laminar field analysis must relate the location of the recording microelectrode with the specific site in the nervous system in which the potential was recorded. For this reason, a careful record of the depth of microelectrode penetration and an actual histological examination of the electrode tract must always be compared with the potential recorded at the different levels in the tract. To this end, Thomas & Wilson's (1965, 1966) techniques for marking single cells, as well as the recording sites, is strongly recommended.

Several simple rules should be observed in the actual analysis of the recorded field potentials. The sites at which the field potentials are the largest do not necessarily correspond with the location of maximum sinks or sources in the tissue (Amassian, 1961). For instance, synchronous synaptic depolarization of a large part of a neurone will not be appreciated by a microelectrode, even if it is recording at the site of maximum activity, if the area activated is very large with respect to the tip of the microelectrode. Since the whole neural surface near the recording site is at a new potential level, little or no current will flow between adjacent points of the membrane and thus only small potential differences will arise between the microelectrode and the reference zero potential electrode. On the other hand, if the microelectrode is moved to a new site where the synaptic distribution is not uniform, large potentials will be recorded at this new site.

A very precise, but rather elaborate means of locating areas of maximum activity is to calculate current densities by measuring the amount of current generated, at a particular time, in a particular small volume in the CNS (Howland *et al.*, 1955).

It should be borne in mind that field potentials can be related to the current fields and thus to sinks and sources only when their values are plotted at a fixed time interval from their initiation. This point should be obvious, yet it is sometimes forgotten that the current fields are instantaneous events.

A very profitable means of obtaining a first approximation of the current flow in a volume conductor such as the nervous system is to assemble isopotential surface maps (Fig. 7.10). The most usual method for this purpose is to work out a series of micro-electrode tracks all in a given plane, and to record the field potential at given positions in each track. The amplitude of the field potentials should then be measured, all at the same time interval after the application of the stimulus, and numerical values and polarities assigned to every recorded site. A map can then be developed which contains the geometrical relation of the recording sites in the plane.

Points having similar numerical values are then united by a continuous line which will demarcate isopotential surfaces. Using the assumption of isotropicity, the current field generating the field potentials can be drawn as orthogonal lines in relation to the isopotential surfaces. An example of this technique is illustrated in Fig. 7.10. The isopotential map was obtained by local stimulation of the surface of the cerebellar cortex (Loc) as shown in the diagram at the lower right corner of Fig. 7.10. The potentials illustrated in A to E were recorded with a microelectrode (ME) at different depths from the surface (ordinate in μ) and at different lateralities from the site of parallel fibre activation (abscissa in μ). o μ corresponds to the middle of a beam of parallel fibres of about 400 μ width. The stimulus was applied in all records at the arrow. In B the first sign of a field is a positive-negative transient produced by the parallel fibre action currents (Eccles, Llinás, & Sasaki, 1966*d*, *e*; Llinás & Bloedel, 1967). The negativity which follows and which reverses to a positivity at a depth lower than 300 μ is interpreted as generated by the excitatory synaptic currents generated by the excitatory synaptic impingement of parallel

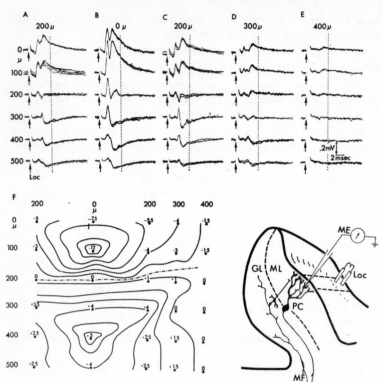

FIG. 7.10. Field potentials recorded at different depths and lateralities in the frog cerebellum following a local activation of the surface of the cerebellar cortex, and, plotting of isopotential contour lines based on these field potentials. A to E, field potentials recorded at 100 steps from a depth of 500 μ to the surface of the cerebellar cortex. A is located 200 μ cranially to B, which is the locus of maximum activity (the parallel fibre beam). B, locus of maximum activity. C, D, and E are located 200, 300, and 400 μ respectively from B in the caudal direction. F, isopotential contour line of the amplitude of the field at every step in depth and laterality. The ordinate represents the depth of the microelectrode tip in microns from the surface of the cerebellum. The abscissa, the laterality from the beam of activated parallel fibres. The numbers at every point indicate the amplitude of the potential field and its electrical sign at the time shown in A to E (dotted line). Right lower corner, diagram of frog cerebellum and experimental arrangement; Loc, local stimulating electrode; ME, microelectrode; GL, granular layer; MF, mossy fibre; ML, molecular layer; PC, Purkinje cell. (Llinás and Bloedel, unpublished observation.)

fibres on the Purkinje cell dendrites. Since in this cerebellum there is not long-lasting inhibition evoked directly on the Purkinje cells, this field can in fact be treated as generated by a single element at $0\ \mu$ having a long dendrite which receives an EPSP at about $100\ \mu$ from the surface. The rest of the field represents the potential generated by the current field as the point of maximum current source at $400\ \mu$ (Purkinje cell soma) gives current to the dendritic sink. Note that the zero isopotential time occurs at about $200\ \mu$ depth. This field can then be described as generated by a simple dipole in a volume conductor.

Note added in proof: Recently Rall and Shepherd have reported a rather novel approach to the study of field potentials in the CNS (1968). These authors have extended Lorente de Nó's concepts on open and closed fields and have introduced the concept of the 'potential divider effect'. The reader is referred to that publication.

APPENDIX

THE most frequently used form of general anaesthesia in neuro-physiology is that provided by the administration of barbiturates. Among these sodium pentobarbital (Nembutal) has been most commonly employed. In the case of adult cats, a dosage of 25 to 35 mg/kg administered intraperitoneally (I.P.) provides two and a half to three hours (and sometimes even longer) of general anaesthesia with almost complete muscular relaxation. This state can be easily maintained for long periods by additional administration of 5 to 10 mg/kg of the barbiturate as the effect of the previous dosage begins to disappear. A venous cannula should be implanted in one of the limbs after the first dose so that later doses can be administered intravenously upon the first signs of recovery from anaesthesia.

The dosages for Nembutal anaesthesia in kittens are given in Table A1. The Nembutal should be administered intraperitone-ally in a concentration of 4 mg/cc. Additional dosages can be administered either intraperitoneally or intravenously and should not be larger than 15 to 20% of the initial dosage.

TABLE A1

Nembutal anaesthesia in kittens

Age of kitten	Dosage in % of adult dosage (40 mg/kg)
24 hours	40
48 hours	45
Up to 4 days	55
Up to 1 week	60
2 weeks	65
3 weeks	70
4 weeks	75
6 weeks	80
8 weeks	90

(Courtesy of R. M. Eccles)

The central action of Nembutal must be remembered when studying the physiology of the central nervous system. This barbiturate has been shown to affect the general excitability of the reticular formation in the cat (Bradley & Key, 1958). More specifically, Crawford & Curtis (1966) suggest that this drug has a general depressant action on the postsynaptic membrane of CNS neurones, such that the response to direct electrophoretic application of acetylcholine (ACh) or excitant amino acids in the vicinity of a cell (pyramidal cells) is markedly and proportionally reduced for both excitants. At spinal cord level Shapovalov (1964) demonstrated that doses of 5 to 10 mg depress spontaneous activity of interneurones. Polysynaptic reflexes were depressed by 10 to 15 mg/kg and the monosynaptic reflex and antidromic invasion of some cells were reduced at levels above 30 mg/kg.

Other general anaesthetics used in neurophysiology are Dial, urethane, surital, and chloralose. *Dial* (diallylbarbituric acid) and *urethane* (ethylcarbamate) have much the same action as Nembutal. The dosage for Dial is 35 to 50 mg/kg (I.P.), while urethane must be used in doses of 400 mg/kg to provide a good general anaesthesia. As in the case of Nembutal, these two anaesthetics have a general depressant action on the postsynaptic membranes of central neurones (Crawford & Curtis, 1966). *Surital* is a convenient form of anaesthetic since its action is very short lasting (generally half an hour), so that it can be used in experimental procedures in which the general anaesthetic action must be kept to a minimum. This barbiturate is used in dosages of 70 to 80 mg/kg—with additional administration of 8 to 10 mg as required (generally every fifteen to twenty minutes). Surital has been shown to act at polysynaptic terminals in the CNS, depressing presynaptically the release of synaptic transmitter without changing the excitability of the neurones directly (Løyning, Oshima, & Yokota, 1964). *Chloralose* is used in doses of 30 to 50 mg/kg intravenously or intraperitoneally administered; it can be used alone or in conjunction with urethane. Chloralose does not seem to have any depressant action on the ACh-receptors in the CNS (Crawford & Curtis, 1966).

Paraldehyde. This form of anaesthesia is especially useful when working with rabbits; 2·3 cc/kg orally will produce 4 to 6 hours of general anaesthesia with quite complete relaxation. The anaesthetic should be made up to 10 cc in warm saline and given with an esophageal cannula one hour before anaesthesia is required.

Mephenesin. This drug produces a short-lasting anaesthesia in doses of 75 to 100 mg/kg intravenously. It is very useful when depression of a polysynaptic pathway is required (Henneman *et al.*, 1949; Kaada, 1950; Funderburk *et al.*, 1953; Wright, 1954; Llinás, 1964*b*).

Volatile anaesthesia. Ether and fluothane seem to be the two volatile anaesthetics more commonly used. Both these drugs are depressant to all cells in the CNS. The anaesthetic dosages are 1·5 to 2·5% in air for fluothane and 3 to 5% for ether.

Unanaesthetized preparations

Certain forms of experimentation in the CNS in which the high-frequency response of units is to be studied (Powell & Mountcastle, 1959) require an unanaesthetized preparation. Besides the decerebrate preparation which is so commonly used in neurophysiology, the encephale 'isole' of Bremer is a very useful preparation since it allows experimentation in the forebrain (Baumgarten & Jung, 1952; Amassian, 1961). A very simple method of producing a cerveux isole preparation with good decerebrate rigidity is to coagulate the mesencephalon with a radio-frequency coagulator (Wyss, 1945; Hunsperger & Wyss, 1953). For this method (Llinás, unpublished technique) four steel needles (No. 30 S.W.G.) are electrically insulated 3 mm from their tips and their ends ground to an oblong shape (Hess, 1954). These bars are then placed 1·5 mm apart so that between them they cover about 6 mm (taking into consideration the diameter of the needles). The fork is then placed stereotaxically at the level desired (generally transcollicular) and lowered into the brain tissues until it enters into contact with the basilar process of the occipital bone. For cats, the needles should be arranged so that the two central ones are a fraction of a millimetre longer than the peripheral ones, in order for all of them to enter into contact with the base of the skull. Once at this point, the electrodes are withdrawn a half to one millimetre and successive coagulations between adjacent pairs of needles are carried out. In this manner, a 'plane' of coagulated tissue which is generally 1·5 to 2 mm in thickness is produced between the uninsulated tips of the needles. In order to have a complete section of the neuraxis, two or three successive coagulation runs should be done after withdrawing the coagulating needles the same distance as the lengths of the uninsulated portion of the needles. It has been found that under these conditions 50 to 80 mA applied for 15 seconds for each pair of electrodes is ample. This form of decerebration has the advantage of not producing much bleeding (the electrodes are inserted through small perforations in the skull) and inducing cerebral edema less frequently than other techniques.

A very successful preparation for neurophysiological research has been developed by Poggio and Mountcastle (Mountcastle, 1961). These investigators produce chronically deafferented preparations which can then be studied without anaesthesia yet without suffering for the experimental animal.

METAL MICROELECTRODES

It should be remembered that although fashionable, microelectrodes are not the only way of recording from and stimulating biological structures. They are just another way of getting the two metal wires used by physiologists from the beginning of electrophysiology into contact with biological tissues. Microelectrodes, as their name implies, have very fine tips. They can thus be placed inside single cells, or be placed extracellularly in such close proximity to cells that they record effectively from only the one cell. Thus if an investigation requires the summed responses of many cells, grosser electrodes should be chosen. Like grosser electrodes the microelectrodes are of two types. One type, the metal microelectrode, can only be placed in the extracellular position because the polarization potentials set up at the metal–biological fluid interface when it is intracellular make recording difficult. The other type, the glass microelectrode, gets around this difficulty to some extent by connecting the metal wire, usually silver, to the inside of cells by a strong electrolyte solution inside the penetrating glass tip. The parallel between metal microelectrodes and the wick electrodes of older physiology can readily be seen. It will also be obvious that very old problems of electrode polarization, together with the new problem of high electrode resistance, have to be kept in mind. It is not the purpose of this book to discuss these problems which are excellently treated in *Physical Techniques in Biological Research* (Nastuk, 1963, 1964), particularly vol. 5, chapter I by Frank & Becker, and vol. 6, chapter 6, by Schwan, and in *Electronic Apparatus for Biological Research* (Donaldson, 1958), chapter X by Kennard.

Although metal microelectrodes have not been used for intracellular recording due to their polarization tendencies, they have met with great success for extracellular analysis of single units. This type of electrode combines low noise level and a sturdiness not found in electrolyte filled micropipettes (Svaetichin, 1951*b*; Dowben & Rose, 1953; Hubel, 1957; Green, 1958; Gesteland *et al.*, 1959; Wolbarsht *et al.*, 1960; Baldwin *et al.*, 1965). Some of these electrodes are believed to be the only recording elements capable of detecting the action currents from single unmyelinated fibres (Gesteland *et al.*, 1959). The metal microelectrodes can be divided into three classes: (1) metal electrodes covered with glass, which are made by heating a glass tube, into which low melting point metal has been introduced, and then pulling metal and glass out together. In this manner, silver solder (600°C melting point) filled electrodes can be made (Svaetichin, 1951*b*). After this procedure, the tip is electrolytically filled with rhodium and covered with a thin filament of platinum black. Svaetichin (1951*b*) gives an interesting table relating resistances and tip diameters; a study of their impedance and of their d.c. stability has also been published (Gray & Svaetichin, 1951). (2) Electrodes made by sharpening metal wires and then insulating them with various materials. Hubel (1957) described a microelectrode made by electro-polishing tungsten wire and insulating it with lacquer. (3) Electrodes made by filling a glass pipette with metal of low melting point after the pipette has been made (Gesteland *et al.*, 1959).

SOLUTIONS FOR ISOLATED PREPARATIONS

All isolated preparations deteriorate sooner or later. The quality of the bathing solution determines how soon. In principle a close resemblance between an ultrafiltrate of the appropriate blood and the bathing solution would seem desirable. The blood concentration of inorganic ions of many species are set out in Prosser & Brown (1961). Some very successful solutions are scattered in the literature and are reproduced below with such comments as we and others have on their usefulness.

Mammalian preparations

Table A2 shows the ionic composition of various saline solutions used for mammalian preparations. The most striking difference

TABLE A2

Mammalian salines (mM)

Authority	NaCl	KCl	CaCl$_2$	MgCl$_2$	MgSO$_4$	NaHCO$_3$	Na$_2$HPO$_4$	NaH$_2$PO$_4$	KH$_2$PO$_4$	Glucose
1 Locke (1901)	154·0	5·64	1·63	—	—	2·38	—	—	—	11·1
2 Tyrode (1910)	136·9	2·68	1·80	0·53	—	11·91	—	0·33	—	5·6
3 Krebs & Henseleit (1932)	127·3	5·10	2·70	—	1·33	—	9·86	—	1·25	—
4 Krebs & Henseleit (1932)	118·4	4·69	2·52	—	1·25	25·0	—	—	1·18	11·1
5 Krebs (1950)*†	94·8	4·74	2·54	—	0·95	24·88	—	—	1·18	11·5
6 Liley (1956a)*†	136·8	5·00	2·00	1·00	—	24·0	—	1·00	—	11·0
7 Earle (1943)	116·4	5·37	1·80	—	0·83	26·2	—	0·92	—	5·55

* Gas with 5% CO_2 + 95% O_2 at least 1 hour (Ling & Smith, 1955).
† Modification; substitution of 24 mM $NaHCO_3$ for 12 mM (Gage & Hubbard, 1966a).

between the composition of the artificial solutions and sera is the higher chloride concentration of the former. This discrepancy is unavoidable in a purely inorganic medium because in serum about 20 m-mole of the anions are organic substances (Krebs, 1950). It is also probable that the ionized calcium concentration of the solutions is higher than that of serum. Recent measurements put the ionized calcium concentration of human serum at only 1·33 mM (Ettori & Scoggar, 1959), the remainder of the 2·5 mM total being divided between a 0·82 mM nondiffusible fraction bound to globulin and albumen and a 0·30 mM fraction complexed with bicarbonate, phosphate, and other anions (Neumann & Neumann, 1958).

It is customary to add at least 1 g/l of glucose to mammalian solutions as an energy source. The amount added to Liley's solution has varied between 2 g/l (Liley, 1956a) and 5 g/l (Krnjevic & Miledi, 1958). Krebs (1950) pointed out that if the sodium salts of pyruvic, fumaric, and glutamic acids were added in addition to glucose, and the amount of sodium chloride reduced in compensation, the oxygen uptake of isolated tissues approximated that of tissues in serum, and the medium itself resembled serum more closely (Table A2, 5).

Both Liley's and Krebs' solution are customarily gassed with 5% CO_2 in 95% O_2 (carbogen). The resultant pH may be calculated from the Henderson–Hesselbach equation (Henderson, 1908) given that the pK of carbonic acid is 6·35

$$pH = pK + \log \frac{HCO_3^-}{CO_2}.$$

It should be noted that for every degree decrease in temperature down to 20°C the bicarbonate concentration should be increased by about 1·88% to give the same pH as at 37°C. Tables of the variables can be found in Dawson, Elliot, Elliot, & Jones (1959).

Some further considerations arise in the actual experimental situation. For instance, Liley's solution (Table A2, 6) with the original 12 mM bicarbonate concentration is acid (pH 7·1). If the bicarbonate is raised to 24 mM (2 g/l) the pH of the gassed solution at 37°C lies between 7·2–7·3 and if the solution is tested as it passes over an isolated preparation its pH will be found to lie between 7·3–7·4, presumably because some of the CO_2 escapes into the ambient atmosphere (Gage & Hubbard, 1966a, and unpublished observations).

Krebs' solution (Table A2, 3) has been used for rat and cat

skeletal muscle (Li, 1958; Boyd & Martin, 1956a) and with the omission of SO_4 ions for guinea pig smooth muscle *in vitro* (Kuriyama, 1963). Liley's solution has also been used for rat and human neuromuscular work (Liley, 1956a; Thesleff, 1959; Elmqvist *et al.*, 1964), and isolated rabbit cervical ganglia survive well in this solution with the magnesium concentration halved (R. M. Eccles, 1955).

Amphibian preparations

Solutions for amphibian preparations have been traditionally known as Ringers, after Sydney Ringer (1883a, b) who showed that the beating of an isolated frog heart was well maintained only if the bathing solution contained salts of sodium, potassium, and calcium, together with a buffer system. Its composition is shown in Table A3, 1. Normally 1–2 g/l of glucose is added. This solution differs from frog plasma most notably in the absence of Mg and SO_4 ions and in the presence of Ca and bicarbonate ions in a much lower concentration. Two trends have been evident in the composition of later amphibian solutions. One has been to raise the $CaCl_2$ concentration nearer to the level of frog plasma, although the original Ringer may have been closer to the actual ionized Ca level of amphibian plasma (0·9 mM, Boyle & Conway, 1941). The other has been to provide a more efficient buffering system. The pH of the original Ringer (Table A3) is 8–8·5, due to the low $NaHCO_3$ concentration in contact only with the ambient CO_2. Such solutions have been used successfully for ganglia (Nishi & Koketsu, 1960; Blackman, Ginsborg, & Ray, 1963a) and for the frog spinal cord *in vitro* (Eccles, 1946b; Araki, Otani, & Furakawa, 1953) despite the alkaline pH. Some workers with muscle preparations have added a phosphate buffer (Gomori, 1955) to obtain a more physiological pH (Table A5, 5), see also Takeuchi & Takeuchi (1959). The presence of a buffer system, while essential for the maintenance of the frog heart beat (Ringer, 1883b), is obviously not necessary for frog neuromuscular work where it is common practice to use a solution containing only NaCl, KCl, and $CaCl_2$ (del Castillo & Katz, 1955b).

Avian preparations (Table A4)

Krebs' solution (Table A2, 3) has also been found quite satisfactory for skeletal muscle and ganglion preparations (Ginsborg, 1960a; Martin & Pilar, 1963a).

TABLE A3

Amphibian saline L (mM)

Authority	NaCl	KCl	CaCl₂	MgCl₂	MgSO₄	NaHCO₃	Na₂HPO₄	NaH₂PO₄	KH₂PO₄	Glucose
1 Ringer (1883b)	111·24	1·88	1·08	—	—	2·38	—	—	—	—
2 Boyle & Conway (1941)*	72·54	1·98	—	—	1·21	25·0	2·51	—	0·5	26·0
3 Förster (1948)	99·23	2·55	1·98	2·1	—	15·0	—	0·58	—	3·1
4 Adrian (1956)	115·0	2·5	1·8	—	—	—	2·15	0·85	—	—
5 Horowitz (1958)†	111·2	3·35	2·7	—	—	—	—†	0·17	—	—
6 Koketsu & Kimura (1960)	112·0	2·0	1·8	—	—	2·4	—	—	—	2·24 sucrose

* Equilibrate with 97% O₂ and 3% CO₂ and add 1·7 mM Ca gluconate and 0·65 mM Na₂SO₄.
† To buffer, obtain a pH of 7·4 with NaOH, then add 0·002 g/l NaH₂PO₄ and sufficient Na₂HPO₄ to get pH 7·4.

TABLE A4

Avian salines (mM)

Authority	NaCl	KCl	CaCl$_2$	MgCl$_2$	MgSO$_4$	NcHCO$_3$	Na$_2$HPO$_4$	NaH$_2$PO$_4$	KH$_2$PO$_4$	Glucose
1 Lewis & Lewis (1911)	119·6	5·63	2·25	—	—	2·38	—	—	—	13·88
2 Hanks (1948)	136·87	5·36	1·80	—	0·91	16·7	0·45	—	0·73	11·1
3 White (1949)*	119·76	5·03	—	—	2·49	6·55	0·33	—	0·19	5·55

* Add also 0·21 g of Ca(NO$_3$)$_2$.2H$_2$O + 0·0013 g of Fe(NO$_3$)$_3$.9H$_2$O per litre.

TABLE A5

Piscine salines (mM)

Authority	NaCl	KCl	CaCl$_2$	MgCl$_2$	NaHCO$_3$	NaH$_2$PO$_4$	Others
1 Lutz (1930)	280·34	7·99	5·00	—	2·00	—	urea 359·6
2 Wasserman et al. (1953)	134·18	2·55	2·55	0·99	40·00	0·5	
3 Schoffeniels (1960)	160·19	4·96	6·04	1·47	—	—	
4 Young (1933)*	111·24	1·88	1·26	—	—*	—	
5 Takeuchi (1959)	128·	2·7	1·8	—	2·3	—	
6 Huggel (1959)	111·21	2·68	0·9	0·42	2·38	to pH 7·2	

* Buffer with either bicarbonate or phosphate buffer.

TABLE A6

Insect salines (mM)

Authority	NaCl	KCl	CaCl₂	MgCl₂	NaHCO₃	NaH₂PO₄	KH₂PO₄	Glucose	Other
1 Pringle (1938)	154·0	2·68	1·84	—	to pH 7·2	—	—	22·2	
2 Hoyle (1953)*	130·0	10·0	2·00	2·00	4·0	6·00	—	—	
3 Yeager (1939)	187·0	21·1	7·66	1·79	—	—	—	—	
4 Hoyle (1952)	119·8	2·68	1·80	1·05	0·6	1·67	—	44·4	
5 Wyatt (1956)	15·0	—	1·0	0·47	—	1·33	1·5	60·0	
6 Wood (1957)	—	18·0	7·5	50·00	—	6·00	—	351·4	Na₂HPO₄ 4·5

* Usherwood & Grundfest (1965) has same composition as Hoyle (1953), except CaCl₂ doubled to 4 mM and MgCl₂ reduced to zero.

TABLE A7

Crustacean salines (mM)

Authority	NaCl	KCl	CaCl$_2$	MgCl$_2$	MgSO$_4$	NaHCO$_3$	Other
1 Cole (1941)	456·61	14·9	—	3·78	5·15	—	CaSO$_4$* 25 Boric acid 0·79 NaOH 0·48
2 Davenport (1941)	491·19	12·21	14·69	12·18	—	1·79	Glucose 5·55
3 Pantin (1934)	530·55	13·28	12·34	24·68	—	2·62	Urea 999
4 Van Harreveld (1936)	195·00	5·4	13·5	2·6	—	—	pH 7·5 with tris-maleate buffer†

* Equivalent amounts are CaSO$_4$, 3·4 g/l; boric acid, 0·54 g/l; NaOH, 0·956 ml of 0·5 M soln. per litre saline.

† From Gomori (1955) trismaleate–NaOH buffer.

TABLE A8

Molluscan salines (mM)

Authority	NaCl	KCl	$CaCl_2$	$MgCl_2$	$MgSO_4$	Glucose	Other
1 Jullien et al. (1955)†	97·6	2·01	10·0	—	—	—	
2 Jullien & Ripplinger (1948)†	46·2	4·02	7·48	—	—	—	
3 Motley (1934)	20·54	0·40	0·54	—	—	—	
4 Cambridge et al. (1959)	484·3	9·93	10·9	28·1	29·32	5·55	
5 Hodgkin & Katz (1949a)†	450	10·0	10·6	52·5	—	—	$NaHCO_3$ 5·52

† Probably best to buffer close to 7·0.

TABLE A9

Annelidan salines (mM)

Authority	NaCl	KCl	CaCl₂	MgCl₂	MgSO₄	NaHCO₃	NaH₂PO₄
1 Ambache et al. (1945)	116·38	1·88	1·08	—	—	2·38	0·08
2 Rushton (1945)	136·92	2·68	1·80	—	0·42	—	—
3 Pantin (1946)	112·96	4·29	1·80	—	—	1·67	—

Piscine preparations (Table A5)

These solutions are for fresh-water fish.

Insect preparations (Table A6)

Insect bloods contain concentrations of calcium and magnesium which are very high by vertebrate standards (Duchateau, Florkin, & Leclercq, 1953). Nevertheless, the optimal medium for insect neuromuscular function contains amounts of the common cations quite similar to those found in frog Ringer (Hoyle, 1955). Salines for herbivorous insects are described by Weevers (1966).

Crustacean preparations (Table A7)

Marine crustaceans may be kept in sea water. For fresh water crustaceans, Van Harreveld's (1936) solution is based on an analysis of the blood of *Astacus trowbridgii* and *Cambarus clarkii*.

Molluscan preparations (Table A8)

Marine molluscs are generally kept in sea water (e.g. Tauc, 1955), but Hodgkin & Katz (1949a) describe an artificial sea water for the squid (Table A8, 5) which they report was a satisfactory replacement.

Annelidan preparations (Table A9).

Lockwood's (1961) review should be consulted for further information, particularly on invertebrate salines.

TEMPERATURE

The Q_{10} or the ratio between the rate of a reaction at one temperature and the rate of the reaction at a temperature 10°C higher is widely used in biochemistry as a quantitative basis for the comparison of the effects of temperature. In biology the same term (Q_{10}) is also commonly used for the ratio between the value of some parameter, e.g., membrane resistance, at one temperature and its value at a temperature 10°C higher. In the following brief account of the effects of temperature changes upon synaptic parameters Q_{10} is used in the second sense except where chemical reactions are being specifically discussed. It is important to note that the temperature range over which a Q_{10} was measured must always be given with the ratio, and that when Q_{10}'s are compared, the comparison is only relevant if the temperature ranges are exactly the same. A further point is that when Q_{10} is used in the second sense of temperature coefficient, it is only meaningful if the parameter under consideration varies linearly with the temperature. For example, Fig. 4.4A shows mean m.e.p.p. frequency at a mammalian neuromuscular junction as a function of the temperature of the bathing solution. Clearly the relation is exponential so that if the frequencies at 25° and 35°C are compared, the ratio obtained will be much smaller than if 30° and 40°C were compared, and either ratio on its own would be misleading.

Temperature changes *in vivo*

An important point when membrane characteristics of neurones are to be analysed is the stabilization of the preparation's temperature. Klee, Pierau, Papajewski (in preparation) have shown that if the temperature of the CNS of mammals is varied by two to three degrees from normal in either direction, significant changes occur in the properties of neuronal membranes. Small decreases in temperature of about two degrees produce a rapid increase in membrane resistance. A further decrease in temperature causes a reduction of the membrane potential which can be as large as 10 mV with a temperature drop of 3°C. Both these changes lead to an increase in the excitability of neurones (Fig. A.1). If the temperature is lowered to 34°C–35°C, the characteristics of the action potentials change. The amplitude and the rate of rise and fall are decreased but the duration may increase to three times the control duration (Fig. A.1). If the temperature is increased to 40–42°, the action potential is unable to invade the neurone's soma so that only the initial segment fires (IS spike).

Similar tests on the amplitude of synaptic potentials (Klee *et al.*, in preparation) demonstrates that cooling increases the amplitude of the synaptic potential by increasing transmitter release, possibly due to the increased duration of the spike at the presynaptic terminals (Katz & Miledi, 1965*a*) as well as the increased input resistance. Temperature increases, on the other hand, tend to decrease the amplitude of the synaptic potentials.

L

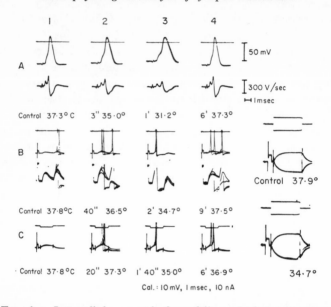

Fig. A.1. Intracellular records from feline spinal motoneurones at different temperatures. In A records 1 to 4 middle trace, antidromically evoked action potentials. Note the marked change in the time course of the IS and SD spikes, the diminution of the spike height and the reduction of the resting potential as the temperature is lowered to 35° in record 2. In record 4 control at 37·3° six minutes later. The lower traces are records of the differentiated action potentials to show changes in the rates of rise and fall. In B increased synaptic efficiency at temperatures of 36·5° and 34·7° (records 2 and 3 respectively). The increased amplitude of the monosynaptic EPSP pair can be observed in lower trace in 2 and 3. Records 1 and 4 are controls. In A and B, upper traces are reference lines. In C intracellular current injection to demonstrate change of excitability of motoneurone. Note that at previously sub-threshold, current (upper trace) evoked action potentials at 37·3°, at 35·0°, and 39·9°. Control in record 1. An increase in membrane resistance can be observed in the two records to the right. The same inward and outward currents in upper trace (control at 37·9°) produce a large IR drop at a temperature of 34·7° (lower record). The amplitude, duration, rates of rise and fall, and current amplitude are all indicated (Klee, Pierau, & Papajewski, unpublished results).

Temperature changes *in vitro*

Neuromuscular transmission is maintained in rats until they are cooled to about 10°C (South, 1961) and for frogs until cooled to below − 1°C (Li & Gouras, 1958).

At rat phrenic nerve–diaphragm junctions ACh produces a larger and longer lasting depolarization at 20°C than at 37°C (Harris & Leach, 1968) and this effect is still demonstrable in the presence of neostigmine in amounts adequate to prevent ChE action. In addition most ChE's have a Q_{10} of 1·3–1·5 in the biological range. A similar temperature dependence is found for the reaction of ChE with competitive inhibitors (reviewed by Chadwick, 1957). As would be expected, prostigmine bromide and eserine have reduced activity as the temperature is lowered (Eccles, Katz, & Kuffler, 1942; Boyd & Martin, 1956*a*, *b*). The decrease in ChE activity together with the increased effectiveness of ACh presumably accounts for the reported increase in e.p.p. amplitudes upon cooling (Eccles, Katz, & Kuffler, 1941; Boyd & Martin, 1956*b*; Takeuchi, 1958).

Form of synaptic potentials

At frog, rat, and cat junctions the amplitude of m.e.p.p.s is little affected by temperature changes which markedly alter e.p.p. amplitudes, but their time course is prolonged (Boyd & Martin, 1956*b*; Liley, 1956*a*; Li, 1958). E.p.p.s are also markedly increased in time course by cooling. The temperature coefficient for the rising phase is higher (2·65, Eccles *et al.*, 1941; 2·7, Takeuchi, 1958) than that for the falling phase (1·29, Eccles *et al.*, 1941; 2.2, Takeuchi, 1958). The lesser activity of cholinesterase at lower temperatures together with the asynchronous quantal emission of ACh (Katz & Miledi, 1965*e*) probably accounts for this prolongation of the rising and falling phases of e.p.p.s and m.e.p.p.s. Voltage-clamp measurements confirm that transmitter action is prolonged on cooling (Takeuchi & Takeuchi, 1959). The small increases in m.e.p.p. amplitude may be explained by the increase in postsynaptic ACh sensitivity upon cooling (Hubbard, Jones, & Landau, in preparation).

Membrane resistance and capacitance

These passive electrical properties appear little affected by temperature changes of 10–20°C in nerve and muscle. Thus for frog muscle the membrane capacitance had a Q_{10} of 1·5 (temperature fall 20–30°C—del Castillo & Machne, 1953), and for cat muscle there was no significant change for a fall of temperature from 37–22°C (Boyd & Martin, 1959). A similar independence of temperature has been reported for frog myelin nerve and nodes of Ranvier between 14–25°C (Tasaki & Spyropoulos, 1957) and for squid axon between 3 and 23°C (Hodgkin & Katz, 1949*b*).

Membrane resistance is more affected by temperature changes but reported Q_{10}'s are still small. Thus for frog muscle R_m increased as the preparation cooled over the range 20–3°C, the Q_{10} being – 1·35 (del Castillo & Machne, 1953). Similarly, in calf and sheep Purkinje fibres there was a negative Q_{10} of 1·5 over the range 10–45°C (Coraboeuf & Weidman, 1954). For cat muscle the Q_{10} (1·6) is positive, resistance falling with temperature over the range 37–22°C (Boyd & Martin, 1959).

Membrane potential

The Nernst equation predicts that the magnitude of the membrane potential, like any diffusion potential, should be proportional to absolute temperature and indeed Bernstein (1902) demonstrated that the injury potential of frog nerve and muscle was proportional to the absolute temperature. Using intracellular electrodes similar results have been reported for frog muscle by Ling & Woodbury (1949) and MacFarlane & Meares (1958). The expected changes are small; for instance, over the range of 10–20°C the predicted Q_{10} would be 1·035. It is perhaps not surprising, therefore, that investigators have failed to detect any change in membrane potential with temperature in frog muscle (0–25°C, Li & Gouras, 1958; Takeuchi, 1958), rat muscle (10–36°C, Li, 1958), squid axon (0–20°C, Hodgkin & Katz, 1949*b*) and heart muscle (25–40°C, Coraboeuf & Weidman, 1954). Falls of 5–10 mV were, however, found in cat muscle fibres when the temperature fell from 37–22°C (Boyd & Martin, 1959). More surprisingly for the temperature range 15–25°C, Kerkut & Ridge (1961, 1962) have observed Q_{10} values of 1·064 (crab muscle), 1·296 (insect muscle), 1·060 (frog muscle) and 1·04 to 1·96 (snail neurones), some of these values being significantly higher than expected from the Nernst equation.

Transmitter release

Lowering of temperature decreases ACh output from the sympathetic ganglia of the cat (Brown, 1954; Kostial & Vouk,

1956) and the rat diaphragm (Straughan, 1960). Similar but not statistically significant results were found when ACh output from rat diaphragms was compared at 37°C and 22°C (Krnjevic & Mitchell, 1961). The amount of transmitter released by single impulses is not much affected by temperature but the rate of synthesis of transmitter is markedly affected. Ganglia stimulated at high frequencies which presumably depleted transmitter stores show a very high Q_{10} for ACh release (Brown, 1954), but no such effect appears with low-frequency stimulation, when there is presumably no depletion (Kostial & Vouk, 1956).

M.e.p.p. frequency

As Fig. 4.4 shows, m.e.p.p. frequency is very sensitive to temperature changes. Q_{10}'s of 2–8 have been reported at all junctions where this point has been investigated (Fatt & Katz, 1952; Boyd & Martin, 1956a; Liley, 1956a; Brooks, 1956; Li, 1958; Li & Gouras, 1958; Takeuchi, 1958; Feigen, Peterson, Hofmann, Genther, & Van Heyningen, 1963; Kuriyama, 1964). These high Q_{10}'s are not reduced in the presence of excess Mg; therefore, depolarization of terminals is probably not responsible (Takeuchi, 1958). A peculiarity of mammalian nerve–muscle junctions is that between 15–25°C there is a hump on the otherwise exponential relationship between frequency and temperature (Liley, 1956a; Li, 1958; Hubbard, Jones, & Landau, 1967).

Quantal content of e.p.p.s.

It would be expected from the ACh and m.e.p.p. findings that e.p.p. quantal content should vary with temperature. In agreement Takeuchi (1958) reported that quantal content of e.p.p.s at frog neuromuscular junctions decreased on cooling below 20°C. In curarized rat neuromuscular junction quantal content of e.p.p.s similarly decreases upon cooling over the range 30–40°C. Analysis shows that this fall is accompanied by a decrease in the immediately available store of transmitter, but there is a compensatory increase in fractional release which is not, however, large enough to overcome the fall in the available store (Hubbard, Jones, & Landau, unpublished observations).

Drug actions

From the studies of Holmes, Jenden, & Taylor (1951), and of Bigland, Goetze, Maclagan, & Zaimis (1958) it appears that the effect of curare decreases with temperature over the range 35–26°C. Below this temperature the effectiveness of curare increases again. The action of depolarizing neuromuscular blocking drugs such as deca- and suxamethonium in contrast is increased in magnitude and duration as the animal is cooled (Bigland *et al.*, 1958; Harris & Leach, 1968). These effects have been discussed by Canepa (1965), and further information about the influence of temperature upon drug actions can be found in the reviews of this subject by Fuhrman (Fuhrman, 1946; Fuhrman & Fuhrman, 1961).

pH

Almost all investigations of the effect of pH changes upon synaptic transmission have been carried out using frog or toad neuromuscular preparations and unless otherwise mentioned, all data refer to amphibian preparations.

Presynaptic effects

E.p.p. amplitudes decreased by about one-third at curarized junctions when the pH changed from 7 to 4 (del Castillo, Nelson, & Sanchez, 1962). This was apparently due to a reduction in ACh output for sensitivity to ACh was increased at the low pH (see below). At the phrenic nerve–rat diaphragm junction there is an increase in the duration of the post-tetanic potentiation of e.p.p. amplitudes as the pH falls from 7·6 to 7·1 and a concomitant decrease of the maximum post-tetanic amplitudes (Gage & Hubbard, 1966*b*). M.e.p.p. frequency rises as pH falls at the rat nerve–muscle junction, the effect being largely due to greater ionization of the bathing Ca as the pH falls below 7·4 (Hubbard *et al.*, 1968*a*).

Membrane potential

Membrane potential was reported by Ling & Gerard (1949*c*) to be unaffected by extracellular pH changes in the range 5–10.

Later investigations have shown that there is a progressive depolarization as the pH is raised from 4–5 to 10–11, the total change over the range being only of the order of 3 or 4 mV. Beyond these extremes the resting potential falls rapidly with further pH changes and contractures develop (Gilbert & Lowenberg, 1964; Kutscha, Pauschenger, & Brecht, 1964).

Membrane capacitance

This is unaffected by pH in the range 5–7·1 (Meves & Volkner, 1958).

Membrane resistance

Membrane resistance increases as pH is lowered (Meves & Volkner, 1958; del Castillo *et al.*, 1962). Hutter and Warner (Brooks & Hutter, 1963*a*, *b*, 1964; Hutter & Warner, 1967*a*, *b*) have established that this effect is due to a decrease in the chloride conductance of the muscle membrane. It appears that in frog muscle there are specific channels for chloride which apparently close as the external solution becomes more acid and open as it becomes more alkaline. There are also small changes of potassium conductance in the same direction as the chloride changes.

The membrane response to applied ACh is increased by a factor of 2·5 when the pH of the bathing solution is reduced from 7 to 4, presumably because of the concomitant increase in the effective muscle membrane resistance (del Castillo *et al.*, 1962).

OSMOTIC PRESSURE

Osmotic pressure increases of the bathing solution produced by addition of non-membrane-penetrating salts or nonelectrolytes produce transient increases in transmitter release. Spontaneous release rates may remain close to the initial increased rate but quantal release by nerve impulses, after an initial enhancement, is reduced. Small changes (5–10%) in the tonicity of bathing solutions do not affect quantal content but produce easily detectable effects on m.e.p.p. frequency. The mechanism by which osmotic pressure changes affect release appears to differ from the mechanism employed by nerve impulses for the initial effects of hypertonic solutions upon transmitter release are insensitive to

variations of the bathing Ca and Mg concentrations and antagonized by depolarization of nerve terminals (Hubbard *et al.*, 1968*c*).
See also Fatt & Katz, 1952; Furshpan, 1956; Boyd & Martin,
1956*a*; Liley, 1956*a*; Blackman, Ginsborg, & Ray, 1963*a*; Gage &
Hubbard, 1966*b*).

Solutions which have an osmotic pressure two to three times
the osmotic pressure of Ringer or Krebs solution have been found
to block excitation-contraction coupling in both frog (Hodgkin &
Horowicz, 1957; Howarth, 1958) and rat muscle (Thesleff, 1959).
Neuromuscular transmission is also blocked due to a reduction in
the amount of ACh released by nerve impulses (Thesleff, 1959;
Lilleheil & Naess, 1961; Hubbard *et al.*, 1968*c*). It may be noted
that after exposure to solutions made hypertonic with glycerol,
when muscles are suddenly returned to a saline solution there is a
period of twitching and then contraction is blocked permanently,
probably due to destruction of transverse tubules. Muscle action
potentials may then be observed at leisure (Eisenberg & Gage,
1967; Gage & Eisenberg, 1967).

STRETCH

The effects of stretch have largely been examined at the frog
neuromuscular junction and all data unless otherwise mentioned
refer to this junction.

Presynaptic effects

Partial block of neuromuscular transmission by fatigue or
curare, or a reduced Ca concentration and/or an increased Mg
concentration in the bathing solution, is relieved upon passive
stretch of the muscle (Kuffler, 1952; Ralston & Libet, 1953;
Hutter & Trautwein, 1956; Hisado, 1958). Analysis of this effect
(Hutter & Trautwein, 1956) has shown that it is brought about by
an increase in the amplitude of e.p.p.s, and that the e.p.p. amplitude varies linearly with muscle length over a wide range. The
increase in e.p.p. amplitude is mainly due to a greater release of
ACh from stretched nerve endings. Stretching also increases
m.e.p.p. frequency in parallel to the increase in e.p.p. amplitude
(Fatt & Katz, 1952; Hutter & Trautwein, 1956). An increase in
m.e.p.p. amplitude also occurs which can be attributed to the
reduction of muscle fibre diameter on stretching (Chapter 2). The

presynaptic effects of stretch are not blocked by increasing the Mg concentration of the bathing medium.

Postsynaptic effects

Membrane potential

Ling & Gerard (1949*b*) found membrane potential independent of muscle fibre length up to 170% of the relaxed length. Later investigators suggest that there is a fall of 3–4 mV on stretching by 130% (Ishiko, 1957, 1958, quoted by Ishiko & Sato, 1960).

Membrane constants

Little or no change of C_m and R_m could be detected when muscle fibres were stretched (Ishiko & Sato, 1960). Similar lack of effect of stretches of two to four times reference length is reported for the earthworm medium giant fibre (Goldman, 1964).

REFERENCES

(Numbers within square brackets indicate pages in which the reference is cited.)

Adrian, R. H. (1956). The effect of internal and external potassium concentration on the membrane potential of frog muscle. *J. Physiol.* **133**, 631–658. [36, 88, 89, 303]
— (1961). Internal chloride concentration and chloride efflux of frog muscle. *J. Physiol.* **156**, 623–632. [107]
— (1964). Membrane properties of striated muscle and the initiation of contraction. In *Cellular Function of Membrane Transport*, ed. Hoffman, J. New York: Prentice Hall. [60]
Agin, D. & Holtzman, D. (1966). Glass microelectrodes: The origin and elimination of tip potentials. *Nature, Lond.* **211**, 1194–1195. [89]
Albe-Fessard, D. & Buser, P. (1953). Explorations de certaines activités du cortex moteur du chat par microélectrodes dérivations endosomatiques. *J. Physiol., Paris* **45**, 14–16. [245]
— (1955). Activités intracellulaires recueillies dans le cortex sigmoide du Chat: Participation des neurones pyramidaux au 'potentiel evoque' somesthesique. *J. Physiol. Paris* **47**, 67–69. [245]
Albert, A. (1965). *Selective Toxicity*, 2nd edn., pp. 69–71. London: Methuen & Sons. [175]
Alnaes, E., Jansen, J. K. S. & Rudord, T. (1964). Spontaneous junctional activity of fast and slow parietal muscle fibres of the Hagfish. *Acta. physiol. scand.* **60**, 240–255. [116]
Alving, B. & Carpenter, D. (1967). The significance of an electrogenic Na^+ pump in Aplysia neurons. *Fed. Proc.* **26**, 329. [68]
Amassian, V. E. (1961). Microelectrode studies of the cerebral cortex. *Int. Rev. Neurobiol.* **3**, 67–136. [290, 297]
Ambache, N., Dixon, St. J. A. & Wright, E. A. (1945). Some observations on the physiology and pharmacology of the nerve endings in the crop and gizzard of the earthworm with special reference to the effects of cooling. *J. exp. Biol.* **21**, 46–57. [309]
Andersen, P. (1960). Interhippocampal impulses. II. Apical dendritic activation of CA1 neurons. *Acta physiol. scand.* **48**, 178–208. [220]
Andersen, P., Eccles, J. C. & Løyning, Y. (1964). Location of postsynaptic inhibitory synapses on hippocampal pyramids. *J. Neurophysiol.* **27**, 592–607. [245, 259]
Andersen, P., Eccles, J. C. & Sears, T. A. (1964). The ventrobasal complex of the thalamus: types of cells, their responses and their functional organization. *J. Physiol.* **174**, 370–399. [245]
Andersen, P., Eccles, J. C. & Voorhoeve, P. E. (1964). Postsynaptic inhibition of cerebellar Purkinje cells. *J. Neurophysiol.* **27**, 1138–1153. [245, 253, 259]

Araki, T., Ito, M. & Oscarsson, O. (1961). Anion permeability of the synaptic and non-synaptic motoneurone membrane. *J. Physiol.* **159**, 410–435. [244]

Araki, T., Ito, M. & Oshima, M. (1961). Potential changes produced by application of current steps to motoneurons. *Nature* **191**, 1104–1105. [222, 244]

Araki, T. & Otani, T. (1955). Response of single motoneurons to direct stimulation in toad's spinal cord. *J. Neurophysiol.* **18**, 472–485. [93, 94, 220, 258]

— (1959). Accommodation and local response in motoneurones of toad's spinal cord. *Jap. J. Physiol.* **9**, 69–83. [221]

Araki, T., Otani, T. & Furukawa, T. (1953). The electrical activities of single motoneurones in toad's spinal cord, recorded with intracellular electrodes. *Jap. J. Physiol.* **3**, 254–267. [219, 302]

Araki, T. & Terzuolo, C. A. (1962). Membrane currents in spinal motoneurons associated with the action potential and synaptic activity. *J. Neurophysiol.* **25**, 772–789. [94, 219, 236, 237, 248, 249]

Ariens, E. J., ed. (1964). *Molecular Pharmacology*, Vol. 1. New York and London: Academic Press. [179]

Ariens, E. J., van Rossum, J. M. & Simonis, A. M. (1956). A theoretical basis of molecular pharmacology. Part 1: Interactions of one or two compounds with one receptor system. *Arzneimittel-forsch.* **6**, 282–293. [176, 179]

Armstrong, C. M. & Binstock, L. (1965). Anomalous rectification in the squid giant axon injected with tetraethylammonium chloride. *J. gen. Physiol.* **48**, 859–872. [61]

Asada, Y. (1963). Effects of intracellularly injected anions on the Mauthner cells of gold fish. *Jap. J. Physiol.* **13**, 583–598. [244]

Axelsson, J. & Thesleff, S. (1958). The 'desensitizing' effect of acetylcholine on the mammalian motor end-plate. *Acta physiol. scand.* **43**, 15–26. [196, 197]

— (1959). A study of supersensitivity in denervated mammalian skeletal muscle. *J. Physiol.* **147**, 178–193. [193]

Bacq, Z. M. & Brown, G. L. (1937). Pharmacological experiments on mammalian voluntary muscle, in relation to the theory of chemical transmission. *J. Physiol.* **89**, 45–60. [7]

Baker, P. F., Hodgkin, A. L. & Meves, H. (1964). The effect of diluting the internal solution on the electrical properties of a perfused giant axon. *J. Physiol.* **170**, 541–560. [39]

Baker, P. F., Hodgkin, A. L. & Shaw, T. I. (1962). The effects of changes in internal ionic concentrations on the electrical properties of perfused giant axons. *J. Physiol.* **164**, 355–374. [31, 36, 60]

Baldwin, H. A., Frenk, S. & Lettvin, J. Y. (1965). Glass coated tungsten microelectrodes. *Science* **148**, 1462–1464. [299]

Barr, L., Dewey, M. M. & Berger, W. (1965). Propagation of action potentials and the structure of the nexus in cardiac muscle. *J. gen. Physiol.* **48**, 797–823. [50]

Barstad, J. A. B. (1962). Presynaptic effect of the neuromuscular transmitter. *Experientia* **8**, 579. [201]

Baumgarten, R. von & Jung, R. (1952). Microelectrode studies on visual cortex. *Rev. Neurol.* **87**, 151–155. [297]

Belt, E. (1955). *Leonardo the Anatomist*, pp. 30–31. Lawrence: University of Kansas Press. [2]

Bennett, M. R. (1967). An analysis of the surface fixed-charge theory of the squid giant axon membrane. *Biophys. J.* **7**, 151–164. [31, 40]

Bennett, M. R. & Burnstock, G. (1966). Application of the sucrose-gap method to determine the ionic basis of the membrane potential of smooth muscle. *J. Physiol.* **183**, 637–648. [10, 87]

Bennett, M. V. L. (1964). Nervous function at the cellular level. *Ann. Rev. Physiol.* **26**, 289–340. [220]

— (1966). Physiology of electrotonic junctions. *Ann. N.Y. Acad Sci.* **137**, 509–539. [11, 50]

Bennett, M. V. L., Crain, S. M. & Grundfest, H. (1959). Electrophysiology of supramedullary neurons in Spheroides maculatus. II. Properties of the electrically excitable membrane. *J. gen. Physiol.* **43**, 189–219. [94]

Bennett, M. V. L. & Fox, S. (1962). Electrophysiology of caudal neurosecretory cells in the skate and fluke. *Gen. Comp. Endocr.* **2**, 77–95. [220]

Bennett, M. V. L., Freeman, A. R. & Thaddeus, P. (1966). 'Reversal' of postsynaptic potentials in non-isopotential systems. *Tenth Annual Meeting of Biophysical Society*. Abst. 122. [247]

Bennett, M. V. L., Nakajima, Y. & Pappas, G. D. (1967*a*). Physiology and ultrastructure of electrotonic junctions. I. Supramedullary neurons. *J. Neurophysiol.* **30**, 161–179. [50]

— (1967*b*). Physiology and ultrastructure of electrotonic junctions. III. Giant electromotor neurons of *Malapterurus electricus*. *J. Neurophysiol.* **30**, 209–235. [50]

Bennett, M. V. L., Pappas, G. D., Aljure, E. & Nakajima, Y. (1967*c*). Physiology and ultrastructure of electrotonic junctions. II. Spinal and medullary electromotor nuclei in mormyrid fish. *J. Neurophysiol.* **30**, 180–208. [50]

Bennett, M. V. L., Pappas, G. D., Giménez, M. & Nakajima, Y. (1967*d*). Physiology and ultrastructure of electrotonic junctions. IV. Medullary electromotor nuclei in gymnotid fish. *J. Neurophysiol.* **30**, 236–300. [50]

Bernard, C. (1856). Analyse physiologique des propriétés des systèmes musculaire et nerveux au moyen du curare. *C.R. Acad. Sci., Paris* **43**, 825–829. [6]

Bernstein, J. (1868). Über den zeitlichen Verlauf der negativen Schwankung des Nervenstroms. *Arch. ges. Physiol.* **1**, 173–207. [5]

Bernstein, T. (1902). Untersuchungen zur Thermodynamik der biolektrischen ströme Erster Theil. *Pflügers. Arch. ges. Physiol.* **92**, 521–562. [31, 314]

Bigland, B., Goetze, B., Maclagan, J. & Zaimis, E. (1958). The effect of lowered muscle temperature on the action of neuromuscular blocking drugs. *J. Physiol.* **141**, 425–434. [316]

Birks, R., Huxley, H. E. & Katz, B. (1960). The fine structure of the neuromuscular junction of the frog. *J. Physiol.* **150**, 134–144. [13]

Birks, R., Katz, B. & Miledi, R. (1960). Physiological and structural changes at the amphibian myoneural junction in the course of nerve degeneration. *J. Physiol.* **150**, 145–168. [12, 117]

Birks, R. & MacIntosh, F. C. (1961). Acetylcholine metabolism of a sympathetic ganglion. *Can. J. Biochem. Physiol.* **39**, 787–827. [114, 144]

Blaber, L. C. & Christ, D. D. (1967). The action of facilitatory drugs on the isolated tenuissimus muscle of the cat. *Int. J. Neuropharmac.* **6**, 473–485. [200]

Blackman, J. G. (1963). Stimulus frequency and neuromuscular block. *Br. J. Pharmacol.* **20**, 5–16. [156]

Blackman, J. G., Ginsborg, B. L. & Ray, C. (1963a). Spontaneous synaptic activity in sympathetic ganglion cells of the frog. *J. Physiol.* **167**, 389–401. [116, 302, 318]

— (1963b). On the quantal release of the transmitter at a sympathetic synapse. *J. Physiol.* **167**, 402–415. [128]

Blankenship, J. E. (1968). Action of tetrodotoxin on spinal motoneurons of the cat. *J. Neurophysiol.* **31**, 186–194. [117]

Blankenship, J. E. & Kuno, M. (1968). Analysis of spontaneous subthreshold activity in spinal motoneurons of the cat. *J. Neurophysiol.* **31**, 195–209. [118, 226, 241]

Blaustein, M. P. & Goldman, D. E. 1966). Action of anionic and cationic nerve-blocking agents: experiment and interpretation. *Science* **153**, 429. [60]

Bloedel, J., Gage, P. W., Llinás, R. & Quastel, D. M. J. (1966). Transmitter release at the squid giant synapse in the presence of tetrodotoxin. *Nature Lond.* **212**, 49–50. [61, 130, 159, 172, 257]

— (1967). Transmission across the squid giant synapse in the presence of tetrodotoxin, *J. Physiol.* **188**, 52–53. [172]

duBois-Reymond, E. (1849). *Untersuchungen über thierische Elektricität*, Vol. 2. Berlin: Reimer. [5]

— (1877). *Gesammelte Abhandlungen zur allgemeinen Muskel und Nervenphysik*, Vol. 2. Leipzig: Veit. [6]

Borelli, A. G. (1608–1679) (published posthumously 1681). *De motu animalium*. Rome: Bernado. (Quoted in *Handbook of Physiology*, Section 1, vol. 1, p. 5. Washington, D.C.: American Physiological Society, 1959.) [2]

Bowman, W. (1840). On the minute structure and movements of voluntary muscle. *Phil. Trans. R. Soc.* **130**, 457–501. [5]

Boyd, I. A. & Martin, A. R. (1956a). Spontaneous subthreshold activity at mammalian neuromuscular junctions. *J. Physiol.* **132**, 61–73. [116, 123, 302, 313, 318]

— (1956b). The end-plate potential in mammalian muscle. *J. Physiol.* **132**, 74–91. [123, 128, 131, 147, 313]

— (1959). Membrane constants of mammalian muscle fibres. *J. Physiol.* **147**, 450–457. [93, 99, 101, 102, 314]

Boyle, P. J. & Conway, E. J. (1941). Potassium accumulation in muscle and associated changes. *J. Physiol.* **100**, 1–63. [302, 303]

Bozler, E. & Cole, K. S. (1935). Electric impedance and phase angle of muscle in rigor. *J. cell. comp. Physiol.* **6**, 229–241. [102]

Bradley, K. & Somjen, G. G. (1961). Accommodation in motoneurones of the rat and the cat. *J. Physiol.* **156**, 75–92. [121]

Bradley, P. B. & Key, B. J. (1958). The effect of drugs on arousal responses produced by electrical stimulation of the reticular formation of the brain. *Electroencephalography, Montreal* **10**, 97–110. [296]

Braun, M. & Schmidt, R. F. (1966). Potential changes recorded from the frog motor nerve terminal during its activation. *Pflügers Arch. ges. Physiol.* **287**, 56–80. [113, 160]

Brock, L. G., Coombs, J. S. & Eccles, J. C. (1952). Synaptic excitation and inhibition. *J. Physiol.* **117**, 8P. [216, 217, 219, 225, 238, 239]

Brooks, A. E. & Hutter, O. F. (1963a). The influence of pH on the chloride conductance of skeletal muscle. *J. Physiol.* **163**, 9–10P. [317]

— (1963b). Effects of extracellular pH on electrical activity of skeletal muscle. *Proc. 2nd Int. Pharm. Congr. Biochem. Pharmacol.* **12**, Part 2, 266–267. [317]

— (1964). The effect of pH on the efflux of ^{36}Cl from skeletal muscle. *J. Physiol.* **172**, 29–30. [317]

Brooks, C. Mc. C. & Eccles, J. C. (1947). Electrical investigation of the monosynaptic pathway through the spinal cord. *J. Neurophysiol.* **10**, 251–274. [159]

Brooks, V. B. (1956). An intracellular study of the action of repetitive nerve volleys and of botulinum toxin on miniature end-plate potentials. *J. Physiol.* **134**, 264–277. [116]

Brooks, V. B. & Thies, R. E. (1962). Reduction of quantal content during neuromuscular transmission. *J. Physiol.* **162**, 298–310. [130, 136, 157]

Brown, G. L. (1937). Action potentials of normal mammalian muscle. Effects of acetylcholine and eserine. *J. Physiol.* **89**, 220–237. [7]

— (1954). The effect of temperature on the release of acetylcholine from sympathetic ganglia. *J. Physiol.* **124**, 26P. [314, 315]

— (1965). The Croonian Lecture: The release and fate of the transmitter liberated by adrenergic nerves. *Proc. R. Soc. B* **162**, 1–19. [202]

Brown, G. L., Dale, H. H. & Feldberg, W. (1936). Reactions of the normal mammalian muscle to acetylcholine and to eserine. *J. Physiol.* **87**, 394–424. [7]

Buchthal, F. & Lindhard, J. (1937). Direct application of acetylcholine to motor endplates of voluntary muscle fibres. *J. Physiol.* **90**, 82–83P. [196]

Bülbring, E. & Tomita, T. (1966). Evidence supporting the assumption that the 'inhibitory potential' in the taenia coli of the guinea pig is a post-synaptic potential due to nerve stimulation. *J. Physiol.* **185**, 24–25P. [173]

Bullock, J. H. & Horridge, G. A. (1965). *Structure and Function in the Nervous System of Invertebrates.* San Francisco and London: Freeman & Co. [v]

Burke, R. E. (1967). Composite nature of the monosynaptic excitatory postsynaptic potential. *J. Neurophysiol.* **30,** 1114–1137. [226–231, 241, 262]

Burke, R. E. & Nelson, P. G. (1966). Synaptic activity in motoneurones during natural stimulation of muscle spindles. *Science* **151,** 1088–1091. [226, 227]

Burke, R. E., Fedina, L. & Lundberg, A. (1968). Differential chloride reversal of IPSPs from group 1a afferents and motor axon collaterals. *Acta physiol. scand.* **73,** 1–2, 3A–4A. [247, 259]

Burke, W. (1957). Spontaneous potentials in slow muscle fibres of the frog. *J. Physiol.* **135,** 511–521. [116, 120]

Burke, W. & Ginsborg, B. L. (1956a). The electrical properties of the slow muscle fibre membrane. *J. Physiol.* **132,** 586–598. [109, 120]

— (1956b). The action of the neuromuscular transmitter on the slow fibre membrane. *J. Physiol.* **132,** 599–610. [105, 120]

Burnstock, G. & Holman, M. E. (1962a). Spontaneous potentials at sympathetic nerve endings in smooth muscle. *J. Physiol.* **160,** 446–460. [116, 203]

— (1962b). Effect of denervation and of reserpine treatment on transmission at sympathetic nerve endings. *J. Physiol.* **160,** 461–469. [203

— (1964). An electrophysiological investigation of the actions of some autonomic blocking drugs on transmission in the guinea pig vas deferens. *Br. J. Pharmacol.* **23,** 600–612. [203]

— (1966). Junction potentials at adrenergic synapses. *Pharmacol. Rev.* 18, part 1, 481–493. [203]

Burnstock, G. & Straub, R. W. (1958). A method for studying the effects of ions and drugs on the resting and action potentials in smooth muscle with external electrodes. *J. Physiol.* **140,** 156–167. [87]

Cambridge, G. W., Holdgate, J. A. & Sharp, J. P. (1959). A pharmacological analysis of the contractile mechanism of Mytilus muscle. *J. Physiol.* **148,** 451–464. [308]

Canepa, F. G. (1965). Anaesthesia and temperature effect mechanism in neuromuscular blocking of N^+ quaternary depolarizing drugs. *Nature Lond.* **207,** 1149–1152. [316]

Cannon, W. B. & Bacq, Z. M. (1931). Studies on the conditions of activity in endocrine organs XXVI. A hormone produced by sympathetic action on smooth muscle. *Am. J. Physiol.* **96,** 392–412. [7]

Cannon, W. B. & Rosenbleuth, A. (1933). Studies on conditions of activity in endocrine organs XXIX. Sympathin E and Sympathin I. *Am. J. Physiol.* **104,** 557–574. [7]

Carey, M. J. & Conway, E. J. (1954). Comparison of various media for immersing frog sartorii at room temperature and evidence for the regional distribution of fibre Na^+. *J. Physiol.* **125,** 232–250. [91]

Carlsson, A. (1966). Pharmacological depletion of catecholamine stores. *Pharmac. Rev.* **18,** 541–549. [202]

Carslaw, H. S. & Jaeger, J. C. (1947). *Conduction of Heat in Solids.* Oxford: Clarendon Press. [76]

Castillo, J. del & Katz, B. (1954a). The effect of magnesium on the activity of motor nerve endings. *J. Physiol.* **124,** 553–559. [128]

Castillo, J. del & Katz, B. (1954*b*). Quantal components of the endplate potential. *J. Physiol.* **124**, 560–573. [8, 12, 115, 127, 128, 129, 130, 131, 149, 226]

— (1954*c*). Statistical factors involved in neuromuscular facilitation and depression. *J. Physiol.* **124**, 574–585. [130, 157, 198]

— (1954*d*). Changes in endplate activity produced by presynaptic polarization. *J. Physiol.* **124**, 586–604. [117, 123, 169, 170, 172]

— (1954*e*). The membrane change produced by the neuromuscular transmitter. *J. Physiol.* **125**, 546–565. [210]

— (1955*a*). On the localization of acetylcholine receptors. *J. Physiol.* **128**, 157–181. [193]

— (1955*b*). Local activity at a depolarised nerve-muscle junction. *J. Physiol.* **128**, 396–411. [12, 89, 90, 302]

— (1956*a*). Localization of active spots within the neuromuscular junction of the frog. *J. Physiol.* **132**, 630–649. [161]

— (1956*b*). Biophysical aspects of neuromuscular transmission. *Prog. Biophys, biophys. Chem.* **6**, 121–170. [12, 115, 116, 130]

— (1957*a*). A study of curare action with an electrical micro-method. *Proc. R. Soc. B.* **146**, 339–356. [194]

— (1957*b*). La base 'quantale' de la transmission neuromusculaire. In *Microphysiologie comparee des elements excitables*, No. 67, pp. 245–258. Paris: Coll. internat. C.N.R.S. [115]

Castillo, J. del & Machne, Xenia (1953). Effect of temperature on the passive electrical properties of frog muscle. *J. Physiol.* **120**, 431–434. [93, 313, 314]

Castillo, J. del, Nelson, T. E., Jr. & Sanchez, V. (1962). Mechanism of the increased acetylcholine sensitivity of skeletal muscle in low pH solutions. *J. cell. comp. Physiol.* **59**, 35–44. [316, 317]

Cavanaugh, D. J. & Hearon, J. Z. (1954). The kinetics of acetylcholine action on skeletal muscle. *Arch. int. Pharmacodyn.* **100**, 68–78. [178]

Chadwick, L. E. (1957). Temperature dependence of cholinesterase activity. In *Influence of Temperature on Biological Systems*, ed. Johnson, F. H. Baltimore: Waverly Press. [313]

Chandler, W. K., Hodgkin, A. L. & Meves, H. (1965). The effect of changing the internal solution on sodium inactivation and related phenomena in giant axons. *J. Physiol.* **180**, 821–836. [39]

Cheymol, J., Bourillet, F. & Ogura, Y. (1962). Action de quelques paralysants neuromusculaires sur la libération de l'acétylcholine au niveau des terminaisons neurveuses motrices. *Arch. int. Pharmacol.* **129**, 187–197. [114]

Ciani, S. & Edwards C. (1963). The effect of acetylcholine on neuromuscular transmission in the frog. *J. Pharmac. exp. Ther.* **142**, 21–23. [123]

Clark, A. J. (1933). *The Mode of Action of Drugs on Cells*. London: Edward Arnold & Co. [176]

— (1937). *General Pharmacology*. Berlin: Springer Verlag. [193]

Clark, J. & Plonsey, R. (1966). A mathematical evaluation of the core conductor model. *Biophys. J.* **6**, 95–112. [269]

Cole, K. S. (1932). Electric phase angle of cell membranes. *J. gen. Physiol.* **15,** 641–649. [43]

— (1941). Rectification and inductance in the squid giant axon. *J. gen. Physiol.* **25,** 29–51. [222]

— (1949). Dynamic electrical characteristics of the squid axon membrane. *Arch. Sci. Physiol.* **3,** 253–258. [53]

— (1962). The advance of electrical models for cells and axons. *Biophys. J.* **2,** No. 2, Part 2, 101–119. [43, 44, 81]

Cole, K. S. & Curtis, H. J. (1938). Electric impedance of Nitella during activity. *J. gen. Physiol.* **22,** 37. [222]

— (1939). Electric impedance of the squid giant axon during activity. *J gen. Physiol.* **22,** 649–670. [44, 52, 70, 222]

Cole, K. S. & Hodgkin, A. L. (1939). Membrane and protoplasm resistance in the squid giant axon. *J. gen. Physiol.* **22,** 671–687. [70]

Cole, W. H. (1941). A perfusing solution for the lobster (Homarus) heart and the effects of its constituent ions on the heart. *J. gen. Physiol.* **25,** 1–6. [307]

Coombs, J. S., Curtis, D. R. & Eccles, J. C. (1957). The interpretation of spike potentials of motoneurons. *J. Physiol.* **139,** 198–231. [94, 219, 258]

— (1959). The electrical constants of the motoneurone membrane. *J. Physiol.* **145,** 505–528. [79, 91–92, 93, 94, 99, 103, 104]

Coombs, J. S., Eccles, J. C. & Fatt, P. (1953). The action of the inhibitory synaptic transmitter. *Aust. J. Sci.* **16,** 1–5. [106]

— (1955a). The electrical properties of the motoneurone membrane. *J. Physiol.* **130,** 291–325. [89, 91, 94, 95, 99, 110, 217, 220, 223, 233, 279]

— (1955b). The specific ionic conductance and the ionic movements across the motoneuronal membrane that produce the inhibitory postsynaptic potential. *J. Physiol.* **130,** 326–373. [89, 239–244, 247]

— (1955c). Excitatory synaptic action in motoneurons. *J. Physiol.* **130,** 374–395. [105, 229, 232–235, 237, 247, 250, 251, 279]

— (1955d). The ionic permeability of the motoneurone membrane. *J. cell. comp. Physiol.* **46,** 362–363. [239, 240]

Coraboeuf, E. & Weidman, S. (1954). Temperature effects on the electrical activity of Purkinje fibres. *Helv. physiol. Acta* **12,** 32–41. [314]

Couteaux, R. (1963). The differentiation of synaptic areas. *Proc. R. Soc.* B **158,** 457–480. [13]

Cowan, S. L. (1934). The action of potassium and other ions on the injury potential and action current in maia nerve. *Proc. R. Soc.* B **115,** 216–260. [36]

Cox, D. R. & Lewis, P. A. W. (1966). *The Statistical Analysis of Series of Events.* London: Methuen. [126]

Cragg, B. G. & Hamlyn, L. H. (1955). Action potentials of the pyramidal neurones in the hippocampus of the rabbit. *J. Physiol.* **129,** 608–627. [220]

Crawford, J. M. & Curtis, D. R. (1966). Pharmacological studies on feline Betz cells. *J. Physiol.* **186,** 121–138. [296]

Creese, R. (1953). Effects of carbon dioxide on muscle. *J. Physiol.* **119,** 16P. [91]

— (1954). Measurement of cation fluxes on rat diaphragm. *Proc. R. Soc. B* **142,** 497–513. [91]

— (1960). Potassium in different layers of isolated diaphragm. *J. Physiol.* **154,** 133–144. [91]

Creese, R. & Northover, J. (1961). Maintenance of isolated diaphragm with normal sodium content. *J. Physiol.* **155,** 343–357. [91]

Creese, R. & Roberts, H. E. (1954). Calcium and muscle sodium. *J. Physiol.* **127,** 32P. [91]

Creese, R., Scholes, N. W. & Whalen, W. J. (1958). Resting potentials of diaphragm muscle after prolonged anoxia. *J. Physiol.* **140,** 301–317. [91]

Creutzfeldt, O. D., Lux, H. D. & Nacimiento, A. C. (1964). Intracelluläre Reizung corticaler Nervenzellen. *Pflügers Arch. ges. Physiol.* **281,** 129–151. [220]

Croone, W. (1633–1684). *De ratione motus musculorum* (London: Hayes 1664) as translated by Leonard G. Wilson; and *An Hypothesis of the Structure of a Muscle and the Reason of its Contraction* (London: Hooke's Philosophical Collections, 1675) as quoted in *Selected readings in the History of Physiology*, 2nd edn., ed. Fulton, John F. & Wilson, L. G. Springfield, Ill.: Charles C Thomas, 1966. [2]

Curtis, D. R. (1963). Direct extracellular application of drugs. *Proc. First Int. Pharmacol. Meeting*, Vol. 5, pp. 205–212. [190, 195]

Curtis, D. R. & Eccles, J. C. (1959). The time courses of excitatory and inhibitory synaptic actions. *J. Physiol.* **145,** 529–546. [237, 240, 249]

— (1960). Synaptic action during and after repetitive stimulation. *J. Physiol.* **150,** 374–398. [147, 237, 248]

Curtis, D. R. & Ryall, R. W. (1966). The synaptic excitation of Renshaw cells. *Exp. Brain Res.* **2,** 81–96. [198]

Dahlbäck, O., Elmqvist, D., Johns, T. R., Radner, S. & Thesleff, S. (1961). An electrophysiologic study of the neuromuscular junction in myasthenia gravis. *J. Physiol.* **156,** 336–343. [192]

Dale, H. H. & Dudley, H. W. (1929). The presence of histamine and acetylcholine in the spleen of the ox and the horse. *J. Physiol.* **68,** 97–123. [7]

Dale, H. H., Feldberg, W. & Vogt, M. (1936). Release of acetylcholine at voluntary motor nerve endings. *J. Physiol.* **86,** 353–380. [7]

Danielli, J. F. & Davson, H. (1935). A contribution to the theory of permeability of thin films. *J. cell. comp. Physiol.* **5,** 495–508. [29]

Davenport, D. (1941). The effects of acetylcholine, atropine, and nicotine on the isolated heart of the commercial crab, *Cancer magister*. *Physiol. Zool.* **14,** 178–185. [307]

Dawson, R. M. C., Elliott, D. C., Elliott, W. H. & Jones, K. M. (1959). *Data for Biochemical Research*. Oxford: Clarendon Press. [301]

Diamond, J. (1968). The activation and distribution of GABA and L-glutamate receptors on goldfish Mauthner neurons: An analysis of dendritic remote inhibition (with appendix by Huxley, A. F.). *J. Physiol.* **194,** 669–723. [259]

Diamond, J., Gray, J. A. B. & Inman, D. R. (1958). The relation between receptor potentials and the concentration of sodium ions. *J. Physiol.* **142,** 382–394. [69]

Diamond, J. & Miledi, R. (1962). A study of foetal and new-born rat muscle fibres. *J. Physiol.* **162,** 393–408. [193]

Dodge, F. A. & Frankenhaeuser, B. (1958). Membrane currents in isolated frog nerve fibre under voltage clamp conditions. *J. Physiol.* **143,** 76–90. [40, 41, 59]

— (1959). Sodium currents in the myelinated nerve fibre of Xenopus laevis investigated with the voltage clamp technique. *J. Physiol.* **148,** 188–200. [40, 41]

Donaldson, P. E. K. (1958). *Electronic Apparatus for Biological Research.* London: Butterworths Scientific Publications. [v, 97, 298]

Dowben, R. M. & Rose, J. E. (1953). Metal-filled microelectrode. *Science* **118,** 22–24. [239]

Duchâteau, G., Florkin, M. & Leclercq, J. (1953). Concentrations des bases fixes et types de composition de la base totale de l'hémolymphe des insects. *Arch. int. Physiol.* **61,** 518–549. [310]

Dudel, J. (1965a). The mechanism of presynaptic inhibition at the crayfish neuromuscular junction. *Pflügers Arch. ges. Physiol.* **284,** 66–80. [160, 161]

— (1965b). The action of inhibitory drugs on nerve terminals in crayfish muscle. *Pflügers Arch. ges. Physiol.* **284,** 81–94. [163]

Dudel, J. & Kuffler, S. W. (1961a). The quantal nature of transmission and spontaneous miniature potentials at the crayfish neuromuscular junction. *J. Physiol.* **155,** 514–529. [116, 128, 141]

— (1961b). Presynaptic inhibition at the crayfish neuromuscular junction. *J. Physiol.* **155,** 543–562. [167]

Dudel, J. & Orkand, R. K. (1960). Spontaneous potential changes at crayfish neuro-muscular junctions. *Nature Lond.* **186,** 476–477. [116]

Earle, W. R. (1943). Production of malignancy *in vitro.* IV. The mouse fibroblast cultures and changes seen in the living cells. *J. Nat. Cancer Inst.* **4,** 165–212. [300]

Eccles, J. C. (1943). Synaptic potentials and transmission in sympathetic ganglion. *J. Physiol.* **101,** 465–483. [204]

— (1946a). An electrical hypothesis of synaptic and neuromuscular transmission. *Ann. N.Y. Acad. Sci.* **47,** 429–455. [6]

— (1946b). Synaptic potentials of motoneurones. *J. Neurophysiol.* **9,** 87–120. [302]

— (1955). The central action of antidromic impulses in motor nerve fibres. *Pflügers Arch. ges. Physiol.* **260,** 385–415. [218, 302]

— (1957). *The Physiology of Nerve Cells.* Baltimore: John Hopkins Press. [96, 216, 227, 230, 233, 239]

— (1963). Postsynaptic and presynaptic inhibitory actions in the spinal cord. In *Progress in Brain Research,* Vol. 1, pp. 1–18, ed. Moruzzi, G., Fessard, A. & Jasper, H. H. Amsterdam and N.Y.: Elsevier. [256]

— (1964). *The Physiology of Synapses.* Berlin-Göttingen-Heidelberg: Springer-Verlag. [v, 61, 166, 208, 244, 248, 254, 257]

Eccles, J. C., Eccles, R. M. & Ito, M. (1964*a*). Effects of intracellular potassium and sodium injections on the inhibitory post-synaptic potentials. *Proc. R. Soc. B* **160**, 181–196. [42, 79, 243]

— (1964*b*). Effects produced on inhibitory postsynaptic potentials by the coupled injections of cations and anions into motoneurones. *Proc. R. Soc. B* **160**, 197–210. [79, 243]

Eccles, J. C., Eccles, R. M. & Lundberg, A. (1957). Synaptic actions on motoneurones in relation to the two components of the group I muscle afferent volleys. *J. Physiol.* **136**, 527–546. [229]

— (1958). The action potentials of the alpha-motoneurones supplying fast and slow muscles. *J. Physiol.* **142**, 275–291. [221]

Eccles, J. C., Eccles, R. M. & Magni, F. (1961). Central inhibitory action attributable to presynaptic depolarization produced by muscle afferent volleys. *J. Physiol.* **159**, 147–166. [254, 255]

Eccles, J. C., Fatt, P. & Koketsu, K. (1954). Cholinergic and inhibitory synapses in a pathway from motor-axon collaterals to motoneurons. *J. Physiol.* **126**, 524–562. [239, 245, 250, 258]

Eccles, J. C., Fatt, P. & Landgren, S. (1954). The 'direct' inhibitory pathway in the spinal cord. *Aust. J. Sci.* **16**, 130–134. [240]

Eccles, J. C., Hubbard, J. I. & Oscarsson, O. (1961). Intracellular recording from cells of the ventral spino-cerebellar tract. *J. Physiol.* **158**, 486–516. [90]

Eccles, J. C., Ito, M. & Szentágothai, J. (1967). *The Cerebellum as a Neuronal Machine*. Berlin-Heidelberg-N.Y.: Springer-Verlag. [253]

Eccles, J. C. & Jaeger, J. C. (1957). The relationship between the mode of operation and the dimensions of the junctional regions at synapses and motor end-organs. *Proc. R. Soc. B* **148**, 38–56. [198]

Eccles, J. C., Katz, B. & Kuffler, S. W. (1941). Nature of the 'end-plate potential' in curarized muscle. *J. Neurophysiol.* **4**, 362–387. [8, 199, 204, 313]

— (1942). Effect of eserine on neuromuscular transmission. *J. Neurophysiol.* **5**, 211–230. [8, 199, 313]

Eccles, J. C., Kostyuk, P. G. & Schmidt, R. F. (1962). The effect of electric polarization of the spinal cord on central afferent fibres and on their excitatory synaptic action. *J. Physiol.* **162**, 138–150. [169]

Eccles, J. C., Libet, B. & Young, R. R. (1958). The behaviour of chromatolysed motoneurones studied by intracellular recording. *J. Physiol.* **143**, 11–40. [219–220]

Eccles, J. C. & Liley, A. W. (1959). Factors controlling the liberation of acetylcholine at the neuromuscular junction. *Am. J. Phys. Med.* **38**, 96–103. [167]

Eccles, J. C., Llinás, R. & Sasaki, K. (1966*a*). The excitatory synaptic actions of climbing fibres on the Purkinje cells of the cerebellum. *J. Physiol.* **182**, 268–296. [105, 234, 235]

— (1966*b*). The action of antidromic impulses on the cerebellar Purkinje cells. *J. Physiol.* **182**, 316–345. [220, 247, 259, 264, 275, 278, 285, 286]

— (1966*c*). The inhibitory interneurones within the cerebellar cortex. *Exp. Brain Res.* **1**, 1–16. [253]

— (1966*d*). Parallel fibre stimulation and responses induced thereby in the Purkinje cells of the cerebellum. *Exp. Brain Res.* **1**, 17–39. [253, 259, 293]

Eccles, J. C. Llinás, R. & Sasaki, K. (1966*e*). The mossy fibre-granule cell relay of the cerebellum and its inhibitory control by Golgi cells. *Exp. Brain Res.* **1**, 82–101. [293]

— (1966*f*). Intracellularly recorded responses of the cerebellar Purkinje cells. *Exp. Brain Res.* **1**, 161–183. [245–247, 253, 259]

Eccles, J. C. & MacFarlane, W. V. (1949). Action of anti-cholinesterases on end-plate potential of frog muscle. *J. Neurophysiol.* **12**, 59–80. [8, 199]

Eccles, J. C., Magni, F. & Willis, W. D. (1962). Depolarization of central terminals of Group I afferent fibres from muscle. *J. Physiol.* **160**, 62–93. [168]

Eccles, J. C., Oscarsson, O. & Willis, W. D. (1961). Synaptic action of Group I and II afferent fibres of muscle on the cells of the dorsal spinocerebellar tract. *J. Physiol.* **158**, 517–543. [147]

Eccles, J. C., Schmidt, R. F. & Willis, W. D. (1962). Presynaptic inhibition of the spinal monosynaptic reflex pathway. *J. Physiol.* **161**, 282–297. [254, 255]

— (1963). Pharmacological studies on presynaptic inhibition. *J. Physiol.* **168**, 500–530. [257]

Eccles, R. M. (1955). Intracellular potentials recorded from a mammalian sympathetic ganglion. *J. Physiol.* **130**, 572–584. [90]

Eccles, R. M., Løyning, Y. & Oshima, T. (1966). Effects of hypoxia on the monosynaptic reflex pathway in the cat spinal cord. *J. Neurophysiol.* **29**, 315–332. [109, 110, 216]

Edmunds, C. W. & Roth, G. B. (1908). Concerning the action of curare and physostigmine upon nerve endings or muscles. *Am. J. Physiol.* **23**, 28–45 [6]

Edwards, C. & Ikeda, K. (1962). Effect of 2-PAM and succinylcholine on neuromuscular transmission in the frog. *J. Pharmacol.* **138**, 322–327. [141].

Eide, E., Lundberg, A. & Voorhoeve, P. (1961). Monosynaptically evoked inhibitory postsynaptic potentials in motoneurones. *Acta physiol. scand.* **53**, 185–195. [240]

Eisenberg, R. S. & Gage, P. W. (1967). Frog skeletal muscle fibers: changes in electrical properties after disruption of transverse tubular system. *Science* **158**, 1700–1701. [318]

Elliott, T. R. (1904). On the action of adrenalin. *J. Physiol.* **31**, 20–21P. [7]

— (1905). The action of adrenalin. *J. Physiol.* **32**, 401–467. [6, 7]

Elmqvist, D. & Feldman, D. S. (1965). Spontaneous activity at a mammalian neuromuscular junction in tetrodotoxin. *Acta physiol. scand.* **64**, 475–476. [118, 172]

Elmqvist, D., Hofmann, W. W., Kugelberg, J. & Quastel, D. M. J. (1964). An electrophysiological investigation of neuromuscular transmission in myasthenia gravis. *J. Physiol.* **174**, 417–434. [93, 118, 122, 126, 144, 147, 302]

Elmqvist, D., Johns, T. R. & Thesleff, S. (1960). A study of some electrophysiological properties of human intercostal muscle. *J. Physiol.* **154**, 602–607. [93, 116]

Elmqvist, D. & Quastel, D. M. J. (1965*a*). Presynaptic action of hemicholinium at the neuromuscular junction. *J. Physiol.* **177**, 463–482. [117, 122, 131, 136, 144, 145]

— (1965*b*). A quantitative study of end-plate potentials in isolated human muscle. *J. Physiol.* **178**, 505–529. [128–130, 136, 143, 146, 147, 149–151, 155–158, 198]

Estable, C. (1923). Notes sur la structure comparative de l'ecorce cerebelleuse et derivées physiologiques possibles. *Trab. Inst. Cajal Invest. biol.* **21**, 169–256. [259]

Ettori, J. & Scoggar, S. M. (1959). Ionised calcium in biological media. *Nature Lond.* **184**, 1315–1316. [301]

Fadiga, E. & Brookhart, J. M (1960). Monosynaptic activation of different portions of the motor neuron membrane. *Am. J. Physiol.* **198**, 693–703. [260]

Fadiga, E. & Brookhart, J. M. (1962). Interactions of excitatory postsynaptic potentials generated at different sites on the frog motoneurons. *J. Neurophysiol.* **25**, 790–804. [238, 260]

Falck, B. (1962). Observations on the possibilities of the cellular localization of mono amines by a fluorescence method. *Acta physiol scand.* **56**, suppl. 197, 1–24. [203]

Falk, G. & Fatt, P. (1964). Linear electrical properties of striated muscle fibres observed with intracellular electrodes. *Proc. R. Soc. B* **160**, 69–123, [29, 74, 81, 83, 84]

— (1965). Electrical impedance of striated muscle and its relation to contraction. In *Studies in Physiology*, ed. Curtis, D. R. & McIntyre, A. K., pp. 64–70. Berlin: Springer-Verlag. [82]

Fatt, P. (1950). The electromotive action of acetylcholine at the motor end-plate. *J. Physiol.* **111**, 408–422. [196]

— (1957). Electric potentials around an antidromically activated motoneurone. *J. Neurophysiol.* **20**, 27–60. [217, 219, 238, 279, 284]

— (1964). An analysis of the transverse electrical impedance of striated muscle. *Proc. R. Soc. B* **159**, 606–651. [81]

Fatt, P. & Ginsborg, B. L. (1958). The ionic requirements for the production of action potentials in crustacean muscle fibres. *J. Physiol.* **142**, 516–543. [59, 60, 103]

Fatt, P. & Katz, B. (1950). Some observations on biological noise. *Nature Lond.* **166**, 597–598. 116]

— (1951). An analysis of the end-plate potential recorded with an intracellular electrode. *J. Physiol.* **115**, 320–370. [6, 8, 41, 62, 76, 78, 105, 142, 199, 208, 288]

— (1952). Spontaneous subthreshold activity at motor nerve endings. *J. Physiol.* **117**, 109–128. [8, 12, 116, 123, 124, 318]

Feigen, S. A., Peterson, N. S., Hofmann, W. W., Genther, G. H. & Van Heyningen, W. E. (1963). The effect of impure tetanus toxin on the frequency of minature end-plate potentials. *J. gen. Microbiol.* **33**, 489–495.[315]

Feldberg, W. (1943). Synthesis of acetylcholine in sympathetic ganglia and cholinergic nerves. *J. Physiol.* **101**, 432–445. [7]

334   *Electrophysiological analysis of synaptic transmission*

Feller, W. (1950). *An Introduction to Probability Theory and Its Applications*, 2nd edn. N.Y. and London: John Wiley & Sons Ltd. [124]

Feng, T. P. & Li, T. H. (1941). Studies on the neuromuscular junction XXIII. A new aspect of the phenomena of eserine potentiation and post-tetanic facilitation in mammalian muscle. *Chin. J. Physiol.* **16**, 37–50. [201]

Fernandez-Morán, H. (1955). Estudios sobre la organizacion submicroscopica del talamo. *Congres Latinoamer. Neurocir.* **6**, 599–753. [13]

Fessard, A. & Tauc, L. (1957). Comparaison entre la dissipation des potentiels postsynaptiques et electrotoniques dans le soma neuronique de l'Aplysie. *J. Physiol., Paris* **49**, 162–164. [93]

Finkelstein, A. & Mauro, A. (1963). Equivalent circuits as related to ionic systems. *Biophys. J.* **3**, 215–237. [38]

Förster, R. P. (1948). Use of thin kidney slices and isolated renal tubules for direct study of cellular transport kinetics. *Science* **108**, 65–67. [303]

Frank, G. B. & Inoue, F. (1966). Large miniature end-plate potentials in partial denervated skeletal muscle. *Nature Lond.* **212**, 596–598. [188]

Frank, K. (1959). Basic mechanisms of synaptic transmission in the central nervous system. IRE, *Inst. Radio Engrs. Trans. Med. Electron* **ME-6**, 85–88. [254]

Frank, K. & Becker, Mary C. (1964). Electrodes for recording and stimulation. In *Physical Techniques for Biological Research*, Vol. V, Ch. 2, ed. Nastuk, W. L. N.Y. and London: Academic Press. [88]

Frank, K. & Fuortes, M. G. F. (1955). Potentials recorded from the spinal cord with microelectrodes. *J. Physiol.* **130**, 625–654. [90]

— (1956). Stimulation of spinal motoneurones with intracellular electrodes. *J. Physiol.* **134**, 451–470. [103, 220, 279]

— (1957). Presynaptic and post-synaptic inhibition of monosynaptic reflex. *Fed. Proc.* **16**, 39–40. [254]

— (1960). Accommodation of spinal motoneurones of cat. *Arch. Ital. Biol.* **98**, 165–170. [221]

— (1961). Excitation and conduction. *A. Rev. Physiol.* **23**, 357–386. [258]

Frankenhaeuser, B. (1960). Quantitative description of sodium currents in myelinated nerve fibres of *Xenopus laevis*. *J. Physiol.* **151**, 49–51. [40]

— (1962). Instantaneous potassium currents in myelinated nerve fibres of *Xenopus laevis*. *J. Physiol.* **160**, 46–53. [41]

Frankenhaeuser, B. & Hodgkin, A. L. (1957). The action of calcium on the electrical properties of squid axons. *J. Physiol.* **137**, 218–244. [169]

Frankenhaeuser, B. & Huxley, A. F. (1964). The action potential in the myelinated nerve fibre of *Xenopus laevis* as computed on the basis of voltage clamp data. *J. Physiol.* **171**, 302–315. [59]

Frankenhaeuser, B. & Vallbo, A. B. (1965). Accommodation in myelinated nerve fibres of *Xenopus laevis* as computed on the basis of voltage clamp data. *Acta. physiol. scand.* **63**, 1–20. [221]

Freygang, W. H. (1958). An analysis of extracellular potentials from single neurons in the lateral geniculate nucleus of the cat. *J. gen. Physiol.* **41**, 543–564. [217, 279, 282]

Freygang, W. H. & Frank, K. (1959). Extracellular potentials from single spinal motoneurons. *J. gen. Physiol.* **42**, 749–760. [217, 275, 279, 282, 285]

Fuhrman, F. A. (1946). The effect of body temperature on drug action. *Physiol. Rev.* **26**, 247–274. [316]

Fuhrman, G. T. & Fuhrman, F. A. (1961). Effects of temperature on the action of drugs. *A. Rev. Pharmacol.* **1**, 65–78. [316]

Fujita, Y. (1968). Activity of dendrites of single Purkinje cells and its relationship to so-called inactivation response in rabbit cerebellum. *J. Neurophysiol.* **31**, 131–141. [220]

Funderburk, W. H. & Unna, K. R. (1953). Site of action of 2,2-diethyl 1,3-propanediol (prenderol) on central nervous system. *J. Pharmac. exp. Ther.* **107**, 344–355. [297]

Fuortes, M. G. F., Frank, K. & Becker, M. C. (1957). Steps in the production of motoneuron spikes. *J. gen. Physiol.* **40**, 735–752. [219]

Furshpan, E. J. (1956). The effects of osmotic pressure changes on the spontaneous activity at motor nerve endings. *J. Physiol.* **134**, 689–697. [318]

Furshpan, E. J. & Potter, D. D. (1959). Transmission of giant motor synapses of the crayfish. *J. Physiol.* **145**, 289–325. [10]

Furukawa, T. (1957). The properties of the procaine end-plate potential. *Jap. J. Physiol.* **7**, 199–212. [195]

Furukawa, T., Sasaoka, T. & Hosoya, Y. (1959). Effects of tetrodotoxin on the neuromuscular junction. *Jap. J. Physiol.* **9**, 143–152. [118]

Gaddum, J. H. (1937). Discussion on pharmacological action. *Proc. R. Soc. B* **121**, 598–601. [188]

— (1943). Part I. Biological aspects: The antagonism of drugs. *Trans. Faraday Soc.* **39**, 323–333. [185]

Gage, P. W. & Eisenberg, R. S. (1967). Action potentials without contraction in frog skeletal muscle fibers with disrupted transverse tubules. *Science* **158**, 1702–1703. [81, 318]

Gage, P. W. & Hubbard, J. I. (1965). Evidence for a Poisson distribution of miniature end-plate potentials and some implications. *Nature Lond.* **208**, 395–396. [125, 171]

— (1966a). The origin of post-tetanic hyperpolarization in mammalian motor nerve terminals. *J. Physiol.* **184**, 335–352. [162, 169, 171, 301]

— (1966b). An investigation of the post-tetanic potentiation of end-plate potentials at a mammalian neuromuscular junction. *J. Physiol.* **184**, 353–375. [316, 318]

Gage, P. W. & Quastel, D. M. J. (1966). Competition between sodium and calcium ions in transmitter release at a mammalian neuromuscular junction. *J. Physiol.* **185**, 95–123. [124, 126]

Galvani, A. (1737–1798), as reported in Fulton, J. F. (1926), *Muscular Contraction and the Reflex Control of Movement*, pp. 34–38. Baltimore: Williams & Wilkins. [4]

Gershon, M. D. (1967). Inhibition of gastrointestinal movement by sympathetic nerve stimulation: The site of action. *J. Physiol.* **189**, 317–327. [173]

Gesteland, R. C., Howland, B., Lettvin, J. Y. & Pitts, W. H. (1959). Comments on microelectrodes. *Proc. I. R. E.* **47**, 1856–1862. [299]

Gilbert, D. L. & Lowenberg, W. E. (1964). Effect of pH on the resting membrane potential of frog sartorius muscle. *J. cell. comp. Physiol.* **63**, 359–364. [317]

Ginetzinsky, A. G. & Shamarina, N. M. (1942). The tonomotor phenomenon in denervated muscle. *Uspekhi Sourenoj Biologii* **15**, 283–294. [193]

Ginsborg, B. L. (1960a). Spontaneous activity in muscle fibres of the chick. *J. Physiol.* **150**, 707–717. [116, 120, 121, 302]

— (1960b). Some properties of avian skeletal muscle fibres with multiple neuromuscular junctions. *J. Physiol.* **154**, 581–598. [120, 121]

Glisson, F. (1677). *Tractatus de ventriculo et intestinis*, Ch. 8, pp. 166–168. London: Henry Brome. Translated in *Selected Readings in the History of Physiology*, 2nd edn., ed. Fulton, John F. & Wilson, L. G. Springfield, Ill.: Charles C Thomas, 1966. [3]

Goldman, D. E. (1943). Potential, impedance and rectification in membranes. *J. gen. Physiol.* **27**, 37–60 (1943). [37]

Goldman, L. (1964). The effects of stretch on cable and spike parameters of single nerve fibres; some implications for the theory of impulse propagation. *J. Physiol.* **175**, 425–444. [319]

Golgi, C. (1907). La dottrina del neurone Teoria e fatti. *Archo Fisiol.* **4**, 187. [213]

Gomori, G. (1955). Preparation of buffers for use in enzyme studies. In *Methods of Enzymology*, Vol. 1, ed. Colowick, S. P. & Kaplan, N. O. New York: Academic Press. [302, 307]

Goodford, P. J. (1964). Chloride content and ^{36}Cl uptake in the smooth muscle of the guinea-pig taenia coli. *J. Physiol.* **170**, 227–237. [42]

Göpfert, H. & Schaefer, H. (1938). Über den direkt und indirekt erregten Aktionsstrom und die Funktion der motorischen Endplatte. *Pflügers Arch. ges. Physiol.* **239**, 597–619. [7]

Gorman, A. L. F., Mirolli, M. & Salmoiraghi, G. C. (1967). Unusual characteristics of an inhibitory potential recorded intracellularly from a molluscan nerve cell. *Fed. Proc.* **26**, 329. [68]

Graham, J. & Gerard, R. W. (1946). Membrane potentials and excitation of impaled single muscle fibres. *J. cell. comp. Physiol.* **28**, 99–117. [89]

Granit, R. (1964). Maintained firing of motoneurones during transmembrane stimulation. In *Progress in Brain Research*, Vol. 12, pp. 35–41, ed. Eccles, J. C. & Schade, J. P. Amsterdam-London-N.Y.: Elsevier. [221]

Granit, R., Henatsch, H. D. & Steg, G. (1956). Tonic and phasic ventral horn cells differentiated by post-tetanic potentiation in cat extensors. *Acta physiol. scand.* **37**, 114–126. [221]

Granit, R., Kernell, D. & Shortess, G. K. (1963). Quantitative aspects of repetitive firing of mammalian motoneurones, as caused by injected currents. *J. Physiol.* **168**, 911–931. [222]

Granit, R. & Phillips, C. G. (1956). Excitatory and inhibitory processes acting upon individual Purkinje cells of the cerebellum in cats. *J. Physiol.* **133**, 520–547. [215, 219, 282]

Gray, E. G. (1959). Axo-somatic and axo-dendritic synapses of the cerebral cortex: An electron microscopic study. *J. Anat.* **93**, 420–433. [13]

Gray, E. G. (1961). Ultra-structure of synapses of the cerebral cortex and of certain specialisations of neuroglial membranes. In *Electron Microscopy in Anatomy*, ed. Boyd *et al.*, pp. 54–73. London: Edward Arnold. [13]

Gray, J. A. B. & Svaetichin, G. (1951). Electrical properties of platinum tipped microelectrodes in Ringer's solution. *Acta physiol. scand.* **24**, 278–284. [299]

Green, S. D. (1958). A simple microelectrode for recording from the central nervous system. *Nature Lond.* **182**, 962–963. [299]

Grinnell, A. D. (1966). A study of the interaction between motoneurones in the frog spinal cord. *J. Physiol.* **182**, 612–648. [220]

Grundfest, H. (1961). Ionic mechanisms in electrogenesis. *Ann. N.Y. Acad. Sci.* **94**, 405–457. [223, 234]

— (1966). Heterogeneity of excitable membrane: Electrophysiological and pharmacological evidence and some consequences. *Ann. N.Y. Acad. Sci.* **137**, 901–949. [52, 60, 172, 220, 223]

Grundfest, H. & Bennett, M. V. L. (1961). Studies on the morphology and electrophysiology of electric organs. I. Electrophysiology of marine electric fishes. In *Biolectrogenesis*, ed. Chagas, C. & de Carvalho, A. P., pp. 57–101. Amsterdam: Elsevier. [105]

Grundfest, H. & Reuben, J. P. (1961). Neuromuscular synaptic activity in lobster. In *Nervous Inhibition*, ed. Florey, E., pp. 92–104. Oxford: Pergamon Press. [116]

Hagiwara, S. (1960). Current voltage relations of nerve cell membranes. In *Electrical Activity of Single Cells*, pp. 145–157. Tokyo: Igakushoin.

— (1966). Membrane properties of the barnacle muscle fibre. *Ann. N.Y. Acad. Sci.* **137**, 1015–1024. [60]

Hagiwara, S. & Naka, K. (1964). The initiation of spike potential in barnacle muscle fibres under low intracellular Ca^{++}. *J. gen. Physiol.* **48**, 141–162. [59]

Hagiwara, S. & Nakajima, S. (1966). Differences in Na and Ca spikes as examined by application of tetrodotoxin, procaine and manganese ions. *J. gen. Physiol.* **49**, 793–806. [59, 61]

Hagiwara, S. & Saito, N. (1957). Mechanism of action potential production in the nerve cell of a puffer. *Proc. Jap. Acad. Sci.* **33**, 682–685. [59]

— (1959a). Voltage-current relations in nerve cell membrane of *Onchidium verruculatum*. *J. Physiol.* **148**, 161–179. [60–61]

— (1959b). Membrane potential change and membrane current in supramedullary nerve cell of puffer. *J. Neurophysiol.* **22**, 204–221. [59]

Hagiwara, S. & Takahashi, K. (1967). Resting and spike potentials of skeletal muscle fibres of salt water elasmobranch and teleost fish. *J. Physiol.* **190**, 499–518. [118]

Hagiwara, S. & Tasaki, I. (1958). A study of the mechanism of impulse transmission across the giant synapse of the squid. *J. Physiol.* **143**, 114–137. [62, 105, 113, 158, 162]

Hagiwara, S., Watanabe, A. & Saito, N. (1959). Potential changes in syncytial neurons of lobster cardiac ganglion. *J. Neurophysiol.* **22**, 544–572. [94, 99–100, 105]

Håkansson, C. H. (1957). Action potentials recorded intra- and extracellularly from the isolated frog muscle fibre in Ringer's solution and in air. *Acta physiol. scand.* **39,** 291–312. [283]

Haller, A. von (1708–1777), quoted in Fulton, J. F. (1926). *Muscular Contraction and the Reflex Control of Movement,* pp. 29–32. Baltimore: Williams & Wilkins. [3]

Hanks, J. H. (1948). The longevity of chick tissue culture without renewal of medium. *J. cell. comp. Physiol.* **31,** 235–268. [304]

Harreveld, A. van (1936). A physiological solution for fresh water crustaceans. *Proc. Soc. Exp. Biol. Med.* **34,** 428–432. [307, 310]

Harreveld, A. van & Biersteker, P. A. (1964). Acute asphyxiation of the spinal cord and cortical cells. *Am. J. Physiol.* **206,** 8–14. [216]

Harreveld, A. van, Crowell, J. & Malhotra, S. K. (1965). A study of extracellular space in central nervous tissue by freeze-substitution. *J. cell Biol.* **25,** 117–137. [215]

Harris, E. J. (1958). Anion interaction in frog muscle. *J. Physiol.* **141,** 351–365. [42, 107]

Harris, E. J. & Steinbach, H. B. (1956). The extraction of ions from muscle by water and sugar solutions with a study of the degree of exchange with tracer of the sodium and potassium in the extracts. *J. Physiol.* **133,** 385–401. [91]

Harris, J. B. & Leach, G. D. H. (1968). The effect of temperature on end-plate depolarization of the rat diaphragm produced by suxamethonium and acetylcholine. *J. Pharm. Pharmac.* **20,** 194–198. [313, 316]

Hartline, H. K. & Ratliff, F. (1957). Inhibitory interaction of receptor units in the eye of limulus. *J. gen. Physiol.* **40,** 357–376. [251]

Hashimoto, Y., Holman, Mollie E. & Tille, J. (1966). Electrical properties of the smooth muscle membrane of the guinea-pig vas deferens. *J. Physiol.* **186,** 27–41. [202]

Heidenhain, R. (1883). Über pseudomotorische Nervenwirkungen. *Arch. Anat. Physiol.* (Physiolog. Abt.), Supp. 7, 133–177. [6]

Henček, M. & Zachar, J. (1965). The electrical constants of single muscle fibres of the crayfish (*Astacus fluviatilis*). *Physiologia bohemoslov.* **14,** 297–311.[102]

Henderson, L. J. (1908). The theory of neutrality regulation in the animal organism. *Am. J. Physiol.* **21,** 427–448. [301]

Hennemann, E., Kaplan, A. & Unna, K. (1949). A neuropharmacological study of the effect of myanesin (tolserol) on motor systems. *J. Pharmac. exp. Ther.* **97,** 331–341. [297]

Hern, J. E. C., Phillips, C. G. & Porter, R. (1962). Electrical thresholds of unimpaled corticospinal cells in the cat. *Q. J. exp. Physiol.* **47,** 134–140. [220]

Hess, A. (1961). The structure of slow and fast extrafusal muscle fibres in the extraocular muscles and their nerve endings in guinea pigs. *J. cell. comp. Physiol.* **58,** 63–80. [120]

— (1965). Developmental changes in the structure of the synapse on the myelinated cell bodies of the chicken ciliary ganglion. *J. cell. Biol.* **25,** Part 2, 1–19. [13]

Hess, A. & Pilar, G. (1964). Slow fibres in the extraocular muscles of the cat. *J. Physiol.* **169**, 780–798. [109, 120]

Hess, W. R. (1957). *Das Zwischenhirn*. Basel: Benno-Schwabe and Co. [297]

Hild, W. & Tasaki, I. (1962). Morphological and physiological properties of neurons and glial cells in tissue culture. *J. Neurophysiol.* **25**, 277–304. [215]

Hille, B. (1966). Common mode of action of three agents that decrease the transient change in sodium permeability in nerve. *Nature Lond.* **210**, 1220–1222. [60]

— (1967). The selective inhibition of delayed potassium currents in nerve by tetraethylammonium ion. *J. gen. Physiol.* **50**, 1287–1302. [60, 61]

His, W. (1890). Histogenese und Zusammenhang der Nervenelemente. *Arch. f. Anat. u. Physiol.*, Anat. Abt. Supplement-Band, 95. [213]

Hisado, M. (1958). Effect of stretch on neuromuscular transmission in a nerve-supplied single muscle fibre. *J. Fac. Sci. Hokkaido Univ.*, Ser. VI, Zoo. **14**, 74–82. [318]

Höber, R. (1910). Eine Methode, die elektrische Leitfähigkeit im Innern von Zellen zu messen. *Arch. ges. Physiol.* **133**, 237–255. [43]

— (1912). Ein zweites Verfahren, die Leitfähigkeit im Innern von Zellen zu messen. *Arch ges. Physiol.* **148**, 189–224. [43]

Hodgkin, A. L. (1937). Evidence for electrical transmission in nerve. I and II. *J. Physiol.* **90**, 183–232. [271]

— (1958). Ionic movements and electrical activity in giant nerve fibres. *Proc. R. Soc. B* **148**, 1–37. [56]

— (1964). *The Conduction of the Nervous Impulse*. Liverpool: Liverpool Univ. Press. [59]

Hodgkin, A. L. & Horowicz, P. (1957). The differential action of hyper-tonic solutions on the twitch and action potential of a muscle fibre. *J. Physiol.* **136**, 17–18P. [318]

— (1959a). Movements of Na and K in single muscle fibres. *J. Physiol.* **145**, 405–432. [29, 37]

— (1959b). The influence of potassium and chloride ions on the membrane potential of single muscle fibres. *J. Physiol.* **148**, 127–160. [37, 41, 42]

Hodgkin, A. L. & Huxley, A. F. (1952a). Currents carried by sodium and potassium ions through the membrane of the giant axon of Loligo. *J. Physiol.* **116**, 449–472. [40, 53, 169, 223]

— (1952b). The components of membrane conductance in the giant axon of Loligo. *J. Physiol.* **116**, 473–496. [53]

— (1952c). The dual effect of membrane potential on sodium conductance in the giant axon of Loligo. *J. Physiol.* **116**, 497–506. [53, 269]

— (1952d). A quantitative description of membrane current and its application to conduction and excitation in nerve. *J. Physiol.* **117**, 500–544. [53, 56]

Hodgkin, A. L., Huxley, A. F. & Katz, B. (1952). Measurement of current-voltage relations in the membrane of the giant axon of Loligo. *J. Physiol.* **116**, 424–448. [53, 221, 222, 223, 236]

Hodgkin, A. L. & Katz, B. (1949a). The effect of sodium ions on the electrical activity of the giant axon of the squid. *J. Physiol.* **108**, 37–77. [37, 52, 217, 308, 310]

— (1949b). The effect of temperature on the electrical activity of the giant axon of the squid. *J. Physiol.* **109**, 240–249. [314]

Hodgkin, A. L. & Keynes, R. D. (1953). The mobility and diffusion co-efficient of potassium in giant axons from Sepia. *J. Physiol.* **119**, 513–528. [29]

— (1955a). Active transport of cations in giant axons from Sepia and Loligo. *J. Physiol.* **128**, 28–60. [59]

Hodgkin, A. L. & Rushton, W. A. H. (1946). The electrical constants of a crustacean nerve fibre. *Proc. R. Soc. B* **133**, 444–479. [29, 76, 78, 79, 92, 101, 102, 206]

Hofmann, W. W., Feigen, G. A. & Genther, G. H. (1962). Effects of veratrine, nitrate ion and aminobutyric acid on mammalian minia-ture end-plate potentials. *Nature Lond.* **193**, 175–176. [107]

Holmes, P. E. B., Jenden, D. J. & Taylor, D. B. (1951). The analysis of the mode of action of curare on neuromuscular transmission; the effect of temperature changes. *J. Pharmac.* **103**, 382–402. [316]

Horowitz, S. B. (1958). The energy requirements of melanin granule aggregation and dispersion in the melanophores of *Anolis carolinensis*. *J. cell. comp. Physiol.* **51**, 341–358. [303]

Horstmann, E. & Meves, H. (1959). Die Feinstruktur des molekularen Rindengraues und ihre physiologische Bedeutung. *A. Zellforsch. v. mikroskop. Anat.* **49**, 569–604. [13]

Howarth, J. V. (1958). The behaviour of frog muscle in hypertonic solu-tions. *J. Physiol.* **144**, 167–175. [318]

Howland, B., Lettvin, J. Y., McCulloch, W. S., Pitts, W. & Wall, P. D. (1955). Reflex inhibition by dorsal root interaction. *J. Neuro-physiol.* **18**, 1–17. [291]

Hoyle, G. (1952). High blood potassium in insects in relation to nerve conduction. *Nature Lond.* **169**, 281–282. [306]

— (1953). Potassium ions and insect nerve muscle. *J. exp. Biol.* **30**, 121–135. [306]

— (1955). The effects of some common cations on neuromuscular trans-mission in insects. *J. Physiol.* **127**, 90–103. [310]

Huang, C., Wheeldon, L. & Thompson, T. E. (1964). The properties of lipid bilayer membranes separating two aqueous phases: formation of membrane of simple composition. *J. molec. Biol.* **8**, 148–160. [29]

Hubbard, J. I. (1959). Post-activation changes at the mammalian neuro-muscular junction. *Nature Lond.* **184**, 1945–1947. [149]

— (1961). The effect of calcium and magnesium on the spontaneous release of transmitter from mammalian motor nerve endings. *J. Physiol.* **159**, 507–517. [123]

— (1963). Repetitive stimulation at the mammalian neuromuscular junction and the mobilisation of transmitter. *J. Physiol.* **169**, 641–662. [143, 149]

Hubbard, J. I., Jones, S. F. & Landau, E. M. (1967). The relationship between the state of nerve-terminal polarization and liberation of acetylcholine. *Ann. N.Y. Acad. Sci.* **144,** 459–471. [315]

— (1968*a*). On the mechanism by which calcium and magnesium affect the spontaneous release of transmitter from mammalian motor nerve terminals. *J. Physiol.* **194,** 381–407. [123]

— (1968*b*). On the mechanism by which calcium and magnesium effect the release of transmitter by nerve impulses. *J. Physiol.* **196,** 75–86. [123]

— (1968*c*). An examination of the effects of osmotic pressure changes upon transmitter release from mammalian motor nerve terminals. *J. Physiol.* **197,** 639–659. [124, 318]

Hubbard, J. I. & Kwanbunbumpen, S. (1968). Evidence for the vesicle hypothesis. *J. Physiol.* **194,** 407–421. [12, 13, 158]

Hubbard, J. I. & Schmidt, R. F. (1963). An electrophysiological investigation of mammalian motor nerve terminals. *J. Physiol.* **166,** 145–167. [119, 161, 163, 164, 168, 169]

Hubbard, J. I., Schmidt, R. F. & Yokota, T. (1965). The effect of acetylcholine upon mammalian motor nerve terminals. *J. Physiol.* **181,** 810–829. [123, 201]

Hubbard, J. I., Stenhouse, D. & Eccles, R. M. (1967). Origin of synaptic noise. *Science,* **157,** 330–331. [117]

Hubbard, J. I. & Willis, W. D. (1962). Hyperpolarization of mammalian motor nerve terminals. *J. Physiol.* **163,** 115–137. [156, 169, 170, 200]

— (1968). The effects of depolarization of motor nerve terminals upon the release of transmitter by nerve impulses. *J. Physiol.* **194,** 381–407. [113, 156, 316]

Hubbard, S. J. (1963). The electrical constants and the component conductances of frog skeletal muscle after denervation. *J. Physiol.* **165,** 443–456. [93, 147]

Hubel, H. D. (1957). Tungsten microelectrodes for recording from single cells. *Science* **125,** 549–550. [299]

Huggel, H (1959). Experimentelle Untersuchungen über die Automatie, Temperaturabhängigkeit und Arbeit des embryonalen Fischherzens, unter besonderer Berücksichtigung der Salmoniden und Scyllbrorhiniden. *Z. vergl. Physiol.* **42,** 63–102. [305]

Hunsperger, R. W. & Wyss, O. A. M. (1953). Quantitative Ausschaltung von Nervengewebe durch Hochfrequenz–Koagulation. *Helv. physiol. pharmac. Acta* **11,** 283–307. [297]

Hutter, O. F. & Noble, D. (1960). The chloride conductance of frog skeletal muscle. *J. Physiol.* **151,** 89–102. [41, 104]

Hutter, O. F. & Padsha, S. M. (1959). Effect of nitrate and other anions on the membrane resistance of frog skeletal muscle. *J. Physiol.* **146,** 117–132. [42, 107]

Hutter, O. F. & Trautwein, W. (1956). Neuromuscular facilitation by stretch of motor nerve endings. *J. Physiol.* **133,** 610–625. [318]

Hutter, O. F. & Warner, A. E. (1967*a*). The pH sensitivity of the chloride conductance of frog skeletal muscle. *J. Physiol.* **189,** 403–426. [317]

Hutter, O. F. & Warner, A. E. (1967b). The effect of pH on the ^{36}C efflux from frog skeletal muscle. *J. Physiol.* **189,** 427–444. [317]

Huxley, A. F. & Stämpfli, R. (1951). Direct determination of membrane resting potential and action potential in single myelinated nerve fibres. *J. Physiol.* **112,** 476–495. [86, 87]

Huxley, A. F. & Taylor, R. E. (1958). Local activation of striated muscle fibres. *J. Physiol.* **144,** 426–441. [172]

Ishiko, N. & Sato, M. (1960). The effect of stretch on the electrical constants of muscle fibre membrane. *Jap. J. Physiol.* **10,** 194–203. [319]

Ito, M. (1957). The electrical activity of spinal ganglion cells investigated with intracellular microelectrodes. *Jap. J. Physiol.* **7,** 297–323. [93, 98, 100]

Ito, M., Kawai, N., Udo, M. & Mano, S. (in course of publication). Axon reflex activation of Deiters' neurones through the cerebellar afferent collaterals. [253]

Ito, M., Kostyuk, P. G. & Oshima, T. (1962). Further study on anion permeability in cat spinal motoneurones. *J. Physiol.* **164,** 150–156. [242, 243, 244]

Ito, M. & Oshima, T. (1964a). The electrogenic action of cations on cat spinal motoneurons. *Proc. R. Soc. B* **161,** 92–108. [79, 89]

— (1964b). The extrusion of sodium from cat spinal motoneurons. *Proc. R. Soc. B.* **161,** 109–131. [110]

— (1964c). Further study on the active transport of sodium across the motoneural membrane. *Proc. R. Soc. B* **161,** 132–141. [110]

— (1965). Electrical behaviour of the motoneuronal membrane during intracellularly applied current steps. *J. Physiol.* **180,** 607–635. [79, 81, 82, 103, 223]

Ito, M. & Yoshida, M. (1964). The cerebellar-evoked monosynaptic inhibition of Deiters' neurones. *Experientia* **20,** 515–516. [253]

— (1966). The origin of cerebellar-induced inhibition of Deiters' neurones. I. Monosynaptic initiation of the inhibitory pstsynaptic potentials. *Exp. Brain Res.* **2,** 330–349.[253]

Iversen, L. L. & Kravitz, E. A. (1966). Uptake of γ–amino-butyric acid (GABA) in lobster nerve-muscle preparation. *Fed. Proc.* **25,** 714. [202]

Jenerick, H. P. & Gerard, W. (1953). Membrane potential and threshold of single muscle fibres. *J. cell. comp. Physiol.* **42,** 79–95. [169]

Jenkinson, D. H. (1957). The nature of the antagonism between Ca and Mg ions at the neuromuscular junction. *J. Physiol.* **138,** 438–444. [123]

— (1960). The antagonism between Tubocurarine and substances which depolarize the motor end-plate. *J. Physiol.* **152,** 309–324. [181, 185, 186, 211]

Johnson, F. H., Eyring, H. & Polissar, M. J. (1955). *Kinetic Basis of Molecular Biology.* New York: Wylie Publishing. [33]

Julian, F. J., Moore, J. W. & Goldman, D. E. (1962). Current-voltage relations in the lobster giant axon membrane under voltage clamp conditions. *J. gen. Physiol.* **45,** 1217–1238. [59]

Jullien, A., Acolat, L., Ripplinger, J., Joy, M. & Vieille-Cessay, Ch. (1955). La teneur en ions Na, K et Ca de l'hemolymph déterminé au photomé être à flamme et ses rapports avec la composition de solutions artificielles aptes à assurer une activité de longue dureé au coeur isolé chez les Helicidés. *C. R. Soc. Biol., Paris* **149**, 723–735. [308]

Jullien, A. & Ripplinger, J. (1948). Sur l'automatisme du ventricule isolé du coeur de Limnée. *C.R. Acad. Sci., Paris* **226**, 1396. [308]

Kaada, B. R. (1950). Site of action of myanesin (mephenesin, tolserol) in the central nervous system. *J. Neurophysiol.* **13**, 89–108. [297]

Kandel, E. R. & Spencer, W. A. (1961). Electrophysiological properties of an Archicortical neuron. In *Current Problems in Electrobiology*, ed. Purpura, D.P. *Ann. N.Y. Acad. Sci.* **94**, 570–603. [245, 246]

Kandel, E. R., Spencer, W. A. & Brinley, F. J. (1961). Electrophysiology of hippocampal neurons. I. Sequential invasion and synaptic organization. *J. Neurophysiol.* **24**, 225–242. [219, 245]

Kandel, E. R. & Tauc, L. (1965). Mechanism of heterosynaptic facilitation in the giant cell of the abdominal ganglion of Aplysia Depilans. *J. Physiol.* **181**, 28–47. [105]

— (1966). Anomalous rectification in the metacerebral giant cells and its consequences for synaptic transmission. *J. Physiol.* **183**, 287–304. [223]

Karis, J. H. Gissen, A. J. & Nastuk, W. L. (1966). Mode of action of diethyl ether in blocking neuromuscular transmission. *Anesthesiology* **27**, 42–51. [200]

Katz, B. (1937). Experimental evidence for a non-conducted response of nerve to subthreshold stimulation. *Proc. R. Soc. B* **124**, 244–276. [103]

— (1939). *Electric Excitation of Nerve*. London: Oxford Univ. Press.

— (1948). The electrical properties of the muscle fibre membrane. *Proc. R. Soc. B* **135**, 506–534. [29, 102]

— (1949). Les constantes électriques de la membrane du muscle *Archs. Sci. physiol.* **3**, 285–299. [41, 60]

— (1962). The transmission of impulses from nerve to muscle, and the subcellular unit of synaptic action. *Proc. R. Soc. B* **155**, 455–477. [116, 122]

— (1966). *Nerve, Muscle and Synapse*. New York: McGraw-Hill. [v, 15]

Katz, B. & Miledi, R. (1963). A study of spontaneous miniature potentials in spinal motoneurones. *J. Physiol.* **168**, 389–422. [116, 117, 141, 226]

— (1965a). Propagation of electric activity in motor nerve terminals. *Proc. R. Soc. B* **161**, 453–482. [113, 160, 311]

— (1965b). The measurement of synaptic delay and the time course of acetylcholine release at the neuromuscular junction. *Proc. R. Soc. B* **161**, 483–495. [128, 164, 165, 173]

— (1965c). The effect of calcium on acetylcholine release from motor nerve endings. *Proc. R. Soc. B* **161**, 496–503. [161, 163]

— (1965d). The effect of temperature on the synaptic delay at the neuromuscular junction. *J. Physiol.* **181**, 656–670. [162, 166]

— (1965e). Release of acetylcholine from a nerve terminal by electric pulses of variable strength and duration. *Nature Lond.* **207**, 1097–1098. [313]

Katz, B. & Miledi, R. (1966). The production of endplate potentials in muscle paralysed by tetrodotoxin. *J. Physiol.* **185**, 5–6P. [61, 172]

— (1967a). Modification of transmitter release by electrical interference with motor nerve endings. *Proc. R. Soc. B* **167**, 1–7. [172]

— (1967b). Tetrodotoxin and neuromuscular transmission. *Proc. R. Soc. B* **167**, 8–22. [172]

— (1967c). The release of acetylcholine from nerve endings by graded electric pulses. *Proc. R. Soc. B* **167**, 23–28. [113, 172]

— (1967d). The timing of calcium action during neuromuscular transmission. *J. Physiol.* **189**, 535–544. [61]

— (1967e). Ionic requirements of synaptic transmitter release. *Nature Lond.* **215**, 651. [61]

Katz, B. & Thesleff, S. (1957a). On the factors which determine the amplitude of the 'miniature end-plate potential'. *J. Physiol.* **137**, 267–278. [103, 106, 145]

— (1957b). A study of the 'desensitization' produced by acetylcholine at the motor end-plate. *J. Physiol.* **138**, 63–80. [174, 196]

— (1957c). The interaction between edrophonium (tensilon) and acetylcholine at the motor end-plate. *Br. J. Pharmac.* **12**, 260–264. [201–202]

Kawai, I. & Sasaki, K. (1964). Effects of strychnine upon supraspinal inhibition. *Jap. J. Physiol.* **14**, 309–318. [222]

Kelly, J. A. (1965). Antagonism between Na^+ and Ca^{2+} at the neuromuscular junction. *Nature Lond.* **205**, 296–297. [124]

Kerkut, G. A. & Ridge, R. M. A. P. (1961). The effect of temperature changes on the resting potential of crab, insect and frog muscle. *Comp. Biochem. Physiol.* **3**, 64–70. [314]

— (1962). The effect of temperature changes on the activity of the neurones of the snail *Helix Aspersa*. *Comp. Biochem. Physiol.* **5**, 283–295. [314]

Kerkut, G. A. & Thomas, R. C. (1964). The effect of anion injection and changes of external potassium and chloride concentration on the reversal potential of the IPSP and acetylcholine. *Comp. Biochem. Physiol.* **11**, 199–213. [244]

Kernan, R. P. (1960). Resting potentials in isolated frog sartorius fibres at low external potassium concentrations. *Nature Lond.* **185**, 471. [90]

Keynes, R. D. (1954). The ionic fluxes in frog muscle. *Proc. R. Soc. B* **142**, 359–382. [91]

— (1963). Chloride in the squid giant axon. *J. Physiol.* **169**, 690–705. [42]

Kirschner, L. B. & Stone, W. E. (1951). Action of inhibitors at the myoneural junction. *J. gen. Physiol.* **34**, 821–834. [182, 183]

Kiyohara, T. & Sato, M. (1967). Membrane constants of red and white muscle fibres in the rat. *Jap. J. Physiol.* **17**, 720–726. [93]

Klee, M. R. & Lux, H. D. (1962). Intracelluläre Untersuchungen über den Einfluss hemmender Potentiale in motorischen Cortex. II. Die Wirkungen elektrischer Reizung des Nucleus caudatus. *Arch. Psychiat. Nervenkr.* **203**, 667–689. [245]

Klee, M. R. & Offenloch, K. (1964). Postsynaptic potentials and spike patterns during augmenting responses in cat's motor cortex. *Science* **143**, 488–489. [245]

Klee, M. R., Pierau, K.-F. & Papajewski, W. Changes in the membrane properties of cat's motoneurone by fast changes of the local temperature. (In preparation). [311, 312]

Koketsu, K. & Kimura, Y. (1960). The resting potential and intracellular potassium of skeletal muscle in frogs. *J. cell. comp. Physiol.* **55,** 239–244. [303]

Kopin, I. J. (1966). Biochemical aspects of release of norepinephrine and other amines from sympathetic nerve endings. *Pharmac. Rev.* **18,** 513–523. [202]

Koppenhöfer, E. (1965). Die Wirkung verschiedener Anionen auf den isolierten Ranvierschen Schnürring. *Pflügers Arch. ges. Physiol.* **282,** 338–350. [61]

Kostial, K. & Vouk, V. B. (1956). The influence of temperature on the acetylcholine output from a sympathetic ganglion. *J. Physiol.* **132,** 239–241. [314, 315]

Krebs, H. A. (1950). Body size and tissue respiration. *Biochim. biophys. Acta* **4,** 249–269. [300, 301]

Krebs, H. A. & Henseleit, K. (1932). Untersuchungen über die Harnstoffbildung in Tierkörper. *Z. Physiol. Chem.* **210,** 33–66. [300]

Krnjević, K. & Miledi, R. (1958). Motor units in the rat diaphragm. *J. Physiol.* **140,** 427–439. [301]

— (1959). Presynaptic failure of neuromuscular propagation in rats. *J. Physiol.* **149,** 1–22. [140]

Krnjević, K. & Mitchell, J. F. (1961). The release of acetylcholine in the isolated rat diaphragm. *J. Physiol.* **155,** 246–262. [114, 315]

Krnjević, K., Randić, M. & Straughan, D. W. (1966). Pharmacology of cortical inhibition. *J. Physiol.* **184,** 78–105. [245]

Kubota, K., Sakata, H. Takahashi, H. & Uno, M. (1965). Location of the recurrent inhibitory synapse on cat pyramidal tract cells. *Proc. Jap. Acad.* **41,** 195–197. [245]

Kuffler, S. W. (1942). Electric potential changes at an isolated nerve muscle junction. *J. Neurophysiol.* **5,** 18–26. [288]

— (1943). Specific excitability of the end-plate region in normal and denervated muscle. *J. Neurophysiol.* **6,** 99–110. [189]

— (1952). Incomplete neuromuscular transmission in twitch system of frog's skeletal muscles. *Fed. Proc.* **11,** 87. [318]

Kuffler, S. W., Nicholls, J. G. & Orkand, R. K. (1966). Physiological properties of glial cells in the central nervous system of amphibia. *J. Neurophysiol.* **29,** 768–787. [216]

Kuffler, S. W. & Potter, D. D. (1964). Glia in the leech central nervous system: physiological properties and neuron-glia relationship. *J. Neurophysiol.* **27,** 290–320. [216]

Kuffler, S. W. & Vaughan Williams, E. M. (1953a). Small-nerve junctional potentials. The distribution of small motor nerves to frog skeletal muscle, and the membrane characteristics of the fibres they innervate. *J. Physiol.* **121,** 289–317. [109, 120]

— (1953b). Properties of the 'slow' skeletal muscle fibres of the frog. *J. Physiol.* **121,** 318–340. [120]

Kuhne, W. (1862). *Über die peripherischen Endorgane der motorischen Nerven.* Leipzig: Engelmann. [5]

— (1888). On the origin and causation of vital movement. *Proc. R. Soc. B* **44**, 427–448. [5, 6, 8]

Kuno, M. (1964*a*). Quantal components of excitatory synaptic potentials in spinal motoneurones. *J. Physiol.* **175**, 81–99. [115, 116, 128, 139, 141, 166, 226, 241]

— (1964*b*). Mechanism of facilitation and depression of the excitatory synaptic potential in spinal motoneurone. *J. Physiol.* **175**, 100–112. [139]

Kuriyama, H. (1963). The influence of potassium, sodium and chloride on the membrane potential of the smooth muscle of taenia coli. *J. Physiol.* **166**, 15–28. [302]

— (1964). The effect of temperature on neuromuscular transmission in the vas deferens of the guinea-pig. *J. Physiol.* **170**, 561–570. [315]

Kuriyama, H. & Tomita, T. (1965). The responses of single smooth muscle cells of guinea-pig taenia coli to intracellularly applied currents, and their effect on the spontaneous electrical activity. *J. Physiol.* **178**, 270–289. [103]

Kusano, K. & Hagiwara, S. (1961). On the integrative synaptic potentials of *Onchidium* nerve cell. *Jap. J. Physiol.* **11**, 96–101. [105]

Kusano, K., Livengood, D. R. & Werman, R. (1967). Tetraethyl-ammonium ions: Effect of presynaptic injection on synaptic transmission. *Science* **155**, 1257–1259. [172]

Kutscha, W., Pauschinger, P. & Brecht, K. (1964). Der Einfluss der H-Ionen auf Elekrolytgehalt, Membran-potential und Kontraktion tonischer and phasischer Skeletmuskeln. *Pflügers Arch. ges. Physiol.* **280**, 1–21. [317]

Langley, J. N. (1905). On the reaction of cells and of nerve-endings to certain poisons, chiefly as regards the reaction of striated muscle to nicotine and to curari. *J. Physiol.* **33**, 374–413. [6, 7]

— (1907). On the contraction of muscle, chiefly in relation to the presence of 'receptive' substances. Part I. *J. Physiol.* **36**, 347–384. [7, 189]

— (1908). On the contraction of muscle, chiefly in relation to the presence of 'receptive' substances. Part III. The reaction of frog's muscle to nicotine after denervation. *J. Physiol.* **37**, 285–300. [6]

— (1909). On the contraction of muscle, chiefly in relation to the presence of 'receptive' substances. Part IV. The effect of curari and of some other substances on the nicotine response of the sartorius and gastrocnemius muscles of the frog. *J. Physiol.* **39**, 235–295. [7]

— (1914). The antagonism of curari and nicotine in skeletal muscle. *J. Physiol.* **48**, 73–108. [7]

Langmuir, I. (1916). Constitution and fundamental properties of solids and liquids. Part I. Solids. *J. Am. Chem. Soc.* **38**, 2219–2295. [176]

Lapicque, L. (1936). Le méchanisme physique et le méchanisme chimique de la transmission nerveuse. *Centre de Documentation Universitaire, Paris.* [6]

Lenhossék, M. V. (1886). Untersuchungen über die Spinal-ganglien des Frosches. *Arch. mikr. Anat.* **26**, 370–453. [98]

Lettvin, J. Y., Pickard, W. F., McCulloch, W. S. & Pitts, W. (1964). A theory of passive ion flux through axon membranes. *Nature Lond.* **202**, 1338. [31]

Levine, L. (1966a). Tip potentials in microelectrodes filled by boiling under reduced pressure. *Experientia* **22**, 559–560. [88, 89]

— (1966b). An electrophysiological study of chelonian skeletal muscle. *J. Physiol.* **183**, 683–713. [93, 109]

Lewis, M. R. & Lewis, W. H. (1911). The cultivation of tissues from chick embryos in solutions of NaCl, $CaCl_2$ and $NaHCO_3$. *Anat. Rec.* **5**, 277–293. [304]

Li, C. H. (1958). Effect of cooling on neuromuscular transmission in the rat. *Am. J. Physiol.* **194**, 200–206. [302, 313]

— (1963). Cortical intracellular synaptic potentials in response to thalamic stimulation. *J. cell. comp. Physiol.* **61**, 165–179. [245]

Li, C. L. & Gouras, P. (1958). Effect of cooling on neuromuscular transmission in the frog. *Am. J. Physiol.* **192**, 464–470. [312, 314]

Liley, A. W. (1956a). An investigation of spontaneous activity at the neuromuscular junction of the rat. *J. Physiol.* **132**, 650–666. [12, 116, 117, 126, 300, 301, 302, 313, 318]

— (1956b). The quantal components of the mammalian endplate potential. *J. Physiol.* **133**, 571–587. [128, 131, 147]

— (1956c). The effects of presynaptic polarization on the spontaneous activity at the mammalian neuromuscular junction. *J. Physiol.* **134**, 427–443. [117, 123, 172]

— (1957). Spontaneous release of transmitter substance in multiquantal units. *J. Physiol.* **136**, 595–605. [118, 119]

Liley, A. W. & North, K. A. K. (1953). An electrical investigation of effects of repetitive stimulation on mammalian neuromuscular junction. *J. Neurophysiol.* **16**, 509–527. [147, 149, 150, 151]

Lilleheil, G. & Naess, K. (1961). Note on the effect of increased NaCl-concentration on the neuromuscular transmission. *Acta physiol. scand.* **52**, 23–31. [318]

Lineweaver, H. & Burk, D. (1934). The determination of enzyme dissociation constants. *J. Am. Chem. Soc.* **56**, 658–666. [178]

Ling, G. & Gerard, R. W. (1949a). The normal membrane potential of frog sartorius fibres. *J. cell. comp. Physiol.* **34**, 383–396. [89]

— (1949b). The influence of stretch on the membrane potential of the striated muscle fibre. *J. cell. comp. Physiol.* **34**, 397–404. [319]

— (1949c). The membrane potential and metabolism of muscle fibres. *J. cell. comp. Physiol.* **34**, 413–438. [89, 316]

Ling, G. & Woodbury, J. (1949). The effect of temperature on the membrane potential of frog muscle fibres. *J. cell. comp. Physiol.* **34**, 407–412. [314]

Ling, G. N. (1962). *A Physical Theory of the Living State: The Association-induction Hypothesis.* New York: Blaisdell Publishing Co. [31]

Ling, H. W. & Smith, R. T. (1955). Changes in pH produced by passing gas mixtures through physiological salt solutions. *Sci. Technologists Assn. Bull.* **4**, 15–19. [300]

Llinás, R. (1964a). Mechanisms of supraspinal actions upon spinal cord activities. Differences between reticular and cerebellar inhibitory actions upon alpha extensor motoneurons. *J. Neurophysiol.* **27,** 1117–1126. [250–251]

— (1964b). Mechanisms of supraspinal actions upon spinal cord activities. Pharmacological studies on reticular inhibition of alpha extensor motoneurons. *J. Neurophysiol.* **27,** 1127–1137. [251, 257, 297]

Llinás, R. & Bloedel, J. (1967). Frog cerebellum: Absence of long-term inhibition upon Purkinje cells. *Science* **155,** 601–603. [293]

Llinás, R., Hillman, D. E. & Precht, W. (1968). Functional aspects of cerebellar evolution. In *The Cerebellum in Health and Disease* (in press). [245, 247]

Llinás, R., Nicholson, C., Freeman, J. & Hillman, D. E. (1968). Dendritic spikes and their inhibition in alligator Purkinje cells. *Science* **160,** 1132–1135. [220, 259, 264, 287]

Llinás, R., Nicholson, C. & Precht, W. (1968). Preferred centripetal conduction of dendritic spikes in alligator Purkinje cells. *Science* **163,** 184–187. [287]

Llinás, R. & Terzuolo, C. A. (1964). Mechanisms of supraspinal actions upon spinal cord activities. Reticular inhibitory mechanism on alpha-extensor motoneurons. *J. Neurophysiol.* **27,** 579–591. [247, 250, 260]

— (1965). Mechanisms of supraspinal actions upon spinal cord activities. Reticular inhibitory mechanisms upon flexor motoneurones. *J. Neurophysiol.* **28,** 413–422. [247, 259, 260]

Lloyd, D. P. C. (1941). A direct central inhibitory action of dromically conducted impulses. *J. Neurophysiol.* **4,** 184–190. [225, 238]

— (1943). Reflex action in relation to pattern and peripheral source of afferent stimulation. *J. Neurophysiol.* **6,** 111–120. [225]

Locke, F. S. (1901). Die Wirkung der Metalle des Blutplasmas und verschiedener Zucker auf das isolierte Säugethierherz. *Pflügers Arch. ges. Physiol.* **14,** 670–672. [300]

Lockwood, A. P. M. (1961). 'Ringer' solutions and some notes on the physiological basis of their ionic composition. *Comp. biochem. Physiol.* **2,** 241–289. [310]

Loewi, O. (1921). Über humorale übertragbarkeit der Herznervenwirkung. *Pflügers. Arch. ges. Physiol.* **189,** 239–242. [7]

Lorente de Nó, R. (1939). Transmission of impulses through cranial motor nuclei. *J. Neurophysiol.* **2,** 402–464. [266, 274, 284]

— (1947a). Action potential of the motoneurones of the hypoglossus nucleus. *J. cell. comp. Physiol.* **29,** 207–288. [276, 277, 278]

— (1947b). A study of nerve physiology. *Studies from the Rockefeller Institute,* Vol. 132, Ch. 16. [92, 169, 270, 273, 275, 276, 279]

— (1953). Conduction of impulses in the neurons of the oculomotor nucleus. In *The Spinal Cord.* (Ciba Fdn. Symp.), pp. 132–173. London: Churchill. [284]

Lorenzo, A. J. de (1960). The fine structure of synapses in the ciliary ganglion of the chick. *J. biophys. biochem. Cytol.* **7,** 31–36. [13, 14]

Løyning, Y., Oshima, T. & Yokota, T. (1964). Site of action of thiamylal sodium on the monosynaptic spinal reflex pathway in cats. *J. Neurophysiol.* **27**, 408–428. [296]

Lundberg, A. & Quilisch, H. (1953*a*). Presynaptic potentiation and depression of neuromuscular transmission in frog and rat. *Acta physiol. scand.* **30**, Suppl. III, 111–120. [147]

— (1953*b*). On the effect of calcium on presynaptic potentiation and depression at the neuromuscular junction. *Acta physiol. scand.* **30**, Suppl. III, 121–129. [149]

Luse, S. A. (1960). Electron microscopic observations of the central nervous system. In *Inhibition in the Nervous System and γ-aminobutyric acid*, ed. Roberts, E. pp. 29–33. New York: Pergamon Press. [215]

Lutz, B. R. (1930). The effect of adrenalin on the auricle of elasmobranch fishes. *Am. J. Physiol.* **94**, 135–139. [305]

Lux, H. D. & Pollen, D. A. (1966). Electrical constants of neurones in the motor cortex of the cat. *J. Neurophysiol.* **29**, 207–220. [13, 94]

Maanen, E. F. van (1950). The antagonism between acetylcholine and the curare alkaloids, *d*-tubocurarine, c. Curare-1, *c*-Toxiferine-II and β-erythroidine in the rectus abdominis of the frog. *J. Pharmac.* **99**, 255–264. [187]

Macfarlane, W. V. & Meares, J. D. (1958). Intracellular recording of action and after-potentials of frog muscle between o and 45°C. *J. Physiol.* **142**, 97–109. [314]

MacIntosh, F. C. (1961). Effect of HC-3 on acetylcholine turnover. *Fed. Proc.* **20**, 562–568. [144]

MacIntosh, F. C., Birks, R. I., & Sastry, P. B. (1956). Pharmacological inhibition of acetylcholine synthesis. *Nature Lond.* **178**, 1181. [144]

Maclagan, Jennifer (1962). A comparison of the responses of the tenuissimus muscle to neuromuscular blocking drugs *in vivo* and *in vitro*. *Br. J. Pharmac. Chemother.* **18**, 204–216. [196]

Maekawa, K. & Purpura, D. P. (1967). Properties of spontaneous and evoked synaptic activities of thalamic ventrobasal neurones. *J. Neurophysiol.* **30**, 360–381. [220]

Maeno, T. (1966). Analysis of sodium and potassium conductances in the procaine end-plate potential. *J. Physiol.* **183**, 592–606. [195, 203, 206, 207, 210]

Malmfors, T. (1964). Release and depletion of the transmitter in adrenergic terminals produced by nerve impulses after the inhibition of noradrenaline synthesis or reabsorption. *Life Sci.* **3**, 1397–1402. [203]

Manthey, A. A. (1966). The effect of calcium on the desensitization of membrane receptors at the neuromuscular junction *J. gen. Physiol.* **49**, 963–976. [196]

Martin, A. R. (1955). A further study of the statistical composition of the end-plate potential. *J. Physiol.* **130**, 114–122. [66, 128, 129, 147]

— (1966). Quantal nature of synaptic transmission. *Physiol. Rev.* **46**, 51–66. [141, 150]

Martin, A. R. & Pilar, G. (1963*a*). The dual mode of synaptic transmission in the avian ciliary ganglion. *J. Physiol.* **168**, 443–463. [14, 302]

Martin, A. R. & Pilar, G. (1963*b*). Transmission through the ciliary ganglion of the chick. *J. Physiol.* **168**, 464–475. [14, 158]

— (1964*a*). Quantal components of the synaptic potential in the ciliary ganglion of the chick. *J. Physiol.* **175**, 1–16. [116, 126, 128, 141, 142]

— (1964*b*). Presynaptic and postsynaptic events during post-tetanic potentiation and facilitation in the avian ciliary ganglion. *J. Physiol.* **175**, 17–30. [158]

Masland, R. L. & Wigton, R. S. (1940). Nerve activity accompanying fasciculation produced by prostigmin. *J. Neurophysiol.* **3**, 269–275. [201]

Matteucci, C. (1838). Sur le courant électrique de la grenouille. *Ann. chim. phys.* **68**, 93. [5]

— (1842*a*). Deuxieme mémoire sur le courant électrique propre de la grenouille et des animaux à sang chard. *Ann. chim. phys.* **80**, 301. [5]

— (1842*b*). Sur une phenomene physiologique produite par les muscle en contraction. *C. r. Acad. Sci.* **4**, 797. [5]

Matteucci, C. & Humboldt, F. H. A. (1843). Sur le courant électrique des muscles des animaux vivants ou récemment tués. *C. r. Acad. Sci.* **16**, 197. [5]

Mendell, L. M. & Henneman, E. (1968). Terminals of single Ia fibers: Distribution within a pool of 300 homonymous motor neurons. *Science* **160**, 96–98. [228]

Meves, H. & Volkner, K. C. (1958). Die Wirkung von CO_2 auf das Ruhemembranpotential und die elektrischen Konstanten der quergestreiften Muskelfaser. *Pflügers Arch. ges. Physiol.* **265**, 457–476. [317]

Miledi, R. (1960*a*). The acetylcholine sensitivity of frog muscle fibres after complete or partial denervation. *J. Physiol.* **151**, 1–23. [192, 193]

— (1960*b*). Junctional and extra-junctional acetylcholine receptors in skeletal muscle fibres. *J. Physiol.* **151**, 24–30. [193]

— (1960*c*). Properties of regenerating neuromuscular synapses in the frog. *J. Physiol.* **154**, 190–205. [192, 193]

— (1962). Induction of receptors. In *Ciba Foundation Symposium on Enzymes and Drug Action*, ed. Mongar, J. L. and de Reuck, A. V. S., pp. 220–235. London: J. & A. Churchill. [189, 192]

— (1967). Spontaneous synaptic potentials and quantal release of transmitter in the stellate ganglion of the squid. *J. Physiol.* **192**, 379–406. [116]

Miledi, R. & Slater, C. R. (1963). A study of rat nerve-muscle junctions after degeneration of the nerve. *J. Physiol.* **169**, 23–24P. [117]

Molina, E. C. (1942). *Poissons Exponential Binomial Limit*, 10th edn. N.Y. & London: D. Van Nostrand Co. Inc. [125]

Monro, A. (1697–1762). *The Works of Alexander Monro* (collected by his son). Edinburgh: Charles Eliot, 1781. [4]

Morrison, J. F. (1965). Kinetic methods for the determinations of enzyme reaction mechanisms. *Aust. J. Sci.* **27**, 317–327. [178]

Moruzzi, G. (1948). L'irradiazione degli effetti paleocerebellari inibitori del tono. *Boll. Soc. ital. Biol. sper.* **24**, 755–756. [253]

Mosher, H. S., Fuhrman, F. A., Buchwald, H. D. & Fischer, A. S. (1964).

Tarichatoxin–Tetrodotoxin: a potent neurotoxin. *Science* **144**, 1100–1104. [172]

Motley, H. L. (1934): Physiological studies concerning the regulation of heartbeats in freshwater mussels. *Physiol. Zool.* **7**, 62–84. [308]

Mountcastle, V. B. (1961). Some functional properties of the somatic afferent system. In *Sensory Communication*, ed. Rosenblith, W. A., pp. 403–436. Cambridge, Mass.: M.I.T. Press. [298]

Mountford, S. (1963). Effects of light and dark adaptation on the vesicle population of receptor bipolar synapses. *J. Ultrastruct. Res.* **9**, 403–416. [12]

Mueller, P. & Rudin, D. O. (1963). Induced excitability in reconstituted cell membrane structure. *J. theor. Biol.* **4**, 268–280. [29]

Mueller, P., Rudin, D. O., Ti Tien, H. & Westcott, W. C. (1964). Formation and properties of bimolecular lipid membranes. In *Recent Progress in Surface Science*, Vol. 1, ed. Danielli, J. F., Pankhurst, K. G. A. and Riddiford, A. L., pp. 379–393. London: Academic Press. [29]

Murakami, M., Watanabe, K. & Tomita, T. (1961). Effect of impalement with a micropipette on the local cell membrane. Study by simultaneous intra- and extracellular recording from the muscle fibre and giant axon. *Jap. J. Physiol.* **11**, 80–88. [283]

Muscholl, E. (1957). Elektrophysiologische Untersuchung einzelner Faseranteile des isolierten Rattenzwerchfelles. *Pflügers Arch. ges. Physiol.* **264**, 467–483. [208]

Nacimiento, A., Lux, H. D. & Creutzefeldt, O. D. (1964). Postsynaptische Potentiale von Nervenzellen des motorischen Cortex nach elektrischer Reizung spezifischer und unspezifischer Thalamuskerne. *Pflügers Arch. ges. Physiol.* **281**, 152–169. [245]

Nakajima, S., Iwasaki, S. & Obata, K. (1962). Delayed rectification and anomalous rectification in frog's skeletal muscle membrane. *J. gen. Physiol.* **46**, 97–115. [60]

Nakamura, Y. Nakajima, S. & Grundfest, H. (1965). The action of tetrodotoxin on electrogenic components of squid giant axons. *J. gen. Physiol.* **48**, 985–996. [60]

Narahashi, T., Moore, J. W. & Scott, W. R. (1964). Tetrodotoxin blockage of sodium conductance increase on lobster giant axons. *J. gen. Physiol.* **47**, 965–974. [60, 172]

Nastuk, W. L. (1951). Membrane potential changes at a single muscle end-plate produced by acetylcholine. *Fed. Proc.* **10**, 96. [189]

— (1953). The electrical activity of the muscle cell membrane at the neuromuscular junction. *J. cell. comp. Physiol.* **42**, 249–272. [89, 189]

— (1963). Physical techniques in biological research. In *Electrophysiological Methods*, Vol. 6, Part B. London and N.Y.: Academic Press. [v. 298]

— (1964). Physical techniques in biological research. In *Electrophysiological Methods*, Vol. 5, Part A. London and N.Y.: Academic Press. [v. 298]

Nastuk, W. L. & Hodgkin, A. L. (1950). The electrical activity of single muscle fibres. *J. cell. comp. Physiol.* **35**, 39–74. [89]

Nastuk, W. L., Manthey, A. A. & Gissen, A. J. (1966). Activation and inactivation of post-junctional membrane receptors. *Ann. N.Y. Acad. Sci.* **137**, 999–1014. [165, 189–191]

Nelson, P. G. (1966). Interaction between spinal motoneurones of the cat. *J. Neurophysiol.* **29**, 275–287. [220]

Nelson, P. G. & Frank, K. (1963). Intracellularly recorded responses of nerve cells to oxygen deprivation. *Am. J. Physiol.* **205**, 208–212. [216]

— (1964a). Extracellular potential fields of single spinal motoneurones. *J. Neurophysiol.* **27**, 913–927. [218]

— (1964b). La production du potential d'action étudiée par la technique du voltage imposée sur le motoneurone du chat. *Actualités Neurophysiol.* Veme Serie. [236]

— (1967). Anomalous rectification in cat spinal motoneurones and effect of polarizing currents on excitatory postsynaptic potential. *J. Neurophysiol.* **30**, 1097–1113. [223, 224]

Neumann, W. F. & Neumann, M. W. (1958). *The Chemical Dynamics of Bone Mineral.* Chicago: Univ. of Chicago Press. [301]

Nishi, S. & Koketsu, K. (1960). Electrical properties and activities of single sympathetic neurons in frogs. *J. cell. comp. Physiol.* **55**, 15–30. [105, 302]

— (1968). Underlying mechanism of ganglionic slow IPSP and posttetanic hyperpolarization of pre- and postsynaptic elements. *Proc. Int. U. Physiol. Sci.* **7**, 321. [68]

Noble, D. (1966). Applications of Hodgkin-Huxley equations to excitable tissues. *Physiol. Rev.* **46**, 3–50. [40, 59]

Offner, F. F. (1954). Triphasic action potential. *Electroen. Neurophysiol.* **6**, 507–508. [269]

Ogston, A. G. (1955). Removal of acetylcholine from a limited volume by diffusion. *J. Physiol.* **128**, 222–223. [198]

Otsuka, M., Endo, M. & Nonomura, Y. (1962). Presynaptic nature of neuromuscular depression. *Jap. J. Physiol.* **12**, 573–584. [129, 152, 197, 198]

Otsuka, M., Iversen, L. L., Hall, Z. W. & Kravitz, E. A. (1966). Release of gamma-amino-butyric acid from inhibitory nerves of lobster. *Proc. natn. Acad. Sci. U.S.A.* **56**, 1110–1116. [244]

Otsuka, M. & Nonomura, Y. (1963). The action of phenolic substances on motor nerve endings. *J. Pharmac. exp. Ther.* **140**, 41–45. [152]

Ottoson, D. & Shepherd, G. M. (1965). Receptor potentials and impulse generation in the isolated spindle during controlled extension. *Symp. Quant. Biol.* **30**, 105–114. [69]

Ozeki, M., Freeman, A. R. & Grundfest, H. (1966). The membrane components of crustacean neuromuscular systems. I. Immunity of different electrogenic components to tetrodotoxin and saxitoxin. *J. gen. Physiol.* **49**, 1319–1334. [60, 172]

Ozeki, M. & Grundfest, H. (1965). Different effects of tetrodotoxin on various electrogenic components. *Fed. Proc.* **24**, 648, Abst. 2868. [60, 118]

Ozeki, M. & Sato, M. (1964). Initiation of impulses at the non-myelinated nerve terminal in Pacinian corpuscles. *J. Physiol.* **170**, 167–185. [69]

Palade, G. E. (1954). Electron microscope observations of interneuronal and neuromuscular synapses. *Anat. Rec.* **118**, 335–336. [13]

Palay, S. L. (1956). Synapses in the central nervous system. *J. biophys. biochem. Cytol.* **2**, suppl. 2, 193–201. [12]

— (1958). The morphology of synapses in the central nervous system. *Exp. Cell Res.*, suppl. **5**, 275–293. [13, 215]

— (1967). Principles of cellular organization in the nervous system. In *The Neurosciences: A Study Program*, ed. Quarton, G. C., Melnechuk, T. and Schmitt, F. O., pp. 24–31. New York: Rockefeller Univ. Press. [215]

Pantin, C. F. A. (1934). On the excitation of crustacean muscle. *J. exp. Biol.* **11**, 11–27. [307]

— (1946). *Notes on Microscopical Techniques for Zoologists*. Cambridge: Cambridge Univ. Press. [309]

Pappas, G. D. & Bennett, M. V. (1966). Specialized junctions involved in electrical transmission between neurons. *Ann. N.Y. Acad. Sci.* **137**, 495–508. [13]

Parsons, R. L., Hofmann, W. W. & Feigen, G. A. (1965). Presynaptic effects of potassium ion on the mammalian neuromuscular juncton. *Nature Lond.* **208**, 590–591. [156]

— (1966). The mode of action of tetanus toxin on the neuromuscular junction. *Am. J. Physiol.* **210**, 84–90. [107]

Paton, W. D. M. (1958). Central and synaptic transmission in the nervous system; pharmacological aspects. *A. Rev. Physiol.* **20**, 431–470. [7]

— (1961). A theory of drug action based on the rate of drug receptor combination. *Proc. R. Soc. B.* **154**, 21–69. [196]

Perry, W. L. (1953). Acetylcholine release in the cat's superior cervical ganglion *J. Physiol.* **119**, 439–454. [199]

Phillips, C. G. (1959). Actions of antidromic pyramidal volleys on single Betz cells in the cat. *Q. J. exp. Physiol.* **44**, 1–25. [219, 245]

— (1961). Some properties of pyramidal neurones of the motor cortex. In *The Nature of Sleep* (Ciba Symposium), ed. Wolstenholme, G. E. W. and O'Connor, M., pp. 4–24. London: Churchill. [245]

Plonsey, R. (1965). An extension of the solid angle potential formulation for an active cell. *Biophys. J.* **5**, 663–667. [266]

Powell, T. P. S. & Mountcastle, V. B. (1959). Some aspects of the functional organization of the cortex of the postcentral gyrus of the monkey: A correlation of findings obtained in a single unit analysis with cytoarchitecture. *Johns Hopkins Hosp. Bull.* **105**, 133–162. [297]

Pringle, J. W. S. (1938). Proprioception in insects. I. A new type of mechanical receptor from the palps of the cockroach. *J. exp. Biol.* **15**, 101–113. [306]

Prosser, C. L. & Brown, F. A., Jr. (1961). *Comparative Animal Physiology*, 2nd edn. Philadelphia and London: W. B. Saunders. [299]

Purple, R. L. (1964). The integration of excitatory and inhibitory influences in the eccentric cell in the eye of *Limulus* Thesis, The Rockefeller Institute. [98]

Purpura, D. P. (1967). Comparative physiology of dendrites. In *The Neurosciences: A Study Program*, ed. Quarton, G. C., Melnechuk, T., and Schmitt, F. O., pp. 372–393. New York: Rockefeller Univ. Press. [285]

Purpura, D. P. & Cohen, B. (1962). Intracellular recording from thalamic neurons during recruiting responses. *J. Neurophysiol.* **25**, 621–635. [245]

Purpura, D. P. & McMurtry, J. G. (1965). Intracellular activities and evoked potential changes during polarization of motor cortex. *J. Neurophysiol.* **28**, 166–185. [220]

Purpura, D. P. & Shofer, R. J. (1963). Intracellular recording from thalamic neurons during reticulocortical activation. *J. Neurophysiol.* **26**, 494–505. [219, 245]

— (1964). Cortical intracellular potentials during augmenting and recruiting responses. I. Effects of injected hyperpolarizing currents on evoked membrane potential changes. *J. Neurophysiol.* **27**, 117–132. [245]

Purpura, D. P., Shofer, R. J. & Musgrave, F. S. (1964). Cortical intracellular potentials during augmenting and recruiting responses. II. Patterns of synaptic activities in pyramidal and non-pyramidal tract neurons. *J. Neurophysiol.* **27**, 133–151. [245]

Purpura, D. P., Shofer, R. J. & Scarff, T. (1965). Properties of synaptic activities and spike potentials of neurones in immature neocortex. *J. Neurophysiol.* **28**, 925–942. [220]

Rall, W. (1957). Membrane time constant of motoneurones. *Science* **126**, 454. [99, 260, 261]

— (1959). Branching dendritic trees and motoneuron membrane resistivity. *Exp. Neurol.* **1**, 491–527. [260]

— (1960). Membrane potential transients and membrane time constant of motoneurons. *Exp. Neurol.* **2**, 503–532. [77, 79, 80, 260]

— (1962a). Electrophysiology of a dendritic neurone model. *Biophys. J.* **2**, 145–167. [97, 99, 236, 260]

— (1962b). Theory of physiological properties of dendrites. *Ann. N.Y. Acad. Sci.* **96**, 1071–1092. [236, 260]

— (1964). Theoretical significance of dendritic trees for neuronal input-output relations. In *Neural Theory and Modeling*, ed. Reies, R. Stanford, Calif.: Stanford Univ. Press. [236, 260, 261, 275, 285]

— (1965). Dendritic synaptic patterns; experiments with a mathematical model. In *Studies in Physiology*, ed. Curtis, D. R. & McIntyre, A. K., pp. 238–242. Berlin: Springer-Verlag. [99, 236, 261]

— (1967). Distinguishing theoretical synaptic potentials computed for different soma-dendritic distributions of synaptic input. *J. Neurophysiol.* **30**, 1138–1168. [66, 231, 232, 235, 236, 259, 260, 261, 262]

Rall, W., Burke, R. E., Smith, T. G., Nelson, P. G. & Frank, K. (1967). Dendritic location of synapses and possible mechanisms for the monosynaptic EPSP in motoneurones. *J. Neurophysiol.* **30**, 1169–1193. [227, 228, 231, 232, 237, 260, 262, 263]

Rall, W. & Shepherd, G. M. (1968). Theoretical reconstruction of field potentials and dendrodendritic synaptic interactions in olfactory bulb. *J. Neurophysiol.* **31**, 884–915. [293]

Ralston, H. J. & Libet, B. (1953). Effect of stretch on action potential of voluntary muscle. *Am. J. Physiol.* **173**, 449–455. [318]

Ralston, A. &. Wilf, H. S. (1960). *Mathematical Methods for Digital Computers*. New York: Wiley. [51]

Ramón, y Cajal, S. (1911). *Histologie du systéme nervoux de l'homme et des vertébrés*, 2 vols. Paris: Maloine. [214, 285]

Reger, J. F. (1957). The ultrastructure of normal and denervated neuromuscular synapses in mouse gastrocnemius muscle. *Exp. Cell Res.* **12**, 662–665. [12]

Renshaw, B. (1940). Activity in the simplest spinal reflex pathways. *J. Neurophysiol.* **3**, 373–387. [225]

— (1941). Influence of discharge of motoneurones upon excitation of neighbouring motoneurones. *J. Neurophysiol.* **4**, 167–183. [252]

Reuter, H. (1967). Dependence of slow inward current in Purkinje fibres on extracellular calcium concentration. *J. Physiol.* **192**, 479–492. [59]

Ringer, S. (1883a). A further contribution regarding the influence of the different constituents of the blood on the contraction of the heart. *J. Physiol.* **4**, 29–42. [302]

— (1883b). A third contribution regarding the influence of the inorganic constituents of the blood on the ventricular contraction. *J. Physiol.* **4**, 222–225. [302, 303]

Ritchie, J. M. & Straub, R. W. (1956). The after-effects of repetitive stimulation on mammalian non-medullated fibres. *J. Physiol.* **134**, 698–711. [87]

Robertis, E. de (1956). Submicroscopic changes of the synapse after nerve section in the acoustic ganglion of the guinea pig. *J. biophys. biochem. Cytol.* **2**, 503–512. [13]

— (1958). Submicroscopic morphology and function of the synapse. *Exp. Cell Res.*, Suppl. **5**, 347–369. [13]

— (1964). *Histophysiology of Synapses and Neurosecretion*, 1st edn. Oxford: Pergamon Press. [12, 112]

Robertis, E. de & Bennett, H. S. (1955). Some features of the submicroscopic morphology of synapses in frog and earthworm. *J. biophys. biochem. Cytol.* **1**, 47–58. [12]

Robertis, E. de & Ferreira, A. V. (1957). Submicroscopic changes of the nerve endings in the adrenal medulla after stimulation of the splanchnic nerve. *J. biophys. biochem. Cytol.* **3**, 611–614. [12]

Robertis, E. de & Franchi, C. M. (1956). Electron microscope observations on synaptic vesicles in synapses of the retinal rods and cones *J. biophys. biochem. Cytol.* **2**, 307–318. [12]

Robertis, E. de, Gerschenfeld, H. M. & Wald, F. (1960). Ultrastructure and function of glial cells. In *Structure and Function of the Cerebral Cortex*, ed. Tower, D. B. and Schade, J. P. Amsterdam: Elsevier. [215]

Robertis, E. de & Gerschenfeld, H. M. (1961). Submicroscopic morphology and function of glial cells. *Int. Rev. Neurobiol.* **3**, 1–65. [215]

Robertson, J. D. (1956). The ultra structure of a reptilian myoneural junction. *J. biophys. biochem. Cytol.* **2**, 381–394. [12]

— (1960). The molecular structure and contact relationship of cell membranes. *Prog. Biophys.* **10**, 343–418. [43]

Rudomin, P. (1966). Pharmacological evidence for the existence of interneurones mediating primary afferent depolarization in the solitary tract neurones of the cat. *Brain Res.* **2**, 181–183. [257]

Rushton, W. A. H. (1937). Initiation of the propagated disturbance. *Proc. R. Soc. B* **124**, 210–243. [270]

— (1945). Action potentials in the isolated nerve cord of the earthworm. *Proc. R. Soc. B* **132**, 423–437. [309]

Samojloff, A. (1925). Zur Frage des Überganges der Erregung vom motorischen Nerven auf den quergestreiften Muskel. *Pflügers Arch. ges. Physiol.* **208**, 508–519. [166]

Sandblom, J. P. & Eisenman, G. (1967). Membrane potentials at zero current. The significance of a constant ionic permeability ratio. *Biophys. J.* **7**, 217–242. [38, 39, 42]

Sasaki, K. & Otani, T. (1961). Accommodation in motoneurones of the cat. *Jap. J. Physiol.* **11**, 443–456. [221]

— (1962). Accommodation in motoneurones as modified by circumstantial conditions. *Jap. J. Physiol.* **12**, 383–396. [221]

Schmidt, H. & Stämpfli, R. (1966). Die Wirkung von Tetraethylammoniumchlorid auf den einzelnen Ranvierschen Schnürring *Pflügers Arch. ges. Physiol.* **287**, 311–325. [61]

Schoffeniels, E. (1960). Les bases physiques et chemiques des potentials bioélectriques chez Electrophorus electricus. *Archs int. Physiol.* **58**, 1–151. [305]

Schueler, F. W. (1960). The mechanism of action of the hemicholiniums. *Int. Rev. Neurobiol.* **2**, 77–97. [144]

Schwan, H. P. (1965). Biological impedance determinations. *J. cell. comp. Physiol.* **66**, Suppl. 2, 5–12. [82, 298]

Segal, J. R. (1967). Electrical capacitance of ion-exchanger membranes. *J. theor. Biol.* **14**, 11–34. [44]

Shanes, A. M. (1958). Electrochemical aspects of physiological and pharmacological action in excitable cells. Part II. The action potential and exitation. *Pharmac. Rev.* **10**, 165–273. [169]

Shanes, A. M., Freygang, W. H., Grundfest, H. & Amatniek, E. (1959). Anesthetic and calcium action in the voltage clamped squid giant axon. *J. gen. Physiol.* **42**, 793–802. [195]

Shapovalov, A. I. (1963). A study of actions of drugs on neuromuscular transmission with the aid of multi-barreled intracellular microelectrodes. *First Int. Pharmac. Meeting*, Vol. 5, pp. 213–220. [193]

— (1964). Intracellular microelectrode investigation of effect of anesthetics on transmission of excitation in the spinal cord. *Fed. Proc.* **23**, Transl. suppl. 1, Part II, T113–T116. [296]

Sherrington, C. S. (1897). The central nervous system. In *A Textbook of Physiology*, 7th edn., Vol. 3, ed. Foster. M. London: MacMillan. [1]

— (1906). *The Integrative Action of the Nervous System*, pp. 16–18. Cambridge: University Press. [1]

Silver, I. A. (1958). Other electrodes. In *Electronic Apparatus for Biological Research*, by Donaldson, P. E., pp. 568–581. London: Butterworth Scientific Publications. [88]

Singer, C. J. (1925). *The evolution of anatomy; a short history of anatomical and physiological discovery to Harvey*. London: Paul, Trench, Trubner. [2]

Smith, T. G., Wuerker, R. B. & Frank, K. (1967). Membrane impedance changes during synaptic transmission in cat spinal motoneurones. *J. Neurophysiol.* **30**, 1072–1096. [235, 237, 238, 248, 249, 250, 260]

South, F. E. (1961). Phrenic nerve-diaphragm preparations in relation to temperature and hibernation. *Am. J. Physiol.* **200**, 565–571. [312]

Spencer, W. A. & Kandel, E. R. (1961a). Electrophysiology of hippocampal neurons. III. Firing level and time constant. *J. Neurophysiol.* **24**, 260–271. [93, 220]

— (1961b). Electrophysiology of hippocampal neurons. IV. Fast prepotentials. *J. Neurophysiol.* **24**, 272–285. [220]

Stämpfli, R. (1954). A new method of measuring membrane potentials with external electrodes. *Experientia* **10**, 508–509. [87]

— (1959). Is the resting potential of Ranvier nodes a potassium potential? *Ann. N. Y. Acad. Sci.* **81**, 265–284. [60]

Stefanis, C. & Jasper, H. (1964). Recurrent collateral inhibition in pyramidal tract neurons. *J. Neurophysiol.* **27**, 855–877. [245]

Stein, R. B. (1967). The frequency of nerve action potentials generated by applied currents. *Proc. R. Soc. B* **167**, 64–86. [58]

Straub, R. (1956). Die Wirkungen von Veratriden und Ionen auf das Ruhepotential markhaltiger Nervenfasern des Frosches. *Helv. physiol. pharmac. Acta* **14**, 1–28. [87]

Straughan, D. W. (1960). The release of acetylcholine from mammalian motor nerve endings. *Br. J. Pharmac.* **15**, 417–424. [114, 315]

Strichholm, A. & Wallin, B. G. (1965). Intracellular chloride activity of crayfish giant axons. *Nature Lond.* **208**, 790–791. [42]

Svaetichin, G. (1951). Low resistance microelectrodes. *Acta physiol. scand.* **24**, suppl. 86, 5–13. [299]

Swammerdam, J. (1637–1680). *The book of nature; on the history of insects* (translated by Thomas Floyd and improved by John Hill). London: C. G. Scyffert 1958. As reported in *Selected Readings in the History of Physiology*, 2nd edn., ed. Fulton, John F. & Wilson, L. G. Springfield, Ill.: Charles C Thomas 1966. [3]

Takata, M., Moore, J. W., Kao C. Y. & Fuhrman, F. A. (1966). Blockage of sodium conductance increase in lobster giant axon by tarichatoxin (tetrodotoxin). *J. gen. Physiol.* **49**, 977–988. [60]

Takata, M., Pickard, W. F., Lettvin, I. Y. & Moore, I. W. (1966). Ionic conductance changes in lobster axon membrane when lanthanum is substituted for calcium. *J. gen. Physiol.* **50**, 461–471. [60]

Takeuchi, A. (1958). The long-lasting depression in neuromuscular transmission of frog. *Jap. J. Physiol.* **8**, 102–113. [147, 149]

— (1959). Neuromuscular transmission of fish skeletal muscles investigated with intracellular microelectrodes. *J. cell. comp. Physiol.* **54**, 211–270. [116, 305]

Takeuchi, A. & Takeuchi, N. (1959). Active phase of frog's end-plate potential. *J. Neurophysiol.* **22**, 395–411. [66, 105, 200, 204, 205, 210, 302, 313]

— (1960a). Further analysis of relationship between end-plate potential and end-plate current. *J. Neurophysiol.* **23**, 397–402. [147, 209]

— (1960b). On the permeability of end-plate membrane during the action of the transmitter. *J. Physiol.* **154**, 52–67. [62, 66, 107, 232]

— (1962). Electrical changes in the pre- and postsynaptic axons of the giant synapse of Loligo. *J. gen. Physiol.* **45**, 1181–1193. [113, 162]

— (1966). A study of the inhibitory action of γ-aminobutyric acid on neuromuscular transmission in the crayfish. *J. Physiol.* **183**, 418–432. [116]

— (1967). Anion permeability of the inhibitory postsynaptic membrane of the crayfish neuromuscular junction. *J. Physiol.* **191**, 575–590. [244]

Takeuchi, N. (1958). The effect of temperature on the neuromuscular junction of the frog. *Jap. J. Physiol.* **8**, 390–404. [108, 313, 314, 315]

— (1963a). Some properties of conductance changes at the endplate membrane during the action of acetylcholine. *J. Physiol.* **167**, 128–140. [208]

— (1963b). Effects of calcium on the conductance change of the end-plate membrane during the action of transmitter. *J. Physiol.* **167**, 141–155. [64, 106, 211]

Tasaki, I. (1964). A new measurement of action currents developed by single nodes of Ranvier. *J. Neurophysiol.* **27**, 1199–1206. [270]

Tasaki, I. & Spyropoulos, C. S. (1957). The influence of changes in temperature and pressure on the nerve fiber. In *Influence of Temperature on Biological Systems*, ed. Johnson, A. S. Baltimore: Waverly Press. [314]

Tauc, L. (1955). Étude de l'activité elementaire des cellules du ganglion abdominal de l'Aplysie. *J. Physiol. Path. gén.* **47**, 769–792. [94, 310]

Taxi, J. (1961). Étude de l'ultrastructure des zones synaptique dans les ganglion sympathiques de la grenouille. *C. r. Sci., Paris* **252**, 174–176. [13]

Taylor, R. E. (1959). Effect of procaine on electrical properties of squid axon membrane. *Am. J. Physiol.* **196**, 1071–1078. [195]

Terzuolo, C. A. (1959). Cerebellar inhibitory and excitatory actions upon spinal extensor motoneurons. *Arch. ital. Biol.* **97**, 316–339. [250]

Terzuolo, C. A. & Araki, T. (1961). An analysis of intra-versus extra-cellular potential changes associated with activity of single spinal motoneurones. *Ann. N. Y. Acad.* **94**, 547–558. [94, 206, 218, 219, 279–284]

Terzuolo, C. A. & Llinás, R. (1966). Distribution of synaptic inputs in the spinal motoneurone and its functional significance. In *Nobel Symposium I. Muscular Afferents and Motor Control*, ed. Granit, R., pp. 373–384. Stockholm: Almqvist & Wiksell; N. Y.-London-Sydney: John Wiley & Sons. [238, 260]

Terzuolo, C. A., Llinás, R. & Green, K. T. (1965). Mechanisms of supraspinal actions upon spinal cord activities. Distribution of synaptic inputs in cat's alpha motoneurons. *Archs. ital. Biol.* **103,** 635–651. [260]

Terzuolo, C. A. & Washizu, Y. (1962). Relation between stimulus strength, generator potential and impulse frequency in stretch receptor of Crustacea. *J. Neurophysiol.* **25,** 56–66. [69]

Thesleff, S. (1955*a*). The mode of neuromuscular block caused by acetylcholine, nicotine, decamethonium and succinylcholine. *Acta physiol. scand.* **34,** 218–231. [196, 318]

— (1955*b*). The effect of acetylcholine, decamethonium and succinylcholine on neuromuscular transmission in the rat. *Acta physiol. scand.* **34,** 386–392. [196]

— (1959). Motor end-plate 'desensitization' by repetitive nerve stimuli. *J. Physiol.* **148,** 659–664. [197, 302]

— (1960). Supersensitivity of skeletal muscle produced by botulinum toxin. *J. Physiol.* **151,** 598–607. [193]

Thies, R. E. (1965). Neuromuscular depression and apparent depletion of transmitter in mammalian muscle. *J. Neurophysiol.* **28,** 427–442 [147, 149, 198]

Thomas, R. C. & Wilson, V. J. (1965). Precise localization of Renshaw cells with a new marking technique. *Nature Lond.* **206,** 211–213. [149, 290]

— (1966). Marking single neurons by staining with intracellular recording microelectrodes. *Science* **151,** 1838–1839. [290]

Thomas-Green, K. (1964). Integration of segmental and supraspinal action on single spinal motoneurones. Thesis, University of Minnesota. [97]

Toida, N. & Osa, T. (1965). Spike generating mechanism of smooth muscle cell membrane. *Proc. XXIII Int. Congr. Physiol. Sci.,* Abst. 171, p. 94. [173]

Toyama, K., Tsukahara, N. & Udo, M. (1967). Nature of cerebellar influences upon red nucleus neurones. *Exp. Brain Res.* **4,** 292–309. [250]

Tsukahara, N. & Kosaka, K. (1966). The mode of cerebral activation of red nucleus neurones. *Experientia* **22,** 193–194. [260, 263]

Tsukahara, N., Toyama, K., Kosaka, K. & Udo, M. (1964). Disfacilitation of red nucleus neurones. *Experientia* **21,** 544. [250, 252]

Tyrode, M. V. (1910). The mode of action of some purgative salts. *Archs. int. Pharmacodyn. Thér.* **20,** 205–223. [300]

Usherwood, P. N. R. (1963). Spontaneous miniature potentials from insect muscle fibres. *J. Physiol.* **169,** 149–160. [116, 123]

Usherwood, P. N. R. & Grundfest, H. (1964). Inhibitory postsynaptic potentials in grasshopper muscle. *Science* **143,** 817–818. [116]

— (1965). Peripheral inhibition in skeletal muscle of insects. *J. Neurophysiol.* **28,** 497–518. [306]

Van der Meer, C. & Meeter, E. (1956). The mechanism of action of anticholinesterases. II. The effect of di-isopropylfluorophosphonate (DFP) on the isolated rat phrenic nerve-diaphragm preparation. A. Irreversible effects. *Acta physiol. pharmac. néerl.* **4,** 454–471. [201]

Vayo, H. W. (1965). Determination of the electrical parameters of vertebrate visceral smooth muscle. *J. theor. Biol.* **9,** 263–277. [103]

Vere-Jones, D. (1966). Simple stochastic models for the release of quanta of transmitter from a nerve terminal. *Aust. J. Statistics* **8**, 53–63. [129]

Volta, A. (1800). On electricity excited by the mere contact of conducting substances of different kinds. *Phil. Trans.* **90**, 403–430. [4]

Waldeyer, W. (1891). Über eininge neuere Forschungen im Gibiete der Anatomie des Central nervensystems. *Dt. med. Wschr.* **17**, 1213. [214]

Wall, P. D. (1958). Excitability changes in afferent fibre terminations and their relation to slow potentials. *J. Physiol.* **142**, 1–21. [168, 256]

Waser, P. G. (1960). The cholinergic receptor. *J. Pharm. Pharmac.* **12**, 577–594. [199]

— (1967). Receptor localization by auto radiographic techniques. *Ann. N. Y. Acad. Sci.* **144**, 737–755. [199]

Washio, H. & Mashima, H. (1963). Effect of some anions and cations on the membrane resistance and twitch tension of frog muscle fibre. *Jap. J. Physiol.* **13**, 617–629. [107]

Washizu, Y. (1960). Single spinal motoneurones excitable from two different antidromic pathways. *Jap. J. Physiol.* **10**, 121–131. [220]

Washizu, Y., Bonewell, G. N. & Terzuolo, C. A. (1961). Effects of strychnine upon the electrical activity of an isolated nerve cell. *Science* **133**, 333–334. [222]

Wasserman, K., Becker, E. L. & Fishman, A. P. (1953). Transport of phenol red in the flounder renal tubule. *J. cell. comp. Physiol.* **42**, 385–393. [305]

Watkins, J. C. (1965). Pharmacological receptors and general permeability phenomena of cell membranes. *J. theor. Biol.* **9**, 37–50. [29, 30]

Weevers, R. G. (1966). A lepidopteran saline and effects of inorganic cation concentrations on sensory, reflex and motor responses in a herbivorous insect. *J. exp. Biol.* **44**, 163–175. [310]

Weidmann, S. (1966). The diffusion of radiopotassium across intercalated disks of mammalian cardiac muscle. *J. Physiol.* **187**, 323–342. [51]

Werman, R. & Grundfest, H. (1961). Graded and all-or-none electrogenesis in arthropod muscle. II. The effects of alkali-earth and onium ions on lobster muscle fibres. *J. gen. Physiol.* **44**, 997–1027. [59]

Werner, E. & Kuperman, A. S. (1963). Actions at the neuromuscular junction. *In Handbuch der Experimentellen Pharmakologie*, Vol. 15, ed. Koelle, G.B., Ch. 13. Berlin: Springer-Verlag. [199]

White, P. R. (1949). Prolonged survival of excised animal tissue *in vitro* in nutrients of known composition. *J. cell. comp. Physiol.* **34**, 221–242. [304]

Whittaker, V. P. (1965). The application of subcellular fractionation techniques to the study of brain function. *Prog. Biophys. molec. Biol.* **15**, 39–96. [12, 112, 113]

— (1966). Some properties of synaptic membranes isolated from the central nervous system. *Ann. N. Y. Acad. Sci.* **137**, 982–998. [12, 112, 113]

Willis, W. D., Letbetter, W. D. & Thompson, W. M. (1968). A small system of neurons in the mammalian spinal cord. *Brain Res.* **9**, 152–155. [228]

Wilson, I. B. (1952). Acetylcholinesterase XII. Further studies of binding forces. *J. biol. Chem.* **197**, 215–225. [211]

Wilson, I. B. & Bergmann, F. (1950a). Studies on cholinesterase VII. The active surface of acetylcholine esterase derived from the effects of pH on inhibitors. *J. biol. Chem.* **185**, 479–489. [211]

— (1950b). Acetylcholinesterase VIII. Dissociation constants of the active groups. *J. Biol. Chem.* **186**, 683–692. [211]

Wilson, V. J. & Burgess, P. R. (1962). Disinhibition in the cat spinal cord. *J. Neurophysiol.* **25**, 392–404. [252, 253]

Winckler, F. H. (1748). Essai sur la Nature. Les effets et les causes avec description de deux nouvelles machines à Électricité. Paris: Jorry. [4]

Wolbarsht, M. L. (1960). Electrical characteristics of insects mechanoreceptors. *J. gen. Physiol.* **44**, 105–122.

Wolbarsht, M. L., MacNichol, E. F. & Wagner, H. G. (1960). Glass insulated platinum microelectrodes. *Science* **132**, 1309–1310. [283, 299]

Wood, D. W. (1957). The effect of ions upon the neuromuscular transmission in a herbivorous insect. *J. Physiol.* **138**, 119–139. [306]

Wright, E. B. (1954). Effect of mephenesin and other depressants on spinal cord transmission in pig and cat. *Am. J. Physiol.* **179**, 390–401. [257, 297]

Wyatt, S. S. (1956). Culture *in vitro* of tissue from the silkworm *Bombyx mori.* *J. gen. Physiol.* **39**, 841–852. [306]

Wyckoff, R. W. G. & Young, J. Z. (1956). The motor-neuron surface. *Proc. R. Soc. B* **144**, 440–450. [13]

Wyss, O. A. M. (1945). Ein Hochfrequenz-Koagulationsgerät zur reizlosen Ausschaltung. *Helv. physiol. Acta* **3**, 437. [297]

Yeager, J. F. (1939). Electrical stimulation of isolated heart preparation from *Periplaneta americana.* *J. Agric. Res.* **59**, 121–137. [306]

Young, J. Z. (1933). The preparation of isotonic solutions for use in experiments with fish. *Pubbl. Staz. zool. Napoli* **12**, 425–431. [305]

SUBJECT INDEX